677.

COPY No. 1

677

A STUDENT'S TEXTBOOK OF
TEXTILE SCIENCE

A STUDENT'S TEXTBOOK
OF TEXTILE SCIENCE

by

A. J. HALL
B.Sc., F.R.I.C., F.T.I., F.S.D.C.

Consulting Chemist to the Textile and related industries
Sometime Examiner to the City and Guilds of London Institute
in the Dyeing and Finishing of Textiles
Gold Medallist for Research (The Worshipful Company of
Dyers of the City of London)

ALLMAN & SON LTD
50 Grafton Way, Fitzroy Square
London W1

Made and printed in Great Britain by
Butler & Tanner Ltd, Frome and London

Table of Contents

Jacquard device; coloured pattern weaving; crepe fabrics; ribbons; knitted fabrics; non-woven fabrics—felts, laces, nets; bonded-fibre fabrics; laminated fabrics; foam-back fabrics; *Questions.*

Preface

Although a large proportion of textile materials are used for industrial purposes—in motor tyres, covering and packing materials, cordage, etc.—the most interesting uses are for wearing apparel and for decorative purposes in the home. For most people clothes are next in importance to food. The fine tenuous fibres (both natural and man-made) of which fabrics and garments are made thus concern everyone.

It is both interesting and useful to know how these fibres are made into yarns, and how these can then be converted by weaving and knitting into fabrics which can be further made more pleasing and serviceable by dyeing and finishing treatments. It is also profitable to know how best to use and wash and clean fabrics and garments, and this knowledge has become more important now that so many different types of synthetic man-made fibres are being used. All these matters are dealt with in this book by the author, who has spent his whole life in the textile industry and would not have wished to do otherwise.

There are many books written about textiles but most of them are highly technical since their appeal is to skilled and trained textile technologists. This book is intended primarily for students up to 'O' level G.C.E. and their teachers but it should also help those having a more general knowledge and interest in textiles. All the essential facts about textiles are presented in an easy readable style yet they are all strictly accurate. It is thus hoped that the book will appeal to a wide range of readers, including those who retail fabrics and garments and all interested in the washing and laundering of clothes.

For the use of students a number of questions are given at the end of each chapter—answering them could assist the assimilation of the chapter's contents.

It is hoped that all interested in textiles from any viewpoint will find from the broad coverage of textile materials in this book much that will be both interesting and profitable to them.

A. J. HALL

CHAPTER I

Textiles in General Use and their Structural Basis

If food be considered the first necessity of mankind then clothes must be second in importance. They keep the body warm and also protect it. Under modern living conditions clothes are further important for adornment and have an aesthetic value—many people derive a sense of well being and sometimes importance from the wearing of correctly styled and well-fitting clothes. But the textile industry is not concerned with clothes and general wearing apparel alone. Much fabric is used for utility and industrial purposes. There are many special types of fabric used for upholstery and home decoration, as bandages and covering materials in hospitals, for the reinforcement of motor tyres and power belting, for strengthening laminated sheet materials prepared with plastics, and for many other purposes connected with agriculture, horticulture, chemical manufacture, fishing and sea-going vessels. But while all such fabrics may differ considerably as regards their properties and usefulness they all have a common basis in that they are made from fibres which usually are fine and tenuous but not necessarily of the same chemical composition.

FIBRES, YARNS AND FABRICS

The normal type of fabric is made by suitably interlacing threads (yarns) with each other and in turn these threads are made from the individual fibres brought together more or less parallel so that the thread can be twisted to give it a satisfactory degree of strength. There are different types of thread interlacing such as can be obtained by weaving or knitting, and also a wide variety of different kinds of threads which may, for instance, be fine or coarse, smooth or fuzzy, and compact (wire-like) or soft according as the thread is hard or soft twisted. Further, the threads may be single or consist of two, three, or more single threads twisted together to give what are often termed *folded* or *multi-ply* threads. In recent years the availability of thermoplastic synthetic fibres has allowed the

9

production of special highly voluminous threads and also threads which have a high degree of stretch or elasticity.

Only a limited number of different types of fibres are in current use. Some of these are produced naturally such as cotton, wool, silk, linen, jute, etc., while others are man-made fibres such as viscose and acetate rayons, nylon, Orlon, Courtelle, Terylene, Kodel, etc. These fibres differ mainly as regards their chemical composition, their physical form, and their other properties which however in turn are largely dependent on their composition and form. It is an important point that the characteristics of man-made fibres can be controlled at the time of their manufacture; the properties of the natural fibres have generally to be accepted as they are, although such fibres as cotton and wool have been improved over many years by selection and breeding control.

FABRIC CHARACTERISTICS

Fundamentally the properties and thus the serviceability of any fabric are determined by the type of fibre used in its construction. For example a cotton fabric will handle cold, be resistant to alkali treatment yet be very easily damaged by treatment with acid, while a wool fabric will handle warm, be easily damaged by alkalis yet be reasonably resistant to acids. These differences stem from the fact that a cotton fibre is made of cellulose while a wool fibre has a protein (keratin) composition. Again, both cotton and wool do not become plastic at high temperatures but rather do they scorch and decompose. By contrast, synthetic fibres such as nylon, Terylene, and Courtelle at high temperatures become thermoplastic so that they can be easily stretched or deformed by pressure. The unique thermoplastic properties of the synthetic fibres are associated with the fact that synthetic fibres are made from organic hydrophobic (water-repellent) polymers—the natural fibres are hydrophile (water-attractive). But in bringing together fibres firstly in thread and then into fabric form there is ample opportunity to mask or obscure one or more natural characteristics of the fibres. Thus by using soft spun cotton threads and then brushing up the surface of the fabric into which these are subsequently woven to give it a hairy surface, a soft warm handling wool-like fabric can ultimately be produced. On the other hand weaving a wool fabric with fine hard twisted threads will give it a firm handle more like a cotton fabric. It is thus evident that there is ample opportunity in the manufacture of a fabric to secure special characteristics not necessarily those of the fibres used.

IMPORTANCE OF DYEING AND FINISHING

Fabrics as obtained from the loom or knitting machine are not often in a state for immediate use—it is generally necessary that they be dyed and finished before being offered to the public. There are many opportunities for dyers and finishers to give fabrics special desired properties and in many instances they may do more than the manufacturer (weaver and knitter) can to change the fabric so that it may have characteristics very different from those of the constituent fibres. In some instances a fabric composed of one type of fibre can be changed in dyeing and finishing so as to have properties suggesting that it is made of quite a different fibre. Thus it is mainly in the dyeing and finishing section of the textile industry that fabrics and garments are brought into a state such that they have the greatest appeal to the intended user.

It may have been inferred from the sole reference to weaving and knitting that these are the only two methods for producing fabrics. But this is not true. Fabrics can also be made by the methods of lace and net manufacturers, by the felting of fibres (wool), and by recently devised methods by which so-called non-woven fabrics are now being produced. These special types of fabrics will be referred to later, but here it is sufficient to note that the characteristics of non-woven fabrics are capable of wide variation quite apart from the type of fibre used.

PROGRESSIVE CHANGES IN FABRIC TYPES

The types of fabric now available today are of course much different from those in use some twenty-five years ago. This arises partly from changing tastes as regards the kind of clothes most useful and attractive and also from the introduction of man-made fibres. Whereas in earlier days only cotton, wool, silk, and flax were considered satisfactory for clothes, the present position is that at least twice as many new additional fibres are now in use as a result of the discovery of methods to manufacture fibres comparable in physical form to the natural fibres. The first important man-made fibres came with the discovery at about the end of the last century of methods for converting cotton and wood pulp cellulose into viscose, cuprammonium, and acetate rayons. A new era in the manufacture of man-made fibres came with the discovery about 1937 of a process for making nylon. Subsequently several new fibres have appeared and each year now sees the introduction of at least one new fibre. Those early man-made fibres are not usually referred to as synthetic fibres but as regenerated cellulose derivatives, since they are made from the natural raw material cellulose. It is only the later fibres commencing with nylon which are termed synthetic fibres for the reason that the raw materials used in their production are synthetically mainly made from primary substances such as coal, petroleum, air, and water. However, both natural and synthetic fibres consist of polymeric substances which are characterised by being composed of long linear molecules, of which more will be said later.

In general, it may be stated that the present generation as distinguished from earlier generations prefers lightweight to heavy clothing and to a large degree this preference can be satisfied only by the use of the newer man-made fibres. Although at present the proportion of synthetic fibres is relatively small their influence on the textile and especially the clothing industry is much greater than this small proportion would at first appear to justify. A partial explanation of this fact is that it is possible to modify profoundly the characteristics of a natural or rayon fabric by introducing into it quite a small proportion of synthetic fibres. Thus if the heels of men's wool socks are reinforced with nylon thread, which has a high resistance to wear, holes will not form in them when they are worn.

HYDROPHILE AND HYDROPHOBIC FABRICS

Since it is the type of fibre which largely determines the characteristics of the fabric made from it, an important fact must now be mentioned—the textile fibres now available can be grouped into two main classes according as they are *hydrophile* or *hydrophobic*, with some other fibres having intermediate properties. An essential difference between these two types is that the hydrophobic fibres are relatively inert towards water. Thus the hydrophobic fibre Terylene absorbs less than $\frac{1}{2}\%$ of moisture from air and but little water when wetted, while the hydrophile fibre wool naturally contains about 18% of moisture in its ordinary air-dry state and may absorb up to 100% of water when wetted. Thus a Terylene fibre does not swell in water whereas a wool fibre may become 30 to 40% thicker.

Over a period of many years manufacturing and dyeing and finishing methods and machinery have been developed for dealing with the hydrophile natural fibres available (cotton, wool, etc.). With the introduction of strongly hydrophobic synthetic fibres it was found that such methods and machinery were not entirely satisfactory. Thus difficulties were encountered during thread and fabric manufacture arising from the tendency for synthetic fibres to accumulate electrostatic electricity in sufficient amount (as a result of fibre-to-fibre friction) to prevent accurate control of the manufacturing operations. In the dyeing of synthetic fibre materials it was found that a large proportion of the dyes suitable for cotton, wool, and silk had no affinity for such fibres as nylon, Terylene, Orlon, and the like, so that new types of dyes have had to be discovered and manufactured. In the finishing of textile goods those made of synthetic fibres have to receive special consideration if high-temperature treatments are involved, since such fibres are highly sensitive to heat and can suffer both adverse and beneficial changes in such treatments. On the whole, synthetic fibre materials are not nearly so amenable to dyeing and finishing processes using aqueous treatment liquors as are goods made of the hydrophile natural fibres.

The above facts have made necessary much expensive adjustment of the older methods of manufacture and equipment employed in dyeing and finishing, and before deciding how to handle any textile fibre it is necessary to ascertain first whether it is hydrophile or hydrophobic. This adjustment is continuing in spite of the difficulties and expense involved because it is now found advantageous for some types of fabric to have hydrophobic properties—for example, hydrophobic fibres lend themselves well to the production of drip-dry and wash-and-wear fabrics and garments. So much so, that special treatments are being developed to make the strongly hydrophile fibres less hydrophile to enable them to compete with the hydrophobic synthetic fibres. Yet, by contrast, because for some purposes the synthetic hydrophobic fibres just fail to be able to compete with natural and cellulose rayon fibres, the methods for manufacturing such fibres are now being modified to make these hydrophobic fibres somewhat more hydrophile.

DISCOVERY OF NEW FIBRES

It has been mentioned above that there are now many more textile fibres available than formerly. This is perhaps a mixed blessing. Each new type of fibre introduced has its own peculiar properties and this creates difficulties for all sections of the textile industry which have to handle it—existing methods and machines have to be modified to suit it. Further, when the new fibre is used in admixture with other fibres some very special difficulties may be encountered—especially in the dyeing and finishing. So each new fibre is liable to encounter a certain amount of resistance on its introduction unless it has some outstanding desirable characteristics. Because of this, many new fibres have in the past few years been discovered but not actually manufactured on the large scale. It has been estimated that the discovery and erection of plant for the first large-scale manufacture of a new fibre can cost up to five million pounds, so that this is a venture not lightly to be undertaken.

Summarising the above observations it is seen that the properties and usefulness of a fabric are determined by (1) the type of fibre of which it is made, (2) the character of the threads, (3) the manner in which the threads are interlaced by weaving, knitting, or twisting, and (4) dyeing and finishing. It will thus now be convenient and useful to consider these sections of textile production in more detail.

CHAPTER II

Textile Fibres—Natural and Man-made

The more important properties of the fibres described in this chapter will be found tabulated on page 109.

IMPORTANCE OF A FIBRE'S PHYSICAL FORM

All the textile fibres now in general use have certain characteristics in common. Of these the most important is that each fibre shall be very much longer than it is thick, say up to 1,000 times as long, and in general it should not be thicker than 1/1,000th of an inch. These dimensional requirements arise from the fact that in making a thread the fibres are brought parallel into bundle form and then twisted—the finer the fibres the more closely can they be brought together by the twisting, and the greater their length the greater is the distance over which they grip each other within the resulting thread. The magnitude of this 'grip' partly determines the strength of the thread, for while a thread under stretch or pull can break by breaking of the fibres, it can also break by a simple slipping of the fibres over each other, and the twist grip hinders this slipping. The other feature which determines thread strength is the strength of the individual fibres.

Surface roughness and irregularity of shape or form along the fibre length are other important features which influence thread strength and other properties. Extremely smooth fibres readily slide over each other. Such sliding is favoured by a symmetry of form, as for example with cylindrical fibres. On the other hand, sliding is hindered by surface roughness such as may, for example, be caused by the pits and striations and twists in cotton fibres, by the crinkled or crimped fibre form and by the overlapping epithelial scales (like those of a fish) which cover wool fibres. In some instances it has been found advantageous to coat fibres with a very thin film of fine inert particles of silica to give them added roughness. Many man-made fibres are given an artificial crimp by passage between hot fluted rollers or by stabilising them while in a highly entangled state since such waviness can assist fibre grip

15

within a thread, although under appropriate conditions this same waviness can lead to the production of more bulky threads, which is sometimes desirable.

INTERNAL STRUCTURE OF FIBRES

But there is another common characteristic of all textile fibres of the utmost importance and this is concerned with their internal structure. Each fibre is built up of molecules and it has been observed with all fibres of use for the production of flexible and durable threads and fabrics that these molecules are long and substantially linear (that is, not branched). Thus an individual fibre has much the same structure as a thread made from a number of such fibres—in a thread the unit of structure is a long fine single fibre, while in the single fibre it is a long, more or less straight molecule. Further, just as the strength of a thread is largely determined by the extreme tenuity of each fibre and the grip existing between the numerous fibres present, so with a single fibre its strength is similarly governed by the extreme length of each molecule compared with its thickness and also by the close packing of these molecules to prevent their sliding over each other when the fibre is subjected to length tension.

Molecular packing within a fibre

By means of X-ray investigations and other methods it has been possible during the past few years to determine with considerable accuracy the nature of the molecules within any type of fibre and also the manner in which they are packed together. Methods have also been perfected which allow the molecule lengths to be measured and to ascertain whether the molecules are arranged parallel to each other within the fibre or are just higgledy-piggledy. It has been found that in wool the molecules are not straight but regularly folded or wave-like. In cotton the molecules are straight but they wind spirally round the fibre. In silk they are straight and mainly aligned parallel to the fibre length. By contrast the molecules in acetate rayon are quite disarranged and higgledy-piggledy.

In general, a textile fibre is stronger in proportion to the degree to which its molecules are long and of uniform length, are straight or linear, closely packed, and are aligned parallel to each other and to the fibre length. In many instances where the fibre in its original state has not this desirable type of structure it can be plasticised sufficiently to allow it to be considerably stretched and by such treatment have its molecules suitably rearranged. For example, Fortisan is an example of a fibre which has been made very strong by simultaneously stretching and saponifying ordinary moderately strong acetate fibres. Most of the synthetic fibres such as nylon and Orlon are at an early stage in their manufacture highly stretched (often termed 'drawing') to a permanently increased length and thus given increased strength and a lower extensibility which is more suitable to weaving and knitting operations.

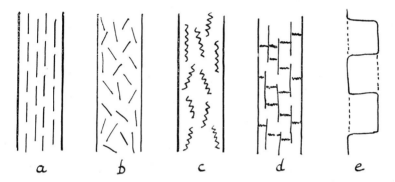

FIG. 1. Showing the different types of molecular structure possible in different fibres: (*a*) molecules aligned parallel to each other and the length axis of the fibre —this allows very close molecular packing which favours high tensile strength and low wet swelling, (*b*) molecules randomly distributed—loose molecular packing associated with high wet swelling and low tensile strength, (*c*) molecules are branched or folded so as not to allow close molecular packing, (*d*) straight molecules which are cross-linked—such a structure gives the fibres enhanced rigidity which is not favourable to softness of handle, and (*e*) a folded single molecule with cross-linked folds—wool molecules have this structure and because of the somewhat weak cross-links they are highly elastic and give the fibre itself a corresponding high degree of elasticity and resilience.

SEARCH FOR NEW MAN-MADE FIBRES

Since it has been found that for a fibre to be satisfactory as a textile fibre it must be composed of long tenuous molecules, it is obvious that only substances built up of such long molecules need be considered in the search for fibre-forming raw materials for use in the manufacture of synthetic fibres. The various polymers now available satisfy these requirements. Our knowledge of numerous

B

polymers of all kinds now allows the manufacture of many polymers which have fibre-forming properties. As will be described later, polyamides, polyesters, polymerised acrylonitriles, polymerised vinyl chlorides and cyanides, and more recently polyolefines, have all become useful for the production of synthetic fibres, and they can be made under controlled conditions so as to have molecules of optimum straightness and length and thus be convertible into fibres having optimum textile properties.

CLASSIFICATION OF FIBRES BY ORIGIN

Although textile fibres from the manufacturing and dyeing and finishing viewpoints can be usefully classified into hydrophile and hydrophobic groups it is also very convenient to use another classification as indicated below:

Natural fibres

Cotton, wool, silk, flax, mohair, cashmere, jute, ramie, hemp, and sisal.

Early man-made fibres (sometimes termed rayons—see page 44)

Viscose, cuprammonium, and acetate rayons. Regenerated protein and zein fibres.

Later man-made fibres (usually termed synthetic fibres)

Polyamides (nylon, Perlon, etc.), polyesters (Terylene, Kodel, Dacron, etc.), acrylics (Dynel, Orlon, Courtelle, Vinyon HH, Creslan, Acrilan, etc.), polyvinyls and polyvinylidenes (Zefran, Rhovyl, Saran, Darvan, Vinylon, etc.), polyolefines (Courlene, Reevon, etc.).

Miscellaneous fibres

Glass fibres, metallic and metallised yarns. All of these are man-made, the last named consisting entirely of metal or having a metal–plastic composite structure.

The essential characteristics of the more important fibres will now be described, *but all the useful properties are tabulated at the end of this chapter.*

Natural fibres (cellulose)

Cultivation of cotton

Cotton fibres are obtained from the cotton plant which is cultivated as an annual in many of the more tropical parts of the world,
including South America and the southern states of America,
Egypt, India, Russia, China, Turkey, Sudan, and Pakistan. The
pinkish flowers which form die in the usual manner, leaving a
pod or boll containing twenty or more seeds from each of which
grow outwardly a very large number of hairs or fibres, say 5 to
20 thousand. In its initial stage of formation each fibre consists of
a uniform hollow cylindrical cellulose tube, and each night there
is deposited on the inside of this a fresh thin layer of so-called
secondary cellulose up to about 30 or 40 such layers. The initial
cellulose tube thus becomes solid except for a central canal,
obviously for the passage of nutriment. Each secondary cellulose
layer has a spiral fibrillar structure. At about this stage the boll
opens, exposing to the drying action of light and warmth a tightly
packed mass of cotton fibres each of which is cylindrical. As drying
of the fibres proceeds they collapse and so change to acquire a
twisted ribbon form with thickened edges, and they also become
twisted irregularly; that is, with two or three right-hand twists
followed by two or three left-hand twists throughout their length
(a typical fibre has somewhat over one hundred twists per inch).

Harvesting, ginning and baling of picked cotton

Then follows the harvesting of these cotton bolls either by hand
or by machine picking. The cotton is then run through a gin of the
saw or roller type to comb away the fibres from the seeds and remove major impurities, so that the ginned cotton can be compressed into bales each containing about 500 lb of raw cotton
ready for export to mills where it can be converted into thread.
After such ginning there remains a proportion of a downy short
fibre cotton covering each seed, and this can be removed by a
special type of gin—the resulting so-called lint is a useful form of
cellulose for conversion into viscose and acetate rayons.

FIG. 2. Showing cotton plants with ripened and burst-open cotton bolls with the cotton fibres (attached to about 32 seeds in each boll) exposed to drying by the wind and sun. A cotton plant takes about 200 days to mature and is sensitive to frost. A large proportion of the world's cotton is grown in the U.S.A. (the southern states) with a suitably damp climate. In other and dry parts, such as Egypt, India, Pakistan, and the Sudan, irrigation schemes are necessary. Brazil, Russia, China, Mexico, Peru, East and West Africa also grow cotton.

By courtesy of The Cotton Board (Manchester)

Growth of a cotton fibre

Ginned cotton consisting of the longer cotton fibres in their collapsed, twisted, ribbon-like form is not homogeneous, since the fibres do not all reach maturity at the same time. The very immature fibres and some which grow imperfectly may consist entirely of the first hollow tube of cellulose without any inner secondary cellulose thickening, so that they collapse to form very thin ribbon-like fibres. These should be removed during the spinning of cotton threads, since they do not dye as does ordinary cotton and are liable to collect as small tangled masses (called neps) on the surface of threads and fabrics made from them and to show up as lustrous non-coloured specks in coloured goods.

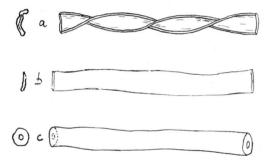

FIG. 3. Showing variations among cotton fibres coming from the same cotton boll. The normal twisted ribbon-like form of a cotton fibre is shown at (*a*) while at (*b*) is shown a thin-walled immature fibre. The thin-walled fibre is much less receptive to dyes than is a normal fibre. A cotton fibre as present in the cotton boll, fully ripened but not yet exposed to the sun and weathering such as takes place when the boll opens, is shown at (*c*) and is seen to be cylindrical; during the drying it contracts to the form shown at (*a*).

Fibre properties

Cotton fibres consist of pure cellulose whose chemical composition is indicated by the simple formula, $C_6H_{10}O_5$, associated with 3 to 4% of impurities among which are waxes, pectins, and mineral substances. While these impurities perform a useful function in the growing fibre it is generally necessary to remove them preparatory to dyeing and finishing. Cellulose molecules as present in cotton and other cellulose fibres consist of many $C_6H_{10}O_5$ units joined end-to-end and may thus be represented by $(C_6H_{10}O_5)_n$ where $n = 100$ or more.

There are several varieties of cotton which can be classified according to their origin or according to their fineness and staple length. It is usual for the finer (more valuable) cottons to be longer than the coarser types. The higher qualities have a staple (fibre) length of 1 to $2\frac{1}{2}$ inches, the lower qualities of up to 1 inch, and the intermediate medium qualities of $\frac{1}{2}$ to $1\frac{1}{2}$ inches approximately. The fibres vary from $1/1,000$ to $1/2,000$th inch in diameter.

Chemical reactivity

Acids. In many ways cotton fibres are very inert to deteriorating influences and cotton mummy wrappings as taken from Egyptian tombs are still in existence. As compared with wool, for example, cotton is not harmed by alkaline treatments except in the presence of oxygen, when oxidation may occur, especially in the presence of a metal catalyst such as iron. But by contrast with wool the treatment of cotton with acids and particularly mineral acids causes a rapid loss of strength. The drying into cotton of very low concentrations of a mineral acid such as hydrochloric or sulphuric acid can cause so profound a deterioration of the cotton cellulose that the fibre can thereafter be easily powdered. Organic acids such as acetic and formic acids have only a deteriorating action if used hot and concentrated, but oxalic acid is more liable to cause weakening.

Alkalis. A strong aqueous solution of a caustic alkali such as caustic soda or caustic potash when applied to cotton causes each fibre to swell and untwist and to regain substantially its original cylindrical form as when growing in the cotton boll at the time of maturity, but before the drying and collapse initiated by the opening of the boll. This swelling in caustic soda of say 50 to 60 Twaddell (1·00 specific gravity or sp. gr. = 200 Twaddell) is accompanied by a length shrinkage, and this was particularly noted by John Mercer about 1850. The caustic soda can be removed by thorough washing with water (it is assisted by also neutralising the alkali with dilute acid), and on drying the fibre retains its new swollen form, but its cellulose content appears to be slightly hydrated in that the fibre is more reactive towards most chemical reagents and it has markedly increased affinity for many dyes. The cotton in this form is generally known as *mercerised* cotton after the name of its discoverer.

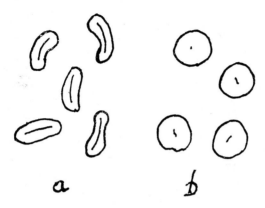

FIG. 4. Showing cross-sections of cotton fibres before (*a*) and after (*b*) mercerisation. The effect of mercerisation with a strong caustic alkali solution is to swell each fibre so that it reverts to its cylindrical form as in the cotton boll before exposure to weathering with consequent drying and contraction.

Some forty years later Horace Lowe, repeating Mercer's experiments, noticed that if the shrinkage of the cotton fibre was prevented by stretching during the treatment with caustic soda and also during the washing out of this alkali, the fibre was left with an enhanced lustre. Also the resulting fibre gained somewhat less reactivity and affinity for dyes.

Mercerisation of cotton

The discoveries of Mercer and Lowe form the basis of a much-used process now known as mercerisation in which cotton yarns and fabrics are given a very useful permanent increase of lustre by impregnating them for about one minute with a cold caustic soda solution of about 55 Twaddell, and then washing out the alkali while the yarn or fabric is held by suitable machinery to about its original dimensions of length or length and width. It has been found that the greatest lustre increase is obtained when the

FIG. 5. Showing part of the plant used for mercerising cotton fabric. In the first stage the fabric is impregnated evenly in open width free from creases with a caustic soda solution of 50 to 55 degrees Twaddell maintained at room temperature (15 to 20° C). It then passes over a number of cylinders to allow sufficient time for this alkaline mercerising liquor to penetrate the fabric thoroughly. The fabric then passes on to the stenter frame where its selvedges are firmly gripped by continuously running clip chains so that it can be suitably stretched in width (it tends to contract strongly in width under the action of the mercerising liquor) and held so stretched while overhead water sprays wash out the mercerising liquor. When washing is practically complete the fabric no longer tends to contract, so it can be led off the stenter to pass through further washing in the usual manner. The alkaline wash liquors are collected for purification and concentration so that the resulting concentrated solution of caustic soda can again be used for mercerising fresh fabric. The permanent high lustre thus produced is dependent on holding out the fabric against width contraction during the washing out of the mercerising liquor—any width contraction which occurs before the fabric reaches the stenter can be corrected by width stretching on the stenter, i.e. by suitably diverging the clip chains in the early part of the travel of the fabric. The fabric requires to be in contact with the mercerising liquid only for $\frac{1}{2}-\frac{3}{4}$ minute to secure the maximum lustre.

By courtesy of The Cotton Board (Manchester)

yarn as such or as present in fabric is a doubled one and of low twist so that after the mercerising treatment the fibres in the yarn lie nearly parallel to the yarn length direction.

Reactivity in conversion of cotton into viscose and acetate rayons

Cotton is inert towards most liquids, so that it is difficult to prepare a solution of it. But if the cotton is degraded by acid treatment or by oxidation it becomes more easy to dissolve in alkaline solutions, especially those containing caustic soda.

Cotton treated with caustic soda and then with carbon disulphide forms cellulose xanthate (yellowish) and this can then be dissolved in a dilute solution of caustic soda to give a viscous liquid which is generally termed *viscose*. By extruding viscose through a jet into an acid liquor, preferably also containing sodium sulphate, a filament of regenerated cellulose can be obtained and this forms the basis of the method by which viscose rayon is manufactured.

By treating cotton with a warm mixture of acetic acid and acetic anhydride it can be converted into cellulose acetate which can be precipitated by dilution of the reaction product, filtered off, dried and dissolved in acetone. The resulting solution can then be extruded through a jet into warm air so that the acetone solvent rapidly evaporates to leave a solidified filament of cellulose acetate. This forms the basis of the manufacture of acetate rayon.

Bleaching of cotton

Raw cotton is generally bleached by treatment with an oxidising liquor containing either sodium hypochlorite, or sodium chlorite, or hydrogen peroxide (the two former agents are used under acid conditions and the last under alkaline conditions). If this process of bleaching is not accurately controlled not only are the impurities oxidised and destroyed but the cotton itself is oxidised and thus damaged. Overbleached cotton containing oxycellulose resists dyeing with direct cotton dyes, so that if this overbleaching is not even, the bleached yarn or fabric is liable to dye unevenly and it is not usually possible to overcome this fault. Overbleached cotton has a higher solubility in alkaline wash liquors than ordinary correctly bleached cotton, so that it can soon become excessively weakened by such repeated washing.

A viscosity test for chemically damaged cotton

The degree of damage or deterioration produced in cotton as a result of any treatment such as bleaching, can be determined by measurement of the viscosity of a solution of the cotton in cuprammonium solution (prepared by dissolving copper hydroxide in aqueous ammonia solution). The damage is proportional to the lowered viscosity as compared with the viscosity under the same standardised conditions of undamaged cotton.

Other forms of damage

Cotton is quite immune to attack by moths but under damp conditions is liable to deterioration by mildew and it is susceptible also to attack by various bacteria. It can be preserved from such attack by a pre-treatment with certain copper and mercurial compounds.

FLAX AND LINEN

Cultivation of flax

Flax is grown in much the same manner as wheat and barley, as an annual. It bears a blue flower which eventually gives place to

FIG. 6. A flax stalk with its flowerhead and root. The fibres, which can ultimately be separated as linen fibres, extend in the form of bundles throughout the whole length of the stalk.

seeds from which linseed oil can be made. The tall upright stalk has below the outer layer or epidermis a concentric layer largely made up of longitudinally disposed bundles of linen fibres embedded in gummy material which also separates the bundles from each other yet holds them together. Each of these fibre bundles extends the full length of the stalk and each long fibre is built up of many short fibres joined end-to-end with a slight overlapping of these ends. In harvesting flax the stalks are pulled up by the root rather than cut (as for wheat, oats, etc.) so as not to waste the fibre present in the root ends; the stalks are then allowed to dry in the open air.

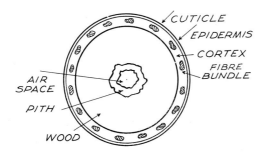

FIG. 7. Diagrammatic view of the cross-section of a flax stalk showing its structure, more particularly in respect of the distribution of the bundles of linen fibres which are spaced within the cortex and which extend the whole length of the stalk from the flowerhead to the roots. It is because the fibres extend so low that flax stalks are pulled (during harvesting) instead of being cut, thus avoiding fibre waste. The central portions of the stalk consist of pith and air space, and the outer portions of cambium, cortex with embedded fibre bundles, epidermis, and cuticle; in between is the wood portion of the stalk. Flax stalks require retting (decomposition by micro-organisms) to allow the fibre bundles to be removed intact for further purification.

Isolation of linen fibres from flax stalks

The further processing of flax stalks is designed to separate the bundles of long fibres from all surrounding gummy impurities and the remainder of the stalk substance, and to do this without breaking each long fibre down into the shorter fibres of which it is built up. Firstly the seed heads are combed off in a so-called rippling machine. The flax stalks, usually in small bundles, are then *retted* by exposing them to sun, rain, and air in the fields or by steeping them in shallow pools of running or stagnant water or in tanks of water under strictly controlled conditions, so that bacteria can loosen or solubilise all parts of the stalks except the bundles of linen fibres. It is essential that the bacterial decomposition which takes place does not involve the linen fibres.

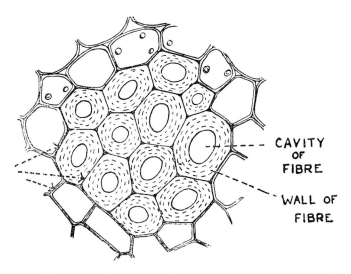

CAVITY
OF
FIBRE

WALL OF
FIBRE

FIG. 8. A cross-section of a bundle of fibres as present in the cortex portion of a flax stalk. The fibres, each having a central cavity, are shown cemented together by a pectin-containing agglutinant.

After the retted flax stalks are dried they are led between fluted rollers under pressure to disintegrate the partly decomposed parts and are then *scutched* by passage through a machine which combs and beats out these disintegrated impurities to leave the long linen fibre bundles substantially intact. Scutched flax is thus comparable to raw cotton after ginning, and it is ready for further processing so that the long fibres become separate by removal of the gummy substance which holds them together in bundle form —a 20 to 30% loss of fibre weight is involved. Further purification is obtained by treatment with boiling alkaline liquors and by bleaching with sodium hypochlorite solution after much the same methods as are employed for bleaching cotton goods.

Linen fibre properties

Linen fibres may be 3 to 4 feet in length according to the length of the stalks from which they are obtained, but the shorter fibres of which they consist joined end-to-end are only up to a maximum of about 2 inches in length. The thickness of the long fibres varies throughout their length but is about 1/1,000th inch. Each fibre has a polygonal cross-section which under high magnification is seen to consist of several polygonal cells joined together. Throughout its length a linen fibre is notched at intervals somewhat after the manner of a bamboo cane.

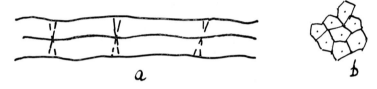

a　　　　*b*

FIG. 9. A longitudinal view of a linen fibre (*a*) and its cross-section (*b*). The fibre is seen to have spaced transverse fissures along its length and to have a polygonal cellular cross-section.

Linen fibres consist of pure cellulose similar to that of cotton but they contain a higher proportion of natural impurities, say 25%. The behaviour of linen towards acids, alkalis, and oxidising agents is similar to that of cotton. Linen absorbs about 12% of moisture from the air as compared with 6% for cotton and it is probably this absorbed moisture and its high power of conducting heat which accounts for much of the cold feel of linen goods.

It is possible to dye linen goods as for cotton but usually it is more difficult for dyes to penetrate the fibres, possibly because the cellulose molecules in linen fibres are packed together more closely than those of cotton. In the same way, linen is more difficult to bleach to a good white than cotton. Linen is adversely affected by those bacteria which attack cotton but also like cotton it is completely immune to attack by moth.

JUTE

This type of fibre, which is very largely used throughout the world for the manufacture of ropes and twines and of coarse packing fabrics including sacks, and also for backing tufted carpets and linoleums, is obtained in much the same manner as linen is from flax stalks except that it is the somewhat large jute plant which provides in its inner bark the raw fibres. Such fibres contain about 20% of the impurity lignin, the remainder being cellulose.

Because of its high content of impurities jute is more durable than flax and cotton especially in respect of liability to deterioration by bacterial attack under damp conditions. In its air-dry state jute contains about 14% of absorbed moisture.

Jute fibres have a polygonal cross-section and are periodically notched along their length, thus resembling linen fibres.

Jute can be dyed in the same way as cotton but it differs from this latter fibre in having a useful strong affinity for acid and basic dyes.

The plant is grown principally in India and Pakistan.

RAMIE

Ramie fibre, which can be used for the production of highly lustrous linen-like fabrics (ramie fabrics were used as Egyptian mummy wrapping some 7,000 years ago), is obtained from stalks of the ramie plant which is widely cultivated throughout the warmer countries such as China, Japan, Egypt, Spain, etc. The long strands of ramie fibre are frequently separated from the ramie stalk bark by hand. Ramie fibres consist of cellulose and can be dyed with most cotton dyes. Fabrics made of ramie can be mercerised to improve their lustre.

HEMP

Hemp fibres are in many ways similar to those of flax except that they are coarser and usually darker in colour and so are difficult to bleach to a good white. They are obtained from the hemp plant which is cultivated in many countries including America, Russia, and also Asian countries (hemp was used in China nearly 5,000 years ago). Grown after the manner of flax, the hemp fibres have to be separated from the much longer hemp stalks by retting and the mechanical processes of breaking and scutching previously described for flax. The long hemp fibres (up to 6 feet or more in length) are built up of shorter fibres each of up to 1 inch in length and joined end-to-end, and they are frequently but irregularly notched along their length. The fibres have a polygonal cross-section and possess a central lumen.

Although hemp can be made into lustrous fabrics its main use is for the manufacture of twines and ropes and for canvas and sacks. Such materials are usually employed as made but they can be dyed with direct cotton dyes, although basic dyes give bright shades after the fibres have first been mordanted with tannic acid + tartar emetic.

SISAL

Sisal fibres are obtained from the large thick leaves of the *Agave sisalana* plant, which is grown mainly in Africa, Java, Mexico, and similarly hot countries. These leaves are fleshy and by suitable machinery the flesh can be scraped away to leave strands of fibres which are then washed and dried to a creamy white colour.

Sisal fibre is largely used for making binder twine and other cordage, but it can also be used for the manufacture of mats which can be dyed with cotton and wool dyes.

Natural fibres (protein)

WOOL

Wool is easily the most important of those natural fibres made of protein (wool protein is known as keratin and its chemical composition is approximately represented by the formula $C_{72}H_{112}N_{18}O_{12}S$). Silk is also a protein fibre but unlike wool it contains no sulphur. Actually wool fibres are not made of a single protein but of many different so-called amino-acids each of the general formula, $NHR—CH_2CH_2\cdots CH_2CH_2COOH$, which are joined together in various ways but mainly end-to-end to form long-chain molecules having some amino-acid molecules attached as side chains at frequent intervals. By suitable methods of hydrolysis these long-chain molecules can be broken down into the score of different amino-acids present in wool molecules.

Sheep and wool

Wool is obtained from sheep to be found throughout the world, but the best qualities of wool are obtained from sheep reared not primarily for the meat they provide but especially for their wool. The Merino sheep give long fine wools of the highest quality and most of this comes from Australia, South Africa, and South America. Merino sheep cross-bred with other types are largely farmed in New Zealand, and these give a coarser but very useful type of wool. It would seem that the soil and climate of a country largely determine what type of sheep and wool can be most satis-factorily produced—it is not possible to produce high quality Merino wool just anywhere and it is interesting to note that Merino sheep do not 'do' so well in Britain as in the countries mentioned above. But throughout the world wool is obtained from sheep of one kind or other and used in the manufacture of wool yarns and fabrics of various kinds and qualities.

Physical characteristics of wool fibres

The wool, which is at appropriate times of the year hand or mechanically sheared from the sheep's back, naturally takes the form of locks which are wavy (crimped), and it is a natural feature of most wool fibres that they strongly retain this form throughout their useful life. This crimp arises indirectly from the fact that each wool fibre is of unequal composition along its length so that it consists of two approximately equal longitudinal halves, one being termed the orthocortex (always present on the inside of a crimp or wave) while the other is termed the paracortex and it is always present on the outside. The finer wool fibres have more crimps per inch (say up to 30) than the coarser fibres (say up to 10).

The length of a wool fibre can vary considerably according to the type of sheep from which it is obtained and it may reach about 16 inches, but the finer Merino wool fibres are nearer to 5 inches in length. The thickness of wool fibre varies from 1/300th to 1/1,000th inch and the fibre is thus somewhat coarser than a cotton fibre. Wool fibres have only about a third of the strength of cotton fibres but they are three to four times more extensible when stretched. An important property of wool is its high resilience. It has the further advantage of having a low specific gravity of 1·32 as compared with 1·54 for cotton. Wool fibres normally retain about 18% of moisture in their air-dry state. In absorbing moisture wool becomes warm and this may partly account for the fact that wet wool materials do not feel so cold as similarly wet cotton goods.

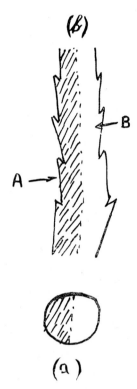

FIG. 10. (*a*) Cross- and (*b*) longitudinal sections of a wool fibre to show its composite structure in so far as one half differs physically and chemically from the other half. The fibre is composed of a paracortex *A* and an orthocortex *B* and this bilateral structure largely determines the crimp or waviness of a wool fibre. This bilateral structure can be readily seen under a microscope, after first having stained the fibre using a method which ensures that the paracortex acquires a colour different from that of the orthocortex.

Scale covering of a wool fibre and its felting properties

Wool fibres differ widely from all other types of fibre in respect of their physical form and structure. Essentially each fibre is cylindrical in cross-section and can be seen to consist of an inner core termed the cortex enclosed within a sheath-like outer covering

c

formed of closely overlapping so-called *epithelial scales*, each of which has a slightly protruding edge with all such edges pointing from the root end towards the tip end of the fibre. These protruding edges give each fibre a roughness which is obviously greater in the tip-to-root rather than the opposite direction. This uni-directional roughness plays an important part in giving wool fibres unique *felting* power, whereby any mass of wool fibres (this may take the form of a thread or fabric) tends to become more compact with corresponding thickening and shrinkage in surface area when washed in a warm aqueous liquor with repeated squeezing and relaxation. In the relaxation which follows each squeeze the fibres are held together by their roughness so that the mass of fibres does not fully return to its original volume. As the process continues this closing-up of the wool fibres becomes greater until a point is reached at which the mass of fibres has reached its maximum density and the fibres are so tightly matted or entangled (felted) that they cannot be separated. In having this power to felt wool differs completely from cotton, silk, and almost all other important textile fibres. Felting accounts for the shrinkage which wool fabrics and garments normally suffer as the result of washing and laundering. Such shrinkage can only be kept to a minimum by avoiding as far as possible all squeezing or compression of the wool material in the washing process.

As will be described later the tendency of wool goods to shrink in washing can be almost eliminated by reducing the felting power of wool by a treatment which will make the wool fibres smoother or at least make their roughness equal in both the root-to-tip and the tip-to-root directions. Such a change can come from removing the epithelial scales (this is not desirable since it weakens the fibres) or by smoothing their protruding edges.

The internal structure of wool fibres

The cortex. The cortex of a wool fibre appears to comprise innumerable small so-called cortical cells of complex non-keratin composition, which are spindle-shaped and embedded in amorphous keratin. There also appears to be a thin membrane (about which little is known) between the cortex and the epithelial scale layer and yet another similar membrane covering this scale layer. In some wool fibres the cortex contains a central hollow channel known as a medulla.

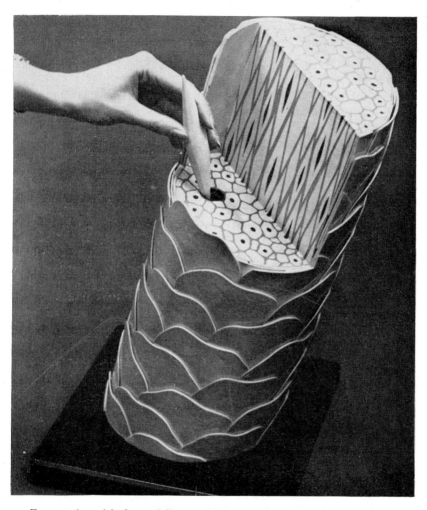

FIG. 11. A model of a wool fibre to show the essential constructional features including the outer covering of epithelial scales (these are tough and protect the inner parts of the fibre) and the cortex which is built up of closely packed so-called spindle cells, one of which is held by the hand. Recent research has shown that the epithelial scale covering is overall covered by a thin membrane which is also protective to the wool fibre as a whole and is now known as the epicuticle.

By courtesy of The International Wool Secretariat

The cortex is of softer material than the scale layer and in fact the scales themselves seem to consist of a much tougher form of keratin. Thus the scales can be considered to protect the cortex. Any treatment of wool fibres which damages or ruptures the scale layer impairs the durability of the fibre, since the cortex then becomes more accessible to deteriorating influences. Thus a fibre having a ruptured scale layer or thinned scales or a proportion of the scales removed becomes more soluble in alkaline washing liquors, is more susceptible to attack by acid and oxidising agents, and can be more easily dyed to a deep shade since the dye can now more easily pass through the scale layer into the cortex. It is normally much more difficult to dye the scales than the cortex and in fact with some dyes the scales may resist dyeing completely so that the colour of the resulting dyed wool fibre is due entirely to the dye which is absorbed into the cortex.

The cortex of a wool fibre has a marked tendency to swell in alkaline liquors and it is largely because of the restraining effect of the surrounding scale layer that the cortex does not swell up to the point of dissolving in such liquor. If the scale layer is ruptured this dissolution of the cortex in the outside alkaline liquor can take place to a degree limited by the extent of the fibre damage (scale layer rupture). Actually an alkali-solubility test is much used to measure the amount of damage to wool.

Special chemical treatments are available which enable the cortical spindle cells, the epithelial scales, and the special thin membranes to be separated from the remainder of the wool substance.

Di-sulphide bonds on wool fibres

The small sulphur content of the wool fibre is very important since it forms part of the so-called disulphide or crystine bonds which hold adjacent wool chain molecules together laterally and so prevent excessive fibre swelling when subjected to dyeing and finishing treatments. These bonds can be broken by suitable treatment with acids, alkalis, oxidising and reducing agents with profound consequent changes in the properties of the wool (mainly harmful) but it is also possible to re-form them to some degree or to replace them by other and sometimes stronger bonds (often with an improvement of the fibre properties in some desired direction). Unfortunately in any such modification of wool fibres the original valuable soft handle of the wool is made harsher. The presence of this sulphur makes wool susceptible to moth damage.

Chemical reactivity of wool

Wool is fairly resistant towards acids and indeed wool materials are frequently dyed (without damage) in dye liquors which have added to them relatively small amounts of acid (mineral or organic) to assist dye absorption by the fibres. On the other hand, wool is very sensitive to alkalis with the exception of the very weak ones such as ammonia. Excessive treatment with an alkaline liquor can cause a loss of weight in the wool material and also a fibre weakening, harshening of handle, and a yellowing in colour.

Wool is especially reactive towards chlorine gas and solutions of hypochlorite, and this can be used as the basis of processes for reducing the felting power of wool materials so that they become resistant to shrinkage in washing. As will be described later, wool can be made unshrinkable by alternative processes which use sulphuryl chloride or a solution containing a mixture of sodium hypochlorite and potassium permanganate, and by processes in which the fibre roughness is masked by deposition of a synthetic resin on the fibres.

Greasy impurities

It is an important point that raw wool contains up to 50% of natural impurities, mainly consisting of a mixture of fats and waxes which is generally termed wool grease and suint—this last-named substance comprises mineral salts and organic substances and is essentially the residue left when sheep's perspiration dries. When raw wool is washed with a weakly alkaline liquor the suint becomes emulsified and then assists removal of the fats and waxes.

Moth attack on wool

As is well known, wool is readily attacked by moths—it is the young larvae, hatched out from eggs laid in the wool by moths, which really do the damage by eating the wool fibres. Bacteria can attack wool also but more particularly under damp conditions.

Warm handle of wool

The scale surface and the crimped nature of wool fibres are conducive to a porous structure in yarns and fabrics made from them, and since air is one of the worst conductors of heat it is natural to find wool garments warm to touch and wear. The valuable warmth and softness of wool materials can be enhanced by making them with soft spun yarns and by ensuring that these yarns are interlaced by weaving and knitting quite loosely.

Recovered wool fibres

The total amount of wool obtained by shearing sheep each year (such wool is called virgin wool) is insufficient by about 3,000 million lb to meet the world's wool requirements, and the deficiency has to be made good by recovering waste wool from all kinds of rags, discarded garments and fabrics, etc. Special machines are used to scratch out loose wool fibres from these sorted waste wool goods which have first to be oiled to assist their mechanical manipulation. The recovered wool passes under various names such as mungo, shoddy, alpaca, and extract (this latter contains cotton fibres also since it is obtained from waste mixture goods). As might be expected the quality of a recovered wool is considerably lower than that of virgin wool, since a proportion of the fibres will have suffered chemical or mechanical damage. Yet for selected types of wool materials it is useful to employ a proportion of recovered wool in admixture with virgin wool.

From the above it may be correctly inferred that a label describing a material as 'made of all wool' can be somewhat misleading since it can include recovered wool. It would be better if the label stated definitely whether the wool was all virgin wool or otherwise.

MOHAIR

Mohair fibres are obtained from the Angora goat which is now largely farmed in America and Turkey. Although similar in structure to wool a mohair fibre is smoother and considerably more lustrous, since the epithelial scales are less numerous and overlap each other to a smaller degree than the epithelial scales of wool. The fibre length varies according to the age of the goat from which the mohair is cut—the variation is between 5 and 12 inches—and the fibres are somewhat stiff and have a circular cross-section. Owing to its compactness of structure mohair is more durable under conditions of hard wear than is wool and thus fabrics made from it are much used for upholstery—in recent years it has met with increasing competition from plastic coverings.

Mohair is attacked by moths as wool. It gives highly lustrous fabrics which can be readily dyed with the usual wool dyes.

Mohair, because of the scale-covering of its fibres, has felting properties but they are less pronounced than those of wool.

CASHMERE

Cashmere fibres are obtained mainly in China from the Tibetan cashmere goat by combing out the downy fibres and discarding the longer coarser fibres or hair. These fibres, of up to 3 inches in length, have a structure similar to that of wool and mohair in that each fibre consists of a cortex (with spindle cells) covered with a scale layer—in the case of cashmere the scale edges protrude considerably so as to give the fibre a high degree of roughness. Cashmere fibres are finer than those of merino wool, and partly because of this the fibres are highly susceptible to deteriorating influences such as alkalis and some chemicals.

Cashmere fibres lend themselves admirably to the production of high quality, lustrous and soft fabrics and garments.

SILK

Cultivation of silk

Silk, which for several centuries commencing nearly 5,000 years ago in China has been the most prized of all textile fibres, is obtained from the cocoon spun around itself by a silkworm just before entering into a pupa stage to emerge a month or so later as a white moth. The cocoon thread is really a double one and it forms from two separate silk filaments which emerge (coated with a gum which eventually hardens to cement them together) through a common spinneret in the head of the silkworm from two more remote glands. The substance of which the two filaments are made is known as fibroin while the cementing gum is termed silk-gum or sericin—these two substances are only slightly different in chemical composition but the difference is sufficient to allow the sericin to be soluble in hot alkaline liquors while the fibroin remains insoluble. Thus the silk-gum can be removed to leave the two silk filaments separate by simply boiling the raw silk thread in a soap solution.

FIG. 12. Cross-section of a raw silk fibre showing it to consist of two single fibres (each having a triangular cross-section) composed of fibroin and held together by a tough coating of silk-gum, otherwise known as sericin. The silk-gum is generally removed at a suitable stage during the manufacture of silk fabrics by treatment with a boiling soap liquor, leaving the separate fibroin or pure silk fibres with a much softer handle and a higher lustre than raw silk fibres.

Before the silkworm spins its cocoon it has had a short but varied life. Originally it hatched out of an egg (somewhat like turnip seed) laid by white moth of the *Bombyx mori* species previously mentioned and kept at a suitable temperature in incubators. Each silkworm is then about $\frac{1}{4}$ inch in length and eagerly devours the cut-up mulberry leaves supplied to it. Within one month this silkworm sheds its skin four times and then climbs on to a twig (also provided for it) and spins its cocoon.

If the cocoon was left to itself the pupa within would later come to life as a moth and moisten that end of the cocoon nearer to its head so as to soften the silk-gum and facilitate the emergence first of its head, then of the remainder of its body, and so be able to fly away, mate, and lay eggs which become a source of a fresh generation of silkworms. But actually the supply of silkworms does not require all the cocoons to hatch out in this manner, and since the emergence of the moth from a cocoon can disturb the silk filament so that entanglement difficulties may arise in the subsequent reeling of the silk thread from the cocoon, it is the practice to keep only a small proportion of the cocoons for moth rearing and to destroy all life within the remainder of the cocoons by steaming or other method of high temperature heating.

The selection of the eggs for the rearing of fresh silkworms is very carefully controlled, since in times past disease has caused very serious losses in silkworm establishments. So only those eggs which have been proved free from disease are used.

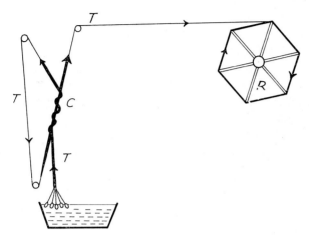

FIG. 13. Showing the method used for reeling silk thread from cocoons. A few cocoons are placed in a basin of hot water to soften the silk-gum which coats a raw silk thread. The ends from these cocoons are then brought together to form a thread *T* which is drawn away from the cocoons over guiding devices and along the path shown so as finally to be wound in the form of a skein on the reel *R*. In this making of a composite silk thread only one silk thread is drawn from each cocoon. The crossing of the composite thread at *C* has the effect of causing the single silk threads to stick together within the composite thread and also to wipe off surplus adhering water. The operator is required to join in a fresh end of silk when the thread from a cocoon breaks and to replace any cocoon as soon as it is fully unwound. Skill is needed to achieve these operations and keep the thickness of the composite thread as constant as possible.

Reeling silk threads from cocoons

The reeling of the double silk thread from the cocoons is largely done by hand, although Japanese silk cultivators have devised machinery for the purpose. A number of cocoons are thrown into a bowl of hot water where they freely float. An end of thread is drawn from each of three, four, or more cocoons (the hot water softens the silk-gum sufficiently to allow this separation and break-down of the cocoons) and together they are drawn through a suitable guide to be wound into a skein. The female labour employed for this purpose skilfully with deft finger movement prevents twisting and entanglement of the threads as they unwind from the moving cocoons to pass forward to give a skein of three- or four-fold silk thread. As any one cocoon becomes fully unwound or becomes so entangled that it has to be discarded, another one is brought in to take its place.

Waste silk for schappe threads

All waste cocoon silk, however formed, is collected and separately freed from silk-gum so as to allow its working up into short fibre silk threads which are known as schappe silk—these threads are not so fine and lustrous as the so-called tram and organzine silk threads which are made from the evenly reeled strands of silk filaments from the cocoon as described above. Tram silk results from twisting together to a moderate degree two or three strands of silk filaments as directly obtained from the cocoons and is thus a moderately strong thread. By contrast, organzine thread results from hard twisting together two or three strands of silk filaments which have themselves been twisted; it is a much stronger thread and is mainly used as the warp in silk fabrics.

De-gumming of silk

It will be noticed that these different types of silk thread have been obtained without removing the silk-gum from the filaments, so that these latter still consist of two silk fibres cemented together. In many instances it is preferred to defer the de-gumming process until such threads have been woven or knitted into fabrics or hose, since the silk-gum serves to protect the fibres from damage in these mechanical operations. De-gumming can at a late stage be carried out by boiling the fabric or hose in a 1% solution of soap for about an hour followed by thorough washing with water. With the removal of the silk-gum the silk material acquires much increased softness and may become whiter if the silk-gum is yellowish coloured, as it frequently is.

Weighting of silk

There is about 20 to 30% of silk-gum associated with the silk fibres so that a weight loss of this order results from de-gumming —it makes the de-gummed silk so much the more expensive. It is for this reason that de-gummed silk is often treated so as to deposit within the fibres insoluble substances which will not appreciably harshen the silk yet restore the loss of weight. This process is usually termed silk weighting. If only the weight loss is restored then the weighted silk has good durability. But there is the temptation to add more weight than that lost and in some cases the weight of the silk may be doubled. This excessive weighting robs the silk of its most valuable characteristics of handle, lustre, and strength, and although sometimes carried out it is not to be recommended.

Silk is weighted by successive treatments with solutions of stannous chloride and sodium phosphate whereby insoluble tin phosphate is deposited within the fibres.

Wild (tussah) silk

Tussah silk is obtained not from the cocoons of silkworms that are bred and cultivated in establishments under carefully controlled conditions, but from the tussah silkworm which lives wild, eating the leaves of a species of oak tree. The cocoons are comparatively large and they are spun with a silk fibre which is much less uniform although stronger than cultivated silk. An important feature of tussah silk is that it is much more resistant to alkalis than is cultivated silk.

Properties of silk

Silk fibres are very fine, say about 1/1,000 to 1/2,000th inch in diameter, and they may be extremely long; the length depends on the breakages which occur in reeling the fibre from the cocoon. Their cross-section is triangular and not circular as is sometimes stated. They consist of the protein fibroin which differs essentially from wool keratin in containing no sulphur and is thus not attacked by moths.

The general behaviour of silk is similar to that of wool in being unharmed by weak acid liquors but it is more resistant to alkalis— tussah silk is even more resistant and may be scoured in hot alkaline liquors without damage. It is harmed by treatment with chlorine and hypochlorite solutions and so is preferably bleached with hydrogen peroxide.

Silk can be easily dyed with a wide range of dyes including many cotton and wool dyes. When treated with organic acids, as for example acetic or formic acid, it acquires a peculiar crisp handle generally termed scroop.

Early man-made fibres

Before embarking on the general subject of man-made fibres, it is desirable to discuss their terminology.

Originally the term rayon included acetate, viscose, and cuprammonium fibres. Then the makers of the acetate fibre Celanese indicated that their fibre should no longer be referred to as a rayon but simply as an acetate fibre.

The practice of confining the term rayon to viscose fibres alone is gaining ground, particularly in America, but it is not universally accepted by any means and has caused confusion to people who are accustomed to using the word rayon in a broader sense. On the other hand acetate and viscose fibres differ in their properties and require different treatment in, e.g., washing, drying and ironing, so that it is important that their names should emphasise the distinction between them. In this book I have allowed the term rayon to apply to both regenerated cellulose and cellulose derivatives, but have qualified the individual fibres wherever appropriate as viscose rayon, acetate rayon, triacetate rayon, and so on. I hope that this practice will underline their separate identities while marking them off from groups of entirely different origin such as the polyamides and polyesters.

Early discoveries in fibre-making

The early man-made fibres, which include more particularly viscose, cuprammonium, and acetate rayons, are now being manufactured from cotton and wood celluloses by processes whose essential details were discovered around 1890. At that time Chardonnet silk was being made on the large scale from cotton by a process of nitration followed by a spinning into filaments of a solution in an organic solvent of the resulting cellulose nitrate—the method used would today be considered completely unsatisfactory and so it can be easily understood why this type of man-made fibre was relatively soon abandoned in favour of the three types mentioned above.

Around 1890 there were discovered in quick succession three different methods for converting cotton into cellulose derivatives which could be dissolved in appropriate solutions sufficiently viscous to allow them to be extruded into a so-called coagulating bath, containing ingredients which both ensured the rapid coagulation of the issuing fine fluid streams into solid filaments, and also that these filaments consisted either of regenerated cellulose or a cellulose derivative which could satisfactorily take the place of regenerated cellulose. In the *viscose* process devised by Cross, Bevan, and Topham the soluble cellulose derivative was cellulose xanthate, in the *cuprammonium* process it was a special hydrated form of cotton, and in the *acetate* process cellulose acetate was the soluble cellulose derivative. The first two processes were developed to large-scale production fairly rapidly, but the acetate process took many years to bring into commercial use. Today the viscose and acetate processes are very largely employed to make viscose (regenerated cellulose) and acetate rayons, while the cuprammonium process which makes regenerated cellulose fibres is used to a relatively quite small extent. Details of these processes can now be described.

VISCOSE RAYON

Viscose rayon was at first made from cotton linters (the shorter fibres which grow with the longer fibres on cotton seeds but which are too short to be used in the manufacture of yarns and fabrics), but in recent years it is made mainly from the cheaper form of cellulose which can be extracted from wood; this cellulose is usually produced in the form of sheets convenient to handle. Essential features of the process are as follows:

Firstly the cellulose (from cotton or wood) in the form of sheets is saturated with a strong solution of caustic soda (about 30% and sp. gr. 1·274 and approximately of mercerising concentration) at room temperature. The cellulose sheets swell and there is formed alkali-cellulose which is a loose combination of cellulose with caustic soda. Excess of caustic soda solution is pressed out and the residual sheets of alkali-cellulose are mechanically shredded into what are usually termed crumbs. These crumbs are then uniformly exposed to air to produce in them a subtle oxidation change which has to be very carefully controlled and which makes the alkali-cellulose desirably more reactive in the next stage of the process.

Preparation of a viscose spinning solution

The matured alkali-cellulose crumbs (slightly yellow) are then mechanically mixed with an appropriate amount of carbon bisulphide until a uniform product of cellulose xanthate is produced having a deep reddish brown colour. This is then dissolved in a moderately strong solution of caustic soda to give a viscous solution generally known as viscose. This is allowed to stand for several hours to undergo another subtle change by which the viscose acquires a viscosity that favours its smooth extrusion and also a composition that favours the coagulation of the extruded streams of viscose as they enter a coagulation bath. This is a solution of sulphuric acid and sodium bisulphate also containing small proportions of zinc sulphate (to assist a stretching of the coagulated viscose threads as they pass through the coagulating liquor and to ensure that they have an indented surface) and glucose (to ensure that the resulting threads are soft and pliable).

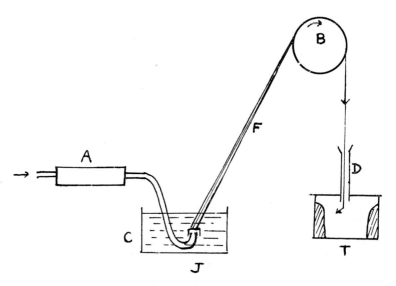

FIG. 14. Showing the essential features of the spinning of viscose rayon. A viscose solution, suitably ripened and having appropriate alkali and cellulose xanthate contents, is very thoroughly filtered in passing through *A* so that it may be extruded without clogging through the many orifices (holes) in spinning jet *J* fully immersed in the coagulating liquor in vessel *C* (this liquor contains sulphuric acid, sodium bisulphate, zinc sulphate, and probably a surface-active agent). It is important that the viscose solution has a viscosity which makes it free-flowing, and also a degree of ripeness so that the fluid streams issuing from the jet are immediately solidified into fibres which are collected into the form of a thread *F* to be drawn over rotating Godet wheel *B* and fall down into the rotating centrifugal Topham pot *T* to be built up inside as a ball or 'cake'.

The spinning process

With the viscose solution correctly ripened by standing and filtered free of suspended insoluble matter which could block the small orifices of the spinneret, it is pumped at a uniform rate through multi-holed spinnerets into the coagulating bath. Thus a number of separate filaments are continuously formed and they are steadily drawn away from the spinnerets under a moderate degree of tension (this stretches them to give improved strength and other properties), to pass through guides (the number of filaments, corresponding to the number of holes in each spinneret, are thus brought together into thread form) and be collected while being given a small degree of twist in a rapidly rotating so-called Topham pot. The thread, as a result of the action of the sulphuric acid in the coagulating bath, now consists of regenerated cellulose and is somewhat highly swollen and weak. But it easily withstands its winding within the Topham pot into the form of a compact cake. In a later stage these cakes are thoroughly washed in special machines, treated with a solution of sodium hypochlorite to bleach the thread (slightly yellow due to the presence of sulphur) to a good white, then treated with a composition which lubricates the individual filaments which form the thread, and finally dried by passage through a tunnel-type drying machine within which hot air circulates.

There are alternative methods for handling the freshly coagulated viscose rayon thread. For example, instead of being collected in a Topham pot it may be continuously led in the form of a close spiral along pairs of tapered rollers termed 'thread-advancing reels' over which water and the other purifying and filament lubricating liquors may be sprayed at appropriate points so that the thread may then be immediately dried in its final purified state. But the essentials of the viscose rayon manufacturing process are those above described. So far as is possible the production of viscose rayon is today carried out in a continuous manner with the raw materials coming into the plant at one point and the fully finished rayon leaving at another, but there are many difficulties to contend with in devising and operating such a system.

Spinning to produce special physical properties

By modifications introduced into the general process of manufacture as outlined above it is possible to produce different types

FIG. 15. A close-up view of part of viscose rayon spinning machine. It shows the extrusion of the viscose solution through the filter and spinneret into the coagulating bath, and the path of travel of the resulting filaments (in thread form) around the Godet wheels and downwards into the Topham 'pot'.

By courtesy of Courtaulds Ltd

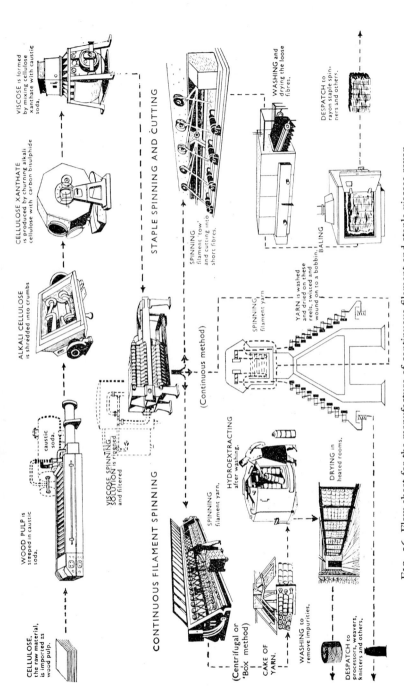

CELLULOSE, the raw material, is imported as wood pulp.

WOOD PULP is steeped in caustic soda.

ALKALI CELLULOSE is shredded into crumbs

CELLULOSE XANTHATE is produced by churning alkali cellulose with carbon bisulphide

VISCOSE is formed by mixing cellulose xanthate with caustic soda.

caustic soda

VISCOSE SPINNING SOLUTION is ripened and filtered

STAPLE SPINNING AND CUTTING

SPINNING filament 'tow' and cutting into short fibres.

WASHING and drying the loose fibres.

DESPATCH to rayon staple spinners and others.

BALING

CONTINUOUS FILAMENT SPINNING

(Continuous method)

SPINNING filament yarn.

YARN is washed and dried on these reels, twisted and wound on to a bobbin.

(Centrifugal or 'Box method)

CAKE OF YARN.

SPINNING filament yarn.

HYDROEXTRACTING after washing.

DRYING in heated rooms.

WASHING to remove impurities.

DESPATCH to processors, weavers, knitters and others.

D

FIG. 16. Flow-sheet for the manufacture of continuous filament and staple viscose rayon.

By courtesy of Courtaulds Ltd

of viscose rayon. Thus the size and number of orifices in the spinnerets determine the number and thickness of the filaments which go to form the freshly formed threads. If the freshly formed filaments are stretched as they travel forward they can be made finer, but what is more important is that they can thus be given a considerably higher strength, although this is generally accompanied by a lower extensibility. If a suitable proportion of opaque white titanium dioxide pigment is added to the viscose solution just before it is spun into filaments, these can be produced with a lower lustre or even be matt—it is seldom that viscose rayon is today required to have the metallic brightness that characterised the rayon produced some thirty or more years ago.

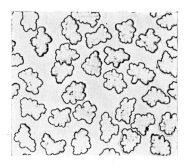

FIG. 17. Cross-sections of bright viscose rayon fibres of 3·75 denier. Magnification × 250. The cross-sections are highly indented and this is favourable to dye receptivity.

By courtesy of Courtaulds Ltd

By adding various substances to the coagulating bath the character of the resulting filaments may be modified. It has already been mentioned that glucose and similar emollients confer softness and pliability and that zinc sulphate causes the filaments to have an indented cross-section—such indents give the filaments improved dyeing properties.

High tenacity viscose rayon

Much viscose rayon thread is today used for reinforcing rubber motor-car tyres, and it is necessary that such threads should have a high tenacity. This property is ensured by subjecting the freshly formed threads to special multi-stage stretching. The effect of this stretching is to align the long cellulose chain molecules within the filaments more parallel to each other (this allows also closer molecular packing within the filaments) and more completely parallel to the length of the fibre, and these changes are favourable to increased tensile strength. It has to be pointed out however that the resulting fibres, because of their increased compactness of structure, are less resistant to abrasion and less absorbent towards dyes. However, by control of the stretching it is possible to produce viscose rayon threads (often termed cords) which are much superior to the cotton threads formerly almost exclusively employed for tyre reinforcement.

Thick 'skin' fibres

Modern research has shown that in the outer layer or skin of a viscose rayon filament the cellulose is denser than in the interior and, further, that stronger filaments result when they are produced under conditions which favour the production of a thicker skin. As a consequence of this, methods of spinning viscose rayon filaments have now been devised by which it can be ensured that the resulting filaments consist almost entirely of skin and have therefore great strength.

FIG. 18. Showing cross-sections of Tenasco (Courtaulds) fibres which possess a thick tough skin (stained black to show this), resulting from a special modification of the usual process for spinning viscose rayon using a higher proportion of zinc sulphate in the coagulation bath and higher stretching of the fibres while being solidified. This thicker skin confers a high tensile strength and lower extensibility to make the fibres suitable for reinforcing motor tyres and industrial belting. Magnification × 500.

By courtesy of Courtaulds Ltd

The chemistry of the viscose rayon manufacture

The viscose process might seem a somewhat roundabout method for converting cotton or wood pulp cellulose into regenerated cellulose (viscose rayon) fibres, but this is because cellulose cannot by itself be dissolved to give a suitably viscous fibre spinning solution. It is much easier to produce a regenerated protein rayon, since this can be accomplished by dissolving the protein (say groundnut protein) in dilute caustic soda solution and then following this by extruding it into a coagulating bath containing sulphuric acid to neutralise the alkali and bring about precipitation of the protein in the form of filaments. However, the viscose process may be made clearer by the following simplified representation of the main chemical reactions involved:

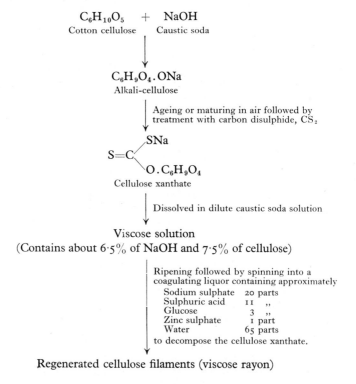

$$C_6H_{10}O_5 \quad + \quad NaOH$$
Cotton cellulose   Caustic soda

$$C_6H_9O_4 . ONa$$
Alkali-cellulose

Ageing or maturing in air followed by treatment with carbon disulphide, CS_2

$$S=C\begin{matrix} {\diagup}SNa \\ {\diagdown}O . C_6H_9O_4 \end{matrix}$$
Cellulose xanthate

Dissolved in dilute caustic soda solution

Viscose solution
(Contains about 6·5% of NaOH and 7·5% of cellulose)

Ripening followed by spinning into a coagulating liquor containing approximately

Sodium sulphate	20 parts
Sulphuric acid	11 ,,
Glucose	3 ,,
Zinc sulphate	1 part
Water	65 parts

to decompose the cellulose xanthate.

Regenerated cellulose filaments (viscose rayon)

Physical properties

Viscose rayon filaments consist of pure regenerated cellulose, but because such cellulose is somewhat more porous than the original cotton or wood cellulose used as the raw material these filaments are more reactive. Thus they can dye to deeper shades than cotton although they have otherwise much the same dyeing properties as cotton. But since so many possible modifications of the manufacturing process are available it is possible to increase or reduce the dye absorptive power of the rayon as desired.

A distinctive feature of viscose rayon filaments as compared with cotton fibres is that on wetting they absorb much more water and in doing so swell laterally about 30 to 40%, thereby temporarily becoming softer with loss of strength; the wet filaments are especially easy to cut with, for instance, scissors. But on drying, the filaments revert to their original non-swollen state and regain their original strength. These facts imply that viscose rayon materials must be carefully handled in the wet state—care is particularly required in mangling wet fabrics. When a wet fabric having thick hard cotton threads in the warp and viscose rayon threads in the weft has been mangled, it has happened that the cotton threads have been pressed through the rayon threads thus completely damaging the fabric. The water in wet viscose rayon materials is best removed by hydroextraction.

Continuous filament and staple fibre viscose rayon

As made by the spinning processes described above viscose rayon is obtained in the form of extremely long fibres (these may be a thousand or more yards long). Yarns containing these filaments may tend to be somewhat wirelike and firm in handle. For this reason it has become the practice to cut up such long continuous filaments into shorter lengths—it has been found that yarns made from these cut-up fibres can be bulkier, softer, and warmer in handle. The practice is to cut the long filaments into lengths which correspond with those of cotton and wool fibres so that the cut-up fibres may be conveniently spun into yarns on machinery already available for spinning cotton and wool yarns. Also if the viscose rayon cut-up fibres have about the same length as cotton or wool fibres it makes their mixing with cotton or other fibres so much the easier. Cut-up viscose rayon fibres are usually referred to as *viscose staple fibre*. It is also obvious that in order to facilitate the mixing of such staple fibre with cotton or wool and thereafter spinning the mixture into yarn, optimum results will be obtained if the viscose rayon fibres are made to have a thickness comparable to that of the cotton or wool fibres.

Ordinary long viscose rayon fibre yarns are usually referred to as *continuous filament* yarns, while those yarns made with cut-up fibres are described as viscose *staple fibre* yarns. At the present time the major proportion of viscose rayon now being produced is in the form of staple fibre.

Bristle fibres

When viscose rayon is required for use as bristles it is necessary that the fibres should be produced much thicker than those for use in the manufacture of clothing. These thicker fibres are usually handled singly and not in the form of yarn containing a number of single fibres twisted together—they are termed monofils.

CUPRAMMONIUM RAYON

At one time this type of regenerated cellulose rayon was known as Pauly silk because it was Pauly who first solved the early difficulties attending its production about 1897. It has never acquired the importance of viscose rayon although both types of rayon consist of regenerated cellulose.

Manufacture

Cuprammonium rayon is made by a somewhat simpler process than is viscose rayon. The process is based on the fact that a cuprammonium solution is able to dissolve cotton or other forms of cellulose and that the resulting solution can then be extruded through spinnerets into water so that coagulation of the extruded streams of cellulose solution rapidly occurs. Regenerated cellulose filaments are formed and can be drawn away in the form of a thread to be subjected to suitable purifying treatments.

A cuprammonium solution is prepared by bubbling air through a strong ammonia solution in which are placed pieces of metallic copper—the copper goes into solution which at the same time becomes intensely blue. The conditions for preparing this solution are such that it finally contains about 3% of dissolved copper (in the form of copper hydrate) and 25% of ammonia. With this an approximately 10% solution of cotton cellulose can be made and this is then ready for spinning into filaments.

Spinning process

In one form of the manufacturing process the cuprammonium solution is extruded downwards into a funnel through which cold water flows, and the resulting freshly formed filaments are highly stretched as they pass downwards and out to be wound as a thread on bobbins. The threads at this stage are blue in colour. Thereafter they are purified by an acid treatment to remove all the copper and ammonia so that they are left white. The stretched filaments have a thickness somewhat less than that of silk fibres and they have a high and desirable softness of handle.

Since cuprammonium rayon has for many years been manufactured by Messrs Bemberg both in Britain and on the Continent it is often called Bemberg rayon. It has properties very similar to those of viscose rayon and thus has a low wet strength and a good affinity for all cotton dyes. At one time Bemberg rayon was much used for the knitting of ladies' stockings but it is now less used for this purpose. However, Bemberg rayon does give high-quality textile materials, largely owing to its softness and subdued lustre coupled with its extreme fineness.

ACETATE RAYONS

Early pioneering efforts

Although considerable research was carried out during the first two decades of the present century with a view to devising a commercial process for manufacturing cellulose acetate rayon, real success came only about 1920 when the Swiss brothers Doctors Henri and Camille Dreyfus saw that some new use would have to be found for the huge production of cellulose acetate at their Spondon works; with the ending of the First World War the demand for this product (used as a dope for covering and tautening the wings of aeroplanes) rapidly diminished. They therefore in a true pioneering spirit introduced the manufacture of cellulose acetate rayon. At first they encountered many difficulties and because the unique properties of this new fibre also caused troubles in all sections of the textile industry the reception of the new fibre was lukewarm. However, after some years during which the new fibre acquired the trade name of Celanese, a number of advantages peculiar to acetate fibres became recognised and so the new fibre has steadily met with such increased favour that its output for purely clothing purposes at one time exceeded that of viscose rayon. Meanwhile both the pioneers of this remarkable fibre have died but they had seen something of the success which attended their efforts.

Manufacturing process

Cellulose obtained from cotton or wood pulp is the raw material for the manufacture of acetate rayon. Each molecule of cellulose is capable of chemically combining under suitable conditions with three molecules of acetic acid to form cellulose triacetate. This is a white water-insoluble solid; around 1920 an American company introduced a new fibre, Lustron, made of this cellulose triacetate, but it fell into disfavour and its manufacture was soon abandoned. Apparently the times were not then suitable for introducing a strongly hydrophobic fibre which required the availability of special dyes for colouring it and which had properties which were so different from the then available textile fibres that much adaptation of processing equipment was required to allow its conversion into useful yarns and fabrics. Yet, within recent years, this same type of acetate fibre has been re-introduced to the textile industry as Tricel and readily accepted because of its valuable textile properties. The explanation is that in the intervening years the hydrophobic fibres nylon, Orlon, Terylene, etc. have been introduced and satisfactory methods have been devised for processing materials of these fibres. These same new methods are applicable to Tricel and other cellulose triacetate fibres such as the American Arnel.

Mono-, di-, and tri-acetates

Celanese, the acetate fibre first produced by the Dreyfus brothers, was not made from cellulose triacetate as such but only after some of its combined acetic acid had been removed by hydrolysis. This modification allowed a cheapening and simplification of the fibre manufacturing process, and ensured that the acetate fibres ultimately obtained were less hydrophobic than triacetate fibres and thus more amenable to the dyeing and finishing processes then in common use for other and more hydrophile textile materials. This step of hydrolysing cellulose triacetate had been discovered by Miles some few years earlier and in view of its importance it is explained here.

The simple molecule of cellulose contains three reactive hydroxyl (OH) groups so that the cellulose molecule $C_6H_{10}O_5$ may be represented by $C_6H_7O_2$ $(OH)_3$. When cotton or other cellulose is reacted with a mixture of acetic acid and acetic anhydride in the presence of a catalyst such as sulphuric acid progressive acetylation of the hydroxyl groups occurs, the three main stages being to the mono-acetate $C_6H_7O_2(OH)_2(O.CO.CH_3)$, diacetate $C_6H_7O_2(OH)$ $(O.CO.CH_3)_2$, and triacetate $C_6H_7O_2(O.CO.CH_3)_3$ according to an esterifying reaction of the kind

$$C_6H_7O_2(OH)_3 + CH_3COOH = C_6H_7O_2(OH)_2(O.CO.CH_3) + H_2O$$

Cellulose   Acetic acid   Cellulose mono-acetic   Water

The resulting cellulose acetates remain dissolved in the reaction mixture but can easily be completely precipitated from this by addition of water. But if at the end of the acetylation in which all the cellulose has been converted into cellulose triacetate there is added only a moderate amount of water sufficient to convert all unreacted acetic anhydride into acetic acid and yet insufficient to precipitate the cellulose triacetate, then a kind of back-acetylation takes place so that some of the acetyl groups $(O.CO.CH_3)$ are split off from the cellulose triacetate. This hydrolysis of acetyl groups is allowed to continue until one out of every six such groups has been hydrolysed by a reaction of the type shown below:

$$C_6H_7O_2(O.CO.CH_3)_3 + H_2O$$

Cellulose triacetate   Water

$$= C_6H_7O_2(OH)(O.CO.CH_3)_2 + CH_3COOH$$

Cellulose diacetate   Acetic acid

and the resulting cellulose acetate has a composition which approximately corresponds to one molecule of cellulose chemically combined with $2\frac{1}{2}$ instead of the original 3 molecules of acetic acid. Whereas the acetyl $(O.CO.CH_3)$ content of cellulose triacetate corresponds to $62 \cdot 5\%$ of combined acetic acid the acetyl content of the hydrolysed acetate (usually termed *secondary* cellulose acetate) corresponds to only 53 to 54%.

Importance of secondary cellulose acetate

Cellulose di- and tri-acetates are insoluble in water so that an organic solvent has to be employed for the preparation of a

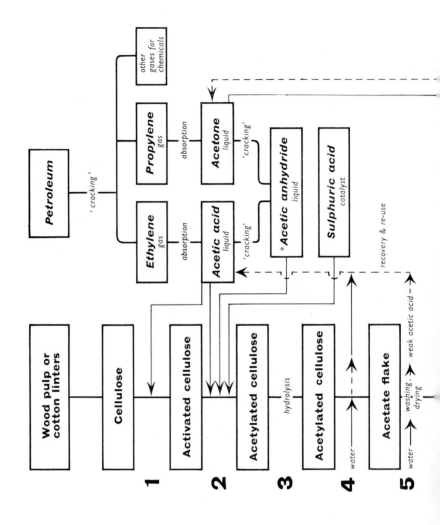

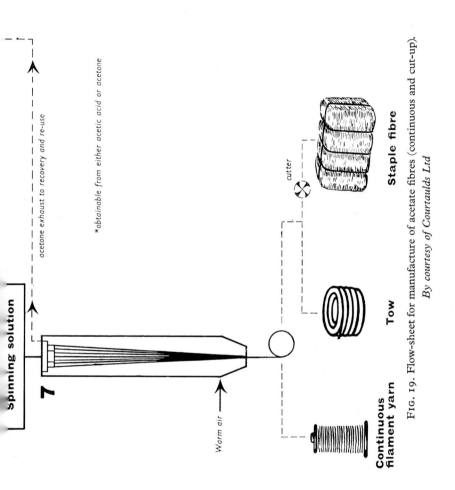

Spinning solution

acetone exhaust to recovery and re-use

*obtainable from either acetic acid or acetone

Warm air

Continuous filament yarn

Tow

cutter

Staple fibre

FIG. 19. Flow-sheet for manufacture of acetate fibres (continuous and cut-up).
By courtesy of Courtaulds Ltd

suitably viscous solution containing them to be used in the spinning of filaments. Cellulose triacetate is soluble only in organic solvents such as chloroform which are either expensive or dangerous to use (from the viewpoint of fire and health risks), whereas secondary cellulose acetate whose preparation is described above just has a sufficient solubility in the cheap volatile solvent acetone to allow this to be employed in making fibre-spinning solutions. It was for this reason that the hydrolysis stage was introduced into the production of cellulose acetate rayon.

Manufacturing stages for acetate rayon

Thus in the manufacture of secondary acetate rayon the first stage is the acetylation of cotton or other form of cellulose to give cellulose triacetate, hydrolysis of this to the secondary cellulose acetate, and the precipitation of this in the form of flakes by suitable dilution of the hydrolysis product. In the acetylation mixture it is usual to have some sulphuric acid present to promote the reaction between the cellulose and the acetic acid and acetic anhydride, and some of this sulphuric acid (quite a small amount) undesirably enters into combination with the cellulose triacetate formed (a small amount of a cellulose sulpho-acetate results from such combination). If this combined sulphuric acid is ultimately to be found in the acetate fibres then these darken and become embrittled on heating. It is therefore important to remove all this combined sulphuric acid, and this is achieved by boiling the precipitated secondary cellulose acetate with dilute sulphuric acid whereby the combined sulphuric acid becomes replaced by hydroxyl groups and the cellulose acetate is thus *stabilised* against further adverse change.

Dry spinning

The stabilised secondary cellulose acetate is then dried and dissolved in acetone to give a 25 to 30% viscous solution, and this is extruded downwards into vertical cells through which warm air is continuously circulated. As the streams of acetate solution emerge from the spinneret their acetone content is rapidly removed by evaporation to leave solid secondary cellulose acetate filaments. These latter are collected into the form of a thread by passing through a guide at the bottom of the cell; this thread is then led out of the cell to be wound on bobbins. If the size and number of holes in the spinneret are suitably determined, then the acetate thread is at once ready for use in manufacturing textile goods.

The process of manufacture of acetate rayon as described above is cheapened by recovering all the waste acetic acid and acetone for purification and re-use.

Fibre properties

As thus manufactured, secondary acetate rayon fibres have about the same strength as viscose rayon fibres and like them lose strength when wet; they are about one-half as strong as cotton fibres and just about as strong as wool. The fibres are less hydrophile than those of viscose rayon for the reason that they contain a smaller proportion of free hydroxyl (OH) groups—hydroxyl groups confer hydrophile properties on a fibre.

Unlike cellulose fibres such as cotton, linen, and viscose rayon the fibres of secondary cellulose acetate become thermoplastic on heating to temperatures around 180° C, and at about 230° C they melt with decomposition. Thus the hot ironing of acetate materials must be conducted with great care. Embossed designs may be very readily impressed on acetate fabrics with the aid of heat and pressure.

Delustred acetate fibres

Unless titanium dioxide pigment is added to the acetate spinning solution with the object of producing low-lustre fibres, those

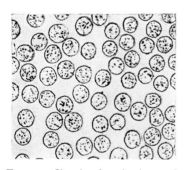 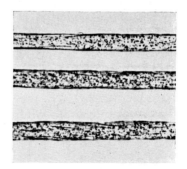

Fig. 20. Showing length view and cross-sections of Courtelle (Courtaulds) matt fibres of 3 denier. Magnification ×500. The cross-sections are circular and the delustring titanium dioxide pigment particles are shown evenly distributed throughout each fibre.

By courtesy of Courtaulds Ltd

normally produced have a high lustre. But it is a peculiar feature of bright acetate rayon that its lustre can be much reduced by boiling the rayon material in a soap liquor—it is important to know that this delustring is hindered by lowering the temperature of the soap liquor, by having present neutral inorganic salts such as sodium sulphate, and by holding the rayon material in a stretched state. The delustring thus produced is not so permanent as that obtained by adding titanium dioxide to the spinning solution since it can under some circumstances be recovered—for instance, by steeping the delustred material in acetic acid and then drying it at a high temperature while held stretched.

Special properties

Secondary acetate rayon is immune to attack by moth and is resistant to mildew. Fishing lines made of this rayon do not so readily deteriorate in sea water as do some others.

While acetate rayon is not harmed by treatment with acids and oxidising agents under mild conditions it is readily saponified by alkalis whereby the acetyl groups are all split off to leave a regenerated cellulose rayon.

Dyeing properties

Secondary acetate rayon resists dyeing with most of the water-soluble dyes which are used for the dyeing of cotton, wool, linen, and other hydrophile fibres. It requires for its colouring a range of specially discovered and so-called disperse dyes which are largely water-insoluble and require to be applied in the form of a dispersion. These dyes are attracted to the acetate fibre surface and then enter to become evenly distributed within by a process of solution—an example of one solid dissolving in another.

Acetate fibres which have been partially or wholly saponified by alkalis are thereby given the usual dyeing properties of cellulose fibres so that they can be dyed with cotton dyes but lose their affinity for the special disperse dyes.

FORTISAN

Secondary acetate fibres can be highly stretched while being maintained in a highly thermoplastic state by exposure to high pressure steam or while in a swollen state such as can be induced by wetting with a liquid which can swell (or in concentrated form actually dissolve) them. The resulting stretched fibres (the process is usually effected on threads rather than single fibres) have a much increased tensile strength but a reduced extensibility. By both stretching and fully saponifying the secondary acetate fibres it is possible to produce a regenerated cellulose type of fibre having exceptionally high strength, yet with the reduced extensibility which usually accompanies a stretched fibre. The high tenacity type of fibre Fortisan is made by such a process—its strength can exceed three times that of silk fibres. Because in these stretched fibres the molecules are very tightly packed together, Fortisan (even before saponification) is much more difficult to dye than is the original secondary cellulose acetate.

CELLULOSE TRIACETATE RAYONS

Triacetate rayon fibres (the first forerunner of this type was the American Lustron now long ago abandoned) have recently been introduced in various countries under various names such as Tricel (in Britain) and Arnel (in America). Although closely related to secondary cellulose acetate rayon these newer fibres have several different and useful properties which are associated with their increased hydrophobicity.

Manufacture

This type of rayon is made by first completely acetylating cotton or other type of cellulose with an acetic acid or methylene chloride solution of acetic anhydride containing also a catalyst such as sulphuric or perchloric acid, then precipitating the cellulose triacetate by dilution with water of the reaction product, stabilising it as with secondary cellulose acetate, washing and drying. Thereafter, the triacetate is made into a viscous spinning solution with methylene chloride containing a small proportion of alcohol (the triacetate is not soluble in the cheaper acetone solvent); and this is then dry spun into filaments (methylene chloride evaporates more easily than acetone) to be collected from the spinning cell in the form of thread.

Since triacetate fibres are definitely hydrophobic they tend to accumulate electrostatic charges of high magnitude during mechanical handling and where they are subject to friction, so that it is necessary to apply to the freshly formed threads an anti-static composition to avoid static trouble. It has been stated that Tricel fibres are not stretched during manufacture.

Properties

It has previously been stated that there is a wide difference in properties between a natural fibre such as cotton and a synthetic fibre such as nylon in that the former is hydrophile and the latter is hydrophobic. Until recently it was considered that secondary acetate rayon occupied a useful intermediate position between these two extreme fibres but now it is thought that the new triacetate rayon, being somewhat more hydrophobic than secondary acetate rayon, more satisfactorily occupies the intermediate position.

Triacetate fibres are similar in many respects to secondary cellulose acetate fibres and particularly in having much the same dry and wet strengths and extensibility and in being thermoplastic so as to require care in hot ironing. However, triacetate fibres have the higher melting point of 290° C approximately as compared with 235° C for ordinary acetate fibres, so that there is less danger in ironing materials made with them especially after a special high temperature treatment which raises their safe ironing temperature to 455° F (235° C).

The normal moisture regain of triacetate fibres is about 4·5% (6·5% for ordinary acetate fibres and 4·2% for nylon). Triacetate fibres are much more resistant to delustring when boiled in water or soap liquors and they do not so readily saponify with alkalis. They can be dyed with the disperse and other dyes usually applied to secondary acetate rayon and the resulting colourings have much the same fastness properties.

High temperature treatment improves fibre properties

There is an important difference between the two types of acetate fibres in respect of their behaviour when exposed to high temperatures. When the triacetate fibres are heated to 180° C and above, the molecules within the fibres acquire increased freedom of movement and as a result they accommodate themselves so as to pack more closely and also pack in such a manner that the fibres become more crystalline. The properties of the fibres thereby undergo some useful changes.

Firstly the softening temperature of the triacetate fibres is raised so that the safe hot ironing temperature is raised from around 200° C to 220° C, and sometimes to 240° C according to the conditions of heating. In the second place the fibres become more difficult to dye to deep shades. On the other hand, if the fibres are already dyed then the high temperature treatment assists the dye particles to move so as to become more evenly distributed within the fibres, and it also causes them to aggregate to some degree into larger particles. The result of these changes is that the colouring acquires increased fastness to washing and sometimes to light. Another result of the high temperature treatment is that a triacetate fabric acquires increased dimensional stability so that it thereafter tends better to retain its shape and size.

Permanent pleating

A further useful advantage is associated with materials made of triacetate fibres—it is concerned with permanent pleating. It is well known that synthetic fibre fabrics can be hot pressed while in a folded or pleated state so that the folds or pleats become permanently set and persist through repeated washing. Triacetate fibre fabrics are now found to have this same property, for if they are pleated and then hot pressed at a sufficiently high temperature these pleats become permanent. In addition, with a triacetate fabric no appreciable shrinkage occurs during the heat-setting of the pleats—an advantage over synthetic fibre materials.

Permanent pleating is possible with cotton or wool fabrics which contain a proportion of triacetate fibres not less than 50%.

Special dyeing properties

Mention has been made of the greater difficulty of dyeing triacetate fibres as compared with secondary acetate fibres, but it is not an insurmountable difficulty. There are available today a number of so-called dye-carriers which can be added to the dyebath and which, by their fibre-swelling action, promote a better and more rapid absorption of the dyes. On the other hand, a similar improvement in dyeing can be obtained by dyeing the triacetate materials at temperatures above 100° C, but this method of dyeing requires special dyeing machines since they must be of a closed type and capable of withstanding the high pressures involved.

E

REGENERATED PROTEIN FIBRES

In view of the high value placed upon wool as a textile fibre it is not surprising that there should be many attempts to manufacture artificial substitute fibres for it. Quite a number of protein fibres have been produced but none of them have proved to be the equal of wool and in recent years some of these substitute fibres have been abandoned. The position now is that regenerated protein fibres have become relatively unimportant.

Manufacture

The production of a regenerated protein fibre is relatively simple from the theoretical viewpoint, although it has difficulties which have never been completely solved. The three stages involved comprise the dissolution of the selected protein in a caustic soda solution, the extrusion of this to produce filaments in a coagulating bath containing sulphuric acid and sodium sulphate, and an after-treatment of the resulting filaments to stabilise them and give them increased strength. A fundamental difficulty encountered is that the freshly formed filaments are very liable to swell and soften in alkaline and acid liquors so as to have a very low wet strength and be easily liable to damage. The after-treatments are designed to reduce such high swelling properties.

Types of fibre

Several types of protein are satisfactory for the production of regenerated protein fibres and among those most used are casein (as obtained from cow's milk), and the natural proteins which can be extracted from groundnuts and soya beans. Casein has been used for the manufacture of the Italian fibre Lanital, and for Courtaulds Fibrolane BX and BC (used to a limited extent in admixture with other fibres), while groundnut protein was used for the I.C.I. fibre Ardil whose manufacture has now been discontinued. The American fibre casein Aralac has also been discontinued, and replaced by Vicara which is made from a corn protein known as zein. Of these various fibres Fibrolane BX and BC are definitely in production because they have special but limited uses.

Properties

Because regenerated protein fibres have their protein content in a relatively highly swollen state as compared with the keratin protein of wool fibres and because they are more liable to swell further during treatment in hot liquors, such fibres can easily be dyed with a wide range of dyes in really deep shades. But because the dye enters the fibres so easily it can also wash out freely and so the fastness of the resulting shades to washing is correspondingly low. The freshly formed fibres are also liable to swell so much as to suffer breakage during dyeing.

Remembering that the long-chain protein molecules in wool fibres are naturally cross-bonded and that this hinders their excessive wet swelling, several after-treatments for the regenerated protein fibres have been devised with the object of introducing such cross-bonding. Preferred treatments involve treating the fibres with an acidic solution of formaldehyde and also with solutions of aluminium or chromium salts. Cross-bonding of the fibres can thus be obtained and considerable improvement of the dimensional stability of regenerated protein fibres has consequently been secured. But in spite of these improvements man-made fibres of this type have not satisfied the demands made upon them.

ALGINATE FIBRES

For many years it has been known that seaweed, some types more than others, contains a gelatinous substance termed alginic acid which is chemically closely related to cellulose in so far that one of the three hydroxyl groups of the cellulose molecule is replaced by a carboxylic acid group (COOH) so that the simple formula for alginic acid is $C_6H_7O_2(OH)_2COOH$. It is this carboxylic acid group which enables alginic acid to become soluble in alkaline solutions such as those of sodium carbonate and caustic soda, whereas cellulose is not thus soluble.

Alginic acid is now being extracted commercially from seaweed gathered around the Scottish coasts and by reason of its gelatinous nature it is being used for many purposes. In recent years it has attracted attention as a raw material for the manufacture of artificial fibres and considerable success has been obtained in this field. However, the alginate fibres now available have only a small number of somewhat restricted uses so that they are being produced only on a small scale.

Manufacture

The simplest means of making alginate fibres is to spin a viscous solution of sodium alginate into a coagulating bath containing either sulphuric acid (this gives alginic acid fibres) or a metal salt, particularly a non-coloured one such as calcium chloride (this gives calcium alginate fibres). When alginic acid and calcium alginate fibres are treated with alkaline liquors they disintegrate. On the other hand, if treated with solutions of other metal salts such as those of iron, chromium, and aluminium they become converted *in situ* to the corresponding metal alginate fibre, for example, iron, chromium, and aluminium alginate fibres.

Properties

Fibres which are so easily dissolved can be used (in thread form) in the production of special embroidery or lace materials where the required final appearance can be made to depend on the removal of specially introduced temporary supporting threads.

All alginate fibres are completely flameproof. They can be produced to have a dry strength comparable to that of viscose rayon fibres but with a lower wet strength. They can be readily dyed with basic dyes. There are special uses for alginate threads in the knitting industry, as for example for linking together successively knitted socks—the linking thread dissolves in later wet processing to leave the socks separate as is required.

Later Man-made Fibres (Synthetic Fibres)

HISTORICAL INTRODUCTION

In recent years, much public interest has been shown in the so-called synthetic fibres, and the first of these, termed nylon, was introduced about 1937 by the E. I. du Pont de Nemours Company Inc. in America. The manufacture of nylon arose out of some far-reaching investigations concerning polymeric substances of various kinds as carried out by Dr Carothers and the team of scientists working for him, and the decision to make nylon commercially was a great adventure which brought even more success than anticipated.

In those early days it was known that the natural fibres, cotton, wool, silk, etc. were composed of very complex molecules and it was discovered with the aid of new X-ray techniques that these molecules were linear or straight. Carothers set out to discover how such long high-molecular-weight molecules could be built up and from his results it was evident that he had discovered how to manufacture polymers made of this particular type of molecule which could be expected to have good fibre-forming properties. The types of polymer most closely investigated by Carothers were polyamides and polyesters, and a decision had to be made as to whether the first synthetic fibre to be made should be of the former or latter type. It appeared from those polyamides and polyesters so far made that the polyamides were likely to give fibres less sensitive to high temperatures and more easily dyed, and thus the choice fell on the particular polyamide which could be made by condensing adipic acid with hexamethylene diamine followed by polymerisation. The name given to this first synthetic fibre was nylon. In due course, after the manufacture of this nylon fibre was successfully established, other polyamides were made into fibres, but so far none has been found superior in textile properties to the first made nylon. The present synthetic fibre epoch is due to Carothers' researches, but he met a tragic death quite early in the commencement of nylon manufacture and so failed to see the far-reaching changes in textile fibre production which he initiated.

The early success of nylon manufacture has during the past twenty years attracted the inventiveness and energies of many textile technologists with a view to the discovery of new fibres to excel or at least equal nylon. Many new fibres have thus become available while many others have been discovered yet not put into large-scale manufacture for one reason or other. Each year sees the manufacture of at least one new fibre. And the search for new fibres continues with unabating energy.

PROPERTIES, STRUCTURE AND CHARACTERISTICS

Synthetic fibre properties

All the synthetic fibres now being produced have a number of characteristics in common—they are based on fibre-forming polymers with some common properties, they are made by similar processes from these polymers, and the fibres themselves have many similar properties. The synthetic fibres are comprised in a group not only because they are made from synthetic polymers but also because the fibres have properties which make it necessary to use special methods and processes in converting them into fabrics and garments. It will thus be convenient here to consider the more general and essential characteristics of synthetic fibres before dealing with the individual fibres such as nylon, Orlon, Courtelle, Terylene, etc.

Molecular structure

In the introduction to this chapter on fibres it was pointed out that all textile fibres are built up of molecules which are relatively straight and very much longer than they are thick and that in the fibre these molecules may be parallel to each other and to the fibre length, or in the other extreme case they may be higgledy-piggledy and aligned in all directions. Within any one fibre it is possible for the molecules to differ in length within reasonable limits but it is generally considered that a fibre will have better textile properties if the molecules have about equal length.

The manner in which the molecules are packed together within a fibre is important, and of course this packing is influenced by the length, shape, and uniformity of the molecules. The straighter and more streamlined are the molecules the more closely and regularly may they be packed and when this packing takes a regular patterned form so does the fibre become crystalline. Thus in any fibre according to whether the molecular packing is at random or patterned so are there crystalline and amorphous regions and it is possible for these regions to merge into each other. Generally it is agreed that the molecules are most closely packed in the crystalline regions and so in dyeing processes it is more difficult for dye particles to penetrate and move within the crystalline regions than the amorphous regions. Similarly a highly crystalline fibre usually has a lower moisture regain than one which is mainly amorphous since it is more difficult for water molecules to penetrate the crystalline regions. It is usual for the melting point of a synthetic fibre to be higher as the molecules are more closely packed.

Comparison with natural fibres

The above considerations apply equally to all types of textile fibres. Thus cotton, linen, and ramie fibres are at least 50%

crystalline, whereas viscose and acetate rayon fibres are mainly amorphous. But they are of special importance for synthetic fibres since in the manufacture of these and also by special high temperature treatments it is often possible advantageously to increase the fibre crystallinity. A crystalline fibre is usually a strong fibre. And just as it is possible to treat fibres to make them more crystalline so is it possible to make them less crystalline. All these possibilities can usually be better and more easily realised with synthetic than with natural fibres.

Characteristics for a fibre-forming polymer

Returning now to the production of synthetic fibres, the first step is the selection and manufacture of the fibre-forming polymer. It is necessary to understand the nature of these polymers.

In general, a polymer is made by joining together of a large number of small molecules—it may be of the same type of molecule or of a mixture of different types of molecules but seldom more than two or three types. These small molecules may join end-to-end to form straight linear polymer molecules or they may join end-to-end and also sideways so as to form three-dimensional or voluminous polymer molecules. It is those polymers having simple long linear molecules which are most suitable for the manufacture of synthetic fibres.

The simplest method for forming a linear polymer is to select a substance (this is termed a monomeric substance or a monomer) whose small molecules have a tendency to join together and then hold this under appropriate conditions to induce the joining-up process (termed polymerisation) to continue until tests indicate that the polymer molecules produced have the desired length and other fibre-forming characteristics. The reaction is then stopped and the polymer separated and purified. Thus using monomer *A*, this is converted into polymer *A-A-A-A-A- - -*. A number of synthetic fibres are made from polymerised acrylonitrile, CH_2CHCN, and this polymerisation is usually effected with the acrylonitrile dissolved in a liquid medium containing a catalyst (often a peroxide such as hydrogen peroxide or benzoyl peroxide) to promote the polymerisation. Polyacrylonitrile such as is used in the manufacture of Orlon is formed thus:

$$nCH_2{=}CHCN$$
Acrylonitrile

$$\downarrow \text{Polymerisation}$$

$$- - -CH_2{-}CH{-}CH_2{-}CH{-}CH_2{-}CH{-}CH_2{-}CH{-} - -$$
$$\qquad\quad\; CN \qquad\;\; CN \qquad\;\; CN \qquad\;\; CN$$
Polyacrylonitrile

Dynel synthetic fibre is made from a linear polymer derived from two different monomers, 60% of vinyl chloride and 40% of acrylonitrile, which are caused to co-polymerise thus:

$$2nCH_2{=}CHCN + 3nCH_2{=}CHCl$$
Acrylonitrile   Vinyl chloride

$$\downarrow \text{Polymerisation}$$

$$- - -CH_2{-}CH{-}CH_2{-}CH{-}CH_2{-}CH{-}CH_2{-}CH{-} - -$$
$$\qquad\quad\; CN \qquad\;\; Cl \qquad\;\; CN \qquad\;\; Cl$$
A copolymer of acrylonitrile and vinyl chloride

It will be noticed above that the polymer results from a simple joining together end-to-end of the monomer molecules without the elimination of any atoms. In some instances, however, polymerisation results from a condensation of the monomer molecules with each other and this involves some elimination of atoms; often the atoms eliminated are in the form of water, H_2O. The polyamide from which nylon is manufactured is made by such a condensation process. Thus starting with an equimolecular mixture of the two monomers adipic acid, $HOOCCH_2CH_2CH_2CH_2COOH$, and hexamethylene diamine, $NH_2CH_2CH_2CH_2CH_2CH_2CH_2NH_2$, these are brought together under high temperature conditions which promote condensation to give

$$HOOCCH_2CH_2CH_2CH_2CO{-}NHCH_2CH_2CH_2CH_2CH_2CH_2NH_2$$
Hexamethylene adipamide $+ H_2O$
Water

This first stage of condensation results in the formation of a monomeric amide having carboxylic acid (COOH) and amino (NH$_2$) terminal groups which are capable of further condensing with hexamethylene diamine and adipic acid molecules respectively to give dimeric amide molecules, and in turn these contain the same terminal groups which can further react with hexamethylene diamine and adipic acid molecules. In fact it is evident that this condensation can continue almost indefinitely to give longer and longer polyamide molecules. By control of the heating the condensation can be arrested when the linear polyamide molecules whose formula may be expressed thus

$$HO—[—OC(CH_2)_4CO.NH(CH_2)_6NH—]_n—H$$

Polyhexamethylene adipamide

have the optimum length for the manufacture of nylon.

Polyamides are characterised by consisting of long molecules in which the monomeric molecules are joined together by amide, —CO—NH—, groups as shown in the formula above and in which n is a large number.

Terylene is made from the polyester which results from similar condensation of terephthalic acid with ethylene glycol having the formulae:

Terephthalic acid   Ethylene glycol

$HOCH_2CH_2OH$

The formation of the polyester known as polyethylene terephthalate proceeds in much the same way under high temperature conditions as in the formation of a polyamide, and the first stage of condensation of terephthalic acid with ethylene glycol results in formation of monomeric molecules having the formula:

$$HOOC\langle\quad\rangle CO.OCH_2CH_2OH$$

Ethylene glycol terephthalate

On further heating these monomeric molecules of ethylene glycol terephthalate add on further molecules of terephthalic acid and ethylene glycol to their terminal carboxylic acid and hydroxyl groups until the process is arrested and the fibre-forming polyethylene terephthalate having the following formula is obtained.

$$HO—\left[—OC\langle\quad\rangle—CO.O.CH_2CH_2O—\right]_n—H$$

Polyethylene terephthalate

Polyesters are characterised in consisting of long molecules in which the monomeric molecules are joined together by ester, —CO.O— ,groups as shown in the above formula.

From the above considerations it will be evident that polyamides and polyesters are made from monomers whose molecules have terminal carboxylic acid, (COOH) and amino (NH$_2$) and carboxylic acid and hydroxyl (OH) groups respectively, since it is these particular pairs of groups which allow the building up of long molecules by a continuing process of condensation.

Selection of polymers for fibre making

Many hundreds of potential fibre-forming polymers of different types are known, but rigorous selection reduces the choice for the large-scale manufacture of a fibre to but a few. Such questions as the ready availability and cost of the raw materials required to make the polymer and the advantages of the new fibre over existing fibres have to be considered. One important feature is concerned with the softening and melting point of the fibre, since not a few fibre-forming polymers have had to be discarded because the fibres made from them would soften at temperatures so low as to make them useless in fabrics for general use. For instance, a fibre which softened in boiling water could only have very limited special uses.

Relation between the melting point and internal structure of a synthetic fibre

The melting point of a synthetic fibre is largely dependent on the degree of close packing of the polymer molecules of which it is composed. It has been found with most substances that as the molecules approach each other they reach a point at which they come under the influence of very powerful so-called van der Waals forces which cause them to attract each other strongly. It is only when the molecules are very close to each other that this attraction becomes effective. So with the polymer molecules in a synthetic fibre; they can, if closely enough packed, be held together very strongly and so resist any separation of them. Now for a substance to melt or soften with a rise of temperature it is necessary for the molecules to move relatively to each other. Obviously the van der Waals forces have the effect of hindering this movement and thus tend to raise the temperature of softening or melting. Since these special forces only come into play when the fibre molecules are very close to each other the more closely they are packed the higher are the softening and melting temperatures of the fibre. It follows that highly crystalline synthetic fibres usually have a high melting point, for in the crystalline regions of the fibre the polymer molecules are most uniformly and closely packed.

Importance of close molecular packing

If it is desired to make synthetic fibres of high melting point, then the fibre-forming polymer used should consist of long straight molecules which allow themselves to be closely packed in the fibres. For this reason it is desirable that there should be no molecules attached to the sides of the main molecules—any such attached side molecules would occupy space between adjacent main molecules and thus prevent their close packing.

It sometimes happens that in the manufacture of a linear polymer there comes a stage where the long molecules so far formed commence to branch instead of simply lengthening. If this is allowed the polymer will become less valuable for fibre manufacture since it could not give fibres of close molecular packing.

THE SPINNING OF SYNTHETIC FIBRES

The second stage in the manufacture of a synthetic fibre is the actual fibre spinning process. The particular method of spinning employed depends on the properties of the fibre-forming polymer. Some of these polymers are soluble in organic solvents (just as secondary cellulose acetate is soluble in acetone) and thus allow the preparation of solutions which can be *dry* spun—that is, into warm air to evaporate off the solvent and leave solidified filaments behind; or *wet* spun—that is, extruded into a coagulating bath after the manner of viscose rayon manufacture. Thus Vinyon HH (made from a copolymer of 88/12 of vinyl chloride and vinyl acetate) can be dry spun from acetone solution while Orlon (made from polymerised acrylonitrile, which is insoluble in acetone) can be dissolved in dimethylformamide and then be either dry spun or wet spun into a coagulating bath of glycerol. Other polymers can be dissolved in concentrated aqueous solutions of inorganic salts such as calcium thiocyanate and then be wet spun into fibres using an aqueous coagulating bath containing a smaller amount of the same salts to ensure polymer precipitation. But with the introduction of nylon an entirely new method of fibre spinning was established—so-called melt-spinning in which the polymer (usually in the form of cut-up ribbon or chips) is melted in a novel device above the spinneret so that it can by means of a pump be extruded through the multi-holed spinneret into cold air to ensure the immediate solidification of the issuing fluid streams into filaments. This method is very attractive since it avoids the use of solvents which can add much expense to the spinning process. One difficulty is sometimes encountered. It is that the polymer may slowly decompose so as to become brownish-coloured while held molten at a few degrees above its melting point, and this colour may be difficult to bleach out of the resulting filaments. Such decomposition with accompanying aerial oxidation of the molten polymer can be largely avoided by blanketing the spinning apparatus with nitrogen gas.

Nylon, Perlon, and Terylene are melt-spun and it would be difficult to spin them by any other method, but many fibre-forming polymers cannot be satisfactorily melt-spun for the reason that they decompose too easily at their melting point. It is possible to add titanium dioxide to the polymer before melt-spinning and thus directly produce delustred fibres.

A special spinning method

Quite recently another new method for spinning synthetic fibres has come into use for those polymers which cannot be spun by the methods already described. In such a spinning process a paste of the finely ground polymer is forced through a suitable die so that the polymer particles agglomerate to give a filament which can then be sintered (compressed at a high temperature) to make the filament homogeneous and strong. This method is employed for the production of Teflon (polytetrafluoroethylene) fibres which only melt at the high temperature of 400° C and then with rapid decomposition; the method is also now being used to produce cellulose triacetate fibres.

Stretching and drawing in fibre manufacture to improve fibre properties

The third stage in the manufacture of synthetic fibres comprises a number of after-treatments which are used to improve the strength and other properties of the freshly formed fibres. It is usual for the fibres as first produced by all the methods of spinning mentioned above to have a relatively low tensile strength, say around 1 gram per denier, and a relatively high extensibility. By suitably stretching them the fibres can have their strength much increased and their extensibility lowered to an acceptable value to make them more serviceable and also more amenable to processing in the machinery which is commonly used in connection with yarns and fabrics. Sometimes the stretching can be achieved at room temperature but otherwise it may be done at an elevated temperature. Such stretching is often referred to as *cold-* or *hot-drawing.*

The stretching which is applied to freshly formed synthetic fibres is drastic, although it may be progressively applied by a general method in which the synthetic fibre thread is run through a pair of 'nip' rollers to another roller on which it is wound. The latter winding-on roller has a higher take-up or peripheral speed than that at which the thread is allowed to pass forward from the nip rollers and thus it becomes stretched on its way to the winding-on roller. In the case of nylon the original thread is thus stretched to about four times its original spun length and by this treatment it has its strength raised from about 1 gram per denier to 4·5–6·0 grams per denier. If the stretching is further increased the tensile strength may be increased up to 8 grams per denier as is required for high tenacity nylon. At the same time the nylon fibres gain considerable lustre. Terylene fibres in thread form from the spinning apparatus are hot stretched to about five times their original length with a corresponding improvement in tensile strength and lustre.

It is to be noted that this type of stretching is so great that it exceeds the elastic properties of the fibres and extends their length to a point at which they show no tendency to return to their original length after release of the stretching force. If only a small stretch is applied to the freshly spun fibres they will return to their original length during subsequent relaxation.

Effect of stretching on internal structure of fibres

The effect of this high degree of stretching on the synthetic fibres is to align their molecules more parallel to the fibre axis and to close up the molecular packing so that crystallisation can also be increased. After stretching the fibres have a lower capacity to absorb moisture and dyes. The greater the degree of stretching, the more pronounced are these effects. Another important effect is that fibres are made less extensible and normally the extensibility will be reduced to 20 to 30%, which is acceptable to those who use the fibres in weaving and knitting.

Although the stretched synthetic fibres are stable under ordinary conditions of use they yet retain a latent tendency to return to their original length. This tendency cannot become effective ordinarily because the molecules within the fibres are closely packed and held together laterally by strong forces such as those of van der Waals mentioned previously. But when the fibres are heated above 100° C (simple immersion in boiling water is often sufficient) the cohesion of the fibre molecules is weakened and they can move relatively to each other so that the fibres shrink, say up to 10% according to the previous degree of stretching. Thus synthetic fibres as found in fabrics and garments in general use are always liable to shrink if suitable conditions prevail—dry or wet heat promotes such shrinkage. It is often a cause of trouble in the dyeing in boiling dye liquors of synthetic fibre goods that undesirable shrinkage occurs. If the dyeing is effected at temperatures above 100° C, as may be required to obtain good dye absorption, then really serious shrinkage can take place.

Stabilisation of stretched fibres

In view of the facts mentioned above and because of the possible high shrinkage which can occur in some types of synthetic fibres, special steps are sometimes taken to stabilise the fibres against such shrinkage. It has been found that if a synthetic fibre is held stretched (that is, *set*) at a particular temperature then it will tend to retain its new length so long as it is not subjected to a temperature nearly approaching the setting temperature. So the stabilising treatments are based on this. They consist of holding the fibres (in thread form) in boiling water or steam or under high-temperature dry conditions while held taut and not free to shrink as they otherwise would do. Thereafter they do not shrink or at most very little when processed in hot conditions. Exposure of non-stabilised synthetic fibre materials to moist steam can often result in shrinkage usually accompanied by loss of strength.

Any shrinkage that is produced in stretched synthetic fibres as a result of high temperature treatment is accompanied by a simultaneous loosening of the structure of the fibres sufficient to give them an increased power to absorb dyes—in this respect it just has the opposite effect to the previous stretching.

Synthetic staple fibre

All synthetic fibres are initially produced in the form of very long fibres because they are spun continuously. But it is usual to cut up such long fibres into shorter ones comparable to the length of the cotton, wool, or other fibres with which they may be mixed for the production of mixture threads and fabrics. Fabrics made from synthetic cut-up or staple fibre, whether or not there are also other types of fibre present, have a softer and warmer handle than those made with continuous filament yarn. Such fabric is more porous and contains an increased number of small air pockets which reduce the heat conductivity of the fabric.

Effect of uneven drawing

In the early days of producing synthetic fibres it proved difficult to ensure that the drawing or stretching of the freshly formed fibres was uniform and always the same from day to day. A relatively small difference in such stretching could reveal itself in a reduced or increased affinity for dyes according as the stretching was higher or lower. This irregularity in stretching would lead to unevenly dyed fabrics if these contained yarns of different degrees of stretching. In cut-up or staple fibre the mixing of the fibres masks any stretching differences and so it is less difficult to dye staple fibre materials evenly.

TYPES OF SYNTHETIC FIBRES—POLYAMIDE FIBRES
NYLON 6,6

Manufacture

Nylon, whose manufacture as the first synthetic polyamide fibre was made possible by some eight years' previous research on polymers by Carothers in America, remains the most popular even among several types which recent research has shown possible. It is made by the melt-spinning of polyhexamethylene adipamide which in its turn is produced by the polycondensation of equimolecular proportions of adipic acid, $HOOC(CH_2)_4$ $COOH$, and hexamethylene diamine, $NH_2(CH_2)_6NH_2$, under high-temperature conditions and under vacua to remove expeditiously the water liberated in the condensation. The resulting polyamide is converted into ribbon which is then cut up into chips and fed to the top of a spinneret where it is first melted electrically

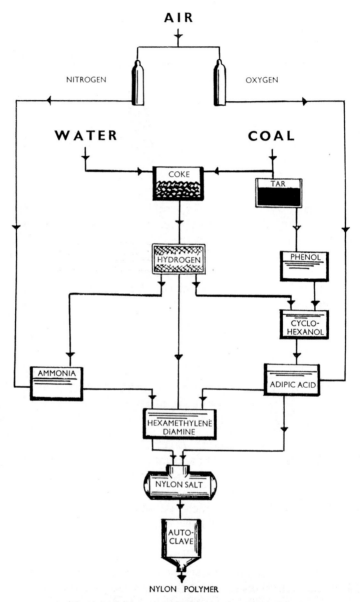

FIG. 21. Showing how a nylon polymer is made.
By courtesy of British Nylon Spinners Ltd

HOW A NYLON YARN IS MADE

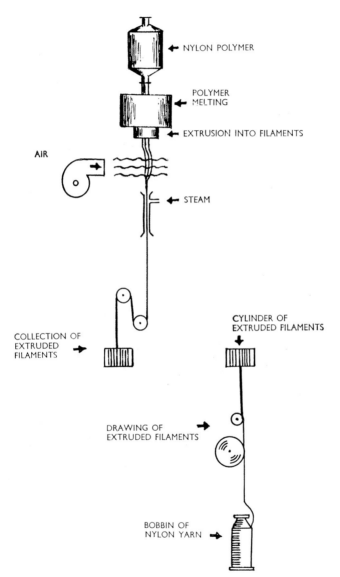

NYLON POLYMER

POLYMER MELTING

EXTRUSION INTO FILAMENTS

AIR

STEAM

CYLINDER OF EXTRUDED FILAMENTS

COLLECTION OF EXTRUDED FILAMENTS

DRAWING OF EXTRUDED FILAMENTS

BOBBIN OF NYLON YARN

FIG. 22. Showing how a nylon yarn is made.
By courtesy of British Nylon Spinners Ltd

F

and then pumped through the multi-holed spinneret to emerge as cooled solidified filaments. These are collected through a guide into thread form which is thereafter cold-drawn (stretched) to about four times its original length and to a degree where the thread no longer tends under ordinary conditions to return to its original length. By such stretching the tensile strength of the original thread (about 1 gram per denier) is increased to about 6 grams per denier or 8 grams if even greater stretching is effected, thus giving ordinary and high tenacity types of nylon. The stretching also reduces the very high extensibility of the original thread to an acceptable value of 20 to 30% for weaving and knitting purposes; a lustre increase is also obtained.

Properties of nylon

Nylon is produced as continuous filaments and as staple fibre. Particular features of this fibre are its low sp. gr. of 1·14, its somewhat less hydrophobic character as compared with other synthetic fibres (for example, Terylene) so that it has a moisture regain of 4·5%, its liability to decompose by hydrolysis into adipic acid and hexamethylene diamine in boiling 5% hydrochloric acid, and its exceptionally high resistance to wear by abrasion. Its high wear value makes it suitable for adding to other materials (particularly for reinforcing the heels of men's socks) to increase their wearing properties.

Nylon is most easily dyed with disperse dyes and these most effectively dye level unevenly stretched nylons. With the aid of dye assistants or by dyeing at temperatures exceeding 100° C, nylon can also be dyed with wool and cotton dyes (notably the acid wool dyes, pre-metallised dyes, and direct cotton dyes).

NYLON 6

A slightly different type of nylon, yet still a polyamide fibre, is made by the simple poly condensation of the monomer ε-caprolactam which is the anhydride of caproic acid, the formulae of these being:

$$CH_2CH_2CH_2CH_2CH_2CO$$
$$| \qquad\qquad\qquad |$$
$$NH\text{——————————}$$

Caprolactam

$$NH_2CH_2CH_2CH_2CH_2CH_2COOH$$

Caproic acid

Caprolactam and caproic acid may be considered equivalent in the manufacture of polycaprolactam, which is carried out by the high temperature heating of caprolactam to effect the following condensation changes:

$$NH_2—(CH_2)_5—COOH$$

Condensation of two molecules

$$NH_2(CH_2)_5CO.NH(CH_2)COOH$$

Continued condensation

$$H—[—NH(CH_2)_5CO—]_n—OH$$
Polycaprolactam

Caprolan and Perlon are American and German brands of nylon 6 and they have the same sp. gr. 1·14 and much the same other properties as nylon 6,6 fibres. An exception is the lower melting point of polycaprolactam which is about 215° C as compared with 250° C for polyhexamethylene adipamide. Nylon 6 fibres appear to be slightly more hydrophile than nylon 6,6 fibres and are more easily dyed. At the present time nylon 6 fibres are coming into increasing favour as polyamide fibres for textile purposes— originally they were mainly employed as bristle fibres.

RILSAN

This is a polyamide fibre of French origin which is available in the usual continuous filament and staple fibre forms. It is made from a polyamide obtained by polycondensation of monomeric 11-amino-undecanoic acid having the formula $NH_2(CH_2)_{10}$ COOH, which in its turn is made from ammonia and the undecylenic acid $CH_2{=}CH(CH_2)_8COOH$, obtained by the controlled decomposition of castor oil. Thus the polyundecanamide used for the spinning of Rilsan fibres has the formula:

$$H—[—NH(CH_2)_{10}CO—]_n—OH$$

It will be noted that Rilsan has a chemical structure more akin to Perlon and Caprolan than to nylon 6,6.

Properties

Continuous Rilsan fibres have the high tensile strength of 6·5 grams per denier and a very compact molecular structure so that they are difficult to dye. It has the low sp. gr. of 1·04 and has a moisture regain of 1·18%. An important property is that Rilsan melts at the relatively low temperature of 189° C while it softens at 170° C. The safe ironing temperature is 80° to 100° C.

Rilsan fabrics can be permanently pleated under appropriate high temperature heat-setting conditions.

POLYESTER FIBRES

TERYLENE

Discovery

The polyethylene terephthalate from which Terylene is melt-spun was originally discovered to be suitable for the manufacture of a polyester type of fibre by Whinfield and Dickson as a result of research carried out in the Manchester laboratories of The Calico Printers Association Ltd. It may be recalled that Dr Carothers in deciding which type of synthetic fibre to make for the first time rejected at least temporarily the polyester type; the polyamide nylon was chosen. It seems that Carothers had never envisaged the possibility of using polyethylene terephthalate, whereas Whinfield and Dickson thought this particular polyester worthy of trial from a reasoning that the high symmetry of its long molecules would ensure that fibres made from it would be strong and durable. These workers actually had great difficulty in scraping together enough of the required terephthalic acid (a rare chemical in those days) to condense with the ethylene glycol component so that fibre-making trials could be made. It thus gave them much satisfaction to find that polyethylene terephthalate yielded a new type of synthetic fibre (afterwards to be named Terylene) having textile properties quite as good as those of the nylon made from polyhexamethylene adipamide. Later the E. I. du Pont de Nemours Company Inc. in America who pioneered nylon obtained the right by licence to manufacture polyethylene terephthalate fibres and these are now being sold under the name of Dacron.

Manufacture

Manufacture of polyethylene terephthalate involves heating together under high temperature conditions and in the presence of a catalyst a mixture of ethylene glycol, $HOCH_2CH_2OH$, and tere-

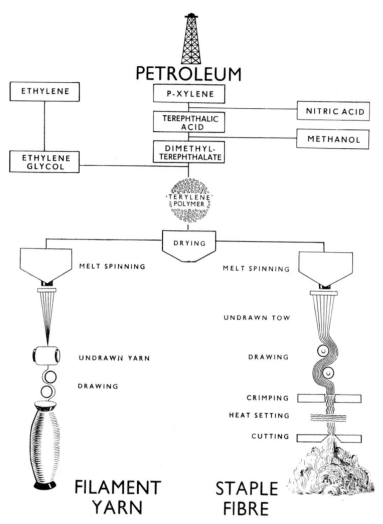

PETROLEUM

ETHYLENE

P-XYLENE

TEREPHTHALIC ACID

NITRIC ACID

METHANOL

DIMETHYL-TEREPHTHALATE

ETHYLENE GLYCOL

'TERYLENE' POLYMER

DRYING

MELT SPINNING

MELT SPINNING

UNDRAWN TOW

UNDRAWN YARN

DRAWING

DRAWING

CRIMPING

HEAT SETTING

CUTTING

FILAMENT YARN

STAPLE FIBRE

FIG. 23. Flow-sheet showing the manufacture of Terylene (polyethylene terephthalate fibre) in the form of continuous filament yarn and also as staple (cut-up) fibre.

By courtesy of Imperial Chemical Industries Ltd

phthalic acid HOOC—⟨　⟩—COOH until the polyethylene terephthalate molecules have attained sufficient length to be suitable
for the melt-spinning of the Terylene fibres. The freshly spun
fibres are much strengthened by hot-stretching (as are most synthetic fibres) to about five times their original length. The resulting fibres may be left in their continuous form or be cut up to any
desired length to give staple fibre. The properties of Terylene
fibres are summarised later on p. 109.

Properties

It is to be noted that in Terylene fibres the molecules of polyethylene terephthalate are especially tightly packed and that the
fibres are highly crystalline. Thus it can be readily understood that
Terylene is very hydrophobic so that it has the exceptionally low
moisture regain of 0·4% and the fibres scarcely swell on wetting.
Terylene shows but little power to absorb dyes and the dyeing of
this type of synthetic fibre has given much trouble to dyers and
printers. Disperse and azoic dyes are mostly used but they can
only be satisfactorily applied under ordinary conditions of dyeing
with the aid of a dye-carrier in the dyebath or (if the use of a dye-
carrier is not desirable) under high temperature, high pressure
dyeing conditions. In either case, the dye-carrier or the high
temperature conditions loosen the internal structure of the Terylene fibres so that dye particles can pass into them more freely and
sufficiently to allow the production of deep shades.

Tumescal D⋆ (diphenyl) and Tumescal OP⋆ (ortho-phenyl-
phenol) are recommended dye-carriers; para-phenylphenol has a
special value in the colour printing of Terylene.

Terylene fibre goods are especially resistant to out-of-doors
conditions of exposure. The fibres have a sp. gr. of 1·38 (comparable to 1·33 for wool and 1·52 for cotton and 1·14 for nylon)
and have good resistance to heat with melting point 260° C.
Terylene yarn shrinks about 7% in boiling water and fabrics will
shrink to a corresponding degree, but this may be almost entirely
prevented by heat-setting, that is holding it to normal dimensions
while being exposed to a temperature about 20° C or more above
the expected usage temperature, but, of course, below the softening
temperature of the Terylene.

⋆ Made by I.C.I. Ltd.

Terylene fabrics are amenable to permanent pleating by a high-temperature treatment which is equivalent to heat-setting with the fabric in a desired folded or pleated state.

DACRON

This American-made type of polyethylene terephthalate fibre is available in the usual continuous filament and staple fibre forms and has properties closely akin to those of Terylene—the rights to manufacture this fibre were obtained by E. I. du Pont de Nemours Co. from the manufacturers of British Terylene (I.C.I. Ltd).

KODEL

This is a polyester fibre made by the Tennessee Eastman Co., U.S.A., and is believed to be a modified polyethylene terephthalate fibre, but its exact composition has not yet been disclosed. The fibres have the very high melting point of 295° C and they shrink only 1% in boiling water. Their sp. gr. is 1·22 (lower than that of Terylene and Dacron) and being produced so far only as staple fibre their tensile strength is about 2·7 grams per denier, which is lower than the 3·5 grams per denier for Terylene staple fibre. It is to be noted that synthetic staple fibres are usually 25% weaker than the corresponding continuous fibres.

An important feature of Kodel is that it can be dyed more easily than Terylene and Dacron so that it is not necessary to use other than conventional dyeing conditions and equipment. Kodel fabrics can be permanently pleated by suitable high temperature treatment but they have very good dimensional stability (retention of shape and size) even without any heat-setting. It is claimed that Kodel materials can be ironed at up to 220° C without damage.

ACRYLIC FIBRES

The acrylic group of synthetic fibres includes many of considerable importance and their number is being steadily increased. This group includes all those fibres made from polymers consisting wholly or partly of acrylonitrile, and important members are Orlon, Acrilan, Courtelle, Verel, Zefran, etc. Acrylonitrile has thus become very important for the manufacture of synthetic fibres. It is a liquid of boiling point 77° C and is made by the direct combination of acetylene with hydrogen cyanide as catalysed by cuprous chloride:

$$
\begin{array}{ccccc}
\text{CH} & & & & \text{CH}_2 \\
\vert\vert\vert & + & \text{HCN} & \rightarrow & \vert\vert \\
\text{CH} & & & & \text{CHCN} \\
\text{Acetylene} & & \text{Hydrocyanide} & & \text{Acrylonitrile}
\end{array}
$$

or by the combination of ethylene oxide with hydrogen cyanide to give ethylene cyanohydrin followed by dehydration of this:

$$
\begin{array}{ccccccc}
\text{CH}_2\!\diagdown & & & & \text{CH}_2\text{OH} & \text{dehydration} & \text{CH}_2 \\
\vert \quad\; \text{O} & + & \text{HCN} & \rightarrow & \vert & \xrightarrow{} & \vert\vert \\
\text{CH}_2\!\diagup & & & & \text{CH}_2\text{CN} & & \text{CHCN} \\
\text{Ethylene} & & \text{Hydrogen} & & \text{Ethylene} & & \text{Acrylonitrile} \\
\text{oxide} & & \text{cyanide} & & \text{cyanohydrin} & &
\end{array}
$$

It very readily undergoes polymerisation by itself (homopolymerisation) and with other polymerisable compounds (copolymerisation). Polymerised acrylonitrile is the basis of Orlon while copolymers of acrylonitrile are the basis of Courtelle, Dynel, Acrilan, Creslan, etc. Acrylonitrile is so favourable to the formation of polymeric substances which can be converted into useful fibres that the fibre-forming copolymers now in use generally contain at least 70% of acrylonitrile.

Most of the copolymers of acrylonitrile are prepared by polymerisation reactions effected in aqueous solutions or dispersions of the components and catalysed with a peroxide such as benzoyl peroxide.

Properties

The presence of the nitrile (CN) group in acrylic fibres gives them a slight yellowish to brown tone which it is difficult to remove by bleaching. Most of the acrylic fibres have lower melting and softening temperatures than nylon and Terylene and are relatively difficult to dye under ordinary conditions with the dyes ordinarily available for cotton and wool. They have good stability towards acids and alkalis and if a stretching or drawing stage is included in their manufacture (the stretching is often about 1,000%) they have the high tensile strength of 3 to 6 grams per denier. Acrylic fibres are strongly hydrophobic and imbibe (absorb) but a small amount of water when wetted so that the fibres swell only to a moderate degree. These fibres also have low moisture regains.

ORLON

Orlon was first manufactured about 1945 and since then has been the subject of much research, mainly carried out with a view to improving its dyeing properties and securing a simplification of details of manufacture. It is made from polymerised acrylonitrile having the formula:

$$- - -CH_2-CH-CH_2-CH-CH_2-CH- - -$$
$$\qquad\quad |\qquad\quad\ |\qquad\quad\ |$$
$$\qquad\quad CN\qquad CN\qquad CN$$

Manufacture

Great difficulty has attended the devising of a satisfactory process for spinning Orlon from polyacrylonitrile, since it decomposes under melt-spinning conditions so as to make this impracticable, while it is difficult to bring it into solution form for spinning into fibres by dry or wet spinning techniques. In the early days of its manufacture special organic solvents had to be prepared for polyacrylonitrile, and among these dimethylformamide, $(CH_3)_2N-OCH$, and dimethylacetamide, $CH_3CON(CH_3)_2$, have proved most useful. Polyacrylonitrile has been found soluble in highly concentrated aqueous solutions of certain inorganic salts such as sodium thiocyanate, zinc chloride, lithium bromide, etc., and spinning techniques have been developed based on spinning such solutions of polyacrylonitrile into aqueous coagulating baths also containing these inorganic salts but in sufficiently low concentration to ensure the precipitation of the extruded polyacrylonitrile in the form of fibres. It is probable that some production of Orlon is based on such a method but it is likely that a larger production comes from dry spinning a solution of polyacrylonitrile in dimethylformamide into warm air to evaporate the organic solvent and leave solidified fibres, or by wet spinning such a solution into a hot glycerol coagulating bath. Exact details of the methods employed for manufacturing Orlon have not been disclosed.

In preparing polyacrylonitrile solutions in dimethylformamide for spinning into fibres it is necessary to use heat and this is liable to result in the formation of yellowish to brown solutions and thus lead to off-white fibres; it is also found that the spinning solutions may tend to gel prematurely. These are two difficulties which have had to receive consideration by Orlon manufacturers.

Properties

The essential properties of Orlon are given in tabular form on p. 109.

The highly compact molecular structure of Orlon fibres (the fibres are highly stretched during manufacture) makes them very difficult to dye, even with disperse dyes, but about 1950 a new method of dyeing with acid wool, and direct cotton dyes, known as the 'cuprous-ion' method, was discovered. It made the dyeing of Orlon (and indeed all acrylic synthetic fibres) much easier and in particular allowed the production of deep shades. In the cuprous-ion method dyeing is effected using a dyebath to which have been added copper sulphate and a reducing agent such as hydroxylamine sulphate, sodium hydrosulphite, sodium bisulphite, etc., so that during the dyeing process cuprous-ions are formed which are absorbed into the Orlon fibres and there act as a mordant to attract the dye into them; dye absorption is thus much assisted.

More recently a special type of basic dye has been developed and the range of these dyes now available much simplifies the dyeing of Orlon fibres goods in a full range of colours. These basic dyes are often referred to as *cationic* dyes and they yield shades having good fastness to light and washing.

The moisture regain of Orlon is about 1·5% and the fibres are characterised by being able to withstand prolonged heating at up to 150° C without appreciable deterioration. The fibres have a sp. gr. of 1·14, which is the same as that of nylon.

Improved types

More recently new whiter and more easily dyed types of Orlon known as Orlon 42 and Orlon 72 have been introduced to replace or supplement the earlier Orlon 41. It is believed that to secure this improvement the polyacrylonitrile has been replaced by a co-polymer of acrylonitrile with a small proportion of another component which may have basic (dye-attractive) properties or which may give bulkier molecules, thus reducing the closeness of molecular packing within the fibres to enable dye particles to enter more freely.

Like all synthetic fibres Orlon is completely resistant to attack by moth, mildew, bacteria, and insects. Orlon fabrics can be permanently pleated. Hot ironing is safe up to 160° C.

CRESLAN

This is a fibre now available mainly as staple fibre which is made by the wet spinning of an organic solution of a copolymer of acrylonitrile with a minor proportion (not more than 10%) of a basic polymerisable component which is probably acrylamide (or a derivative of this), CH_2=$CH.CONH_2$. The use of this copolymer ensures that the Creslan fibres are less hydrophobic than those of Orlon while at the same time its basic component (acrylamide) ensures that the fibres have an attraction for acid wool and some direct cotton dyes.

If Creslan fibres are made from the copolymer mentioned above, their molecules will differ from those of Orlon in that at spaced intervals along the length of each molecule there will be attached basic amide, —$CO.NH_2$, groups as shown below:

$$- - -CH_2—CH—CH_2—CH—CH_2—CH—CH_2—CH- - -$$
$$CN \qquad CN \qquad CONH_2 \qquad CN$$

Properties

As indicated above it is an important feature of Creslan that it can be easily dyed with a wide range of dyes which include direct cotton dyes, premetallised dyes, acid wool dyes, basic (cationic) and chrome mordant dyes. The fibres have the relatively low strength of about 3 grams per denier but have a usefully low sp. gr. of 1.17. Creslan yarn shrinks only 1% in boiling water and has a 1% moisture regain.

It is claimed that Creslan materials are naturally highly resistant to creasing but they can be permanently pleated by the usual high temperature heat-setting treatments. Creslan goods can be dry-cleaned without suffering damage. The fibre is slightly off-white in colour.

ACRILAN

Acrilan (an American fibre but now also being made in Northern Ireland) is made from a complex copolymer containing over 80% of acrylonitrile and probably not more than 10% of acid and basic components (the latter type was thought to be a vinylpyridine in earlier types of Acrilan). It is believed that Acrilan fibres are made by the wet spinning of a solution of the copolymer in dimethylacetamide.

Properties

Acrilan fibres have the moderate tensile strength of about 2·5 grams per denier with a somewhat high 35% extensibility. They have a moisture regain of 1·2 to 1·6% according as they are brought to equilibrium from a dry or a wet state and they have a sp. gr. of 1·17.

The basic component in Acrilan fibres ensures that they can be readily dyed with the acid and chrome mordant dyes commonly employed for wool, but dyeing can also be effected with disperse, basic, azoic and vat dyes. A feature of Acrilan fabrics is that they resist creasing yet can be permanently pleated and they can also be safely ironed up to about 150° C. It is claimed that while Acrilan has less resistance to abrasion than nylon and Terylene it is better in this respect than wool.

Acrilan fibres which have been highly stretched but not stabilised readily shrink when entered into hot (about 65° C) water. Thus a so-called Hi-Bulk Acrilan yarn is being produced with a mixture of stretched and non-stretched fibres so that by treatment in hot water it shrinks irregularly to give a highly porous yarn which is suitable for making garments which are required to handle especially warm and soft; such garments retain the quick-drying properties of ordinary Acrilan materials.

VEREL

This is a modified acrylic fibre consisting of a copolymer of acrylonitrile and minor proportions of one or more other polymerisable components introduced with the object of giving the fibres less hydrophobic properties and improved dyeing properties. Thus Verel fibres have the relatively high moisture regain of 3·5 to 4·0% and can be readily dyed by the use of ordinary procedures and, more particularly, with cationic, disperse, and the neutral-dyeing pre-metallised dyes—for really deep shades it is necessary to use a dye-carrier in the dyebath.

Properties

The ordinary Verel yarns are heat stabilised so as to shrink only up to 3% in boiling water but a yarn containing highly stretched non-stabilised fibres is available so that in boiling water it shrinks to give a very bulky yarn.

Verel fibres have the relatively high sp. gr. of 1·38, which is the same as that of the early acrylic fibre Vinyon (this was spun from a copolymer of 88% vinyl chloride and 12% of vinyl acetate) and thus it may be that Verel and Vinyon have similar compositions.

It is a special feature of Verel that it will not burn; however, it melts easily, so that it must not be ironed above 150° C.

Verel fibres have but moderate strength (2·4 to 2·7 grams per denier). They have very good durability and resist deterioration during outdoor exposure better than cotton and wool.

Verel does not respond to heat-setting treatments and in this respect it differs from most synthetic fibres. Garments made with Verel have only a small tendency to pill.

COURTELLE

Courtelle is the first British discovered and manufactured acrylic fibre. It is made from a copolymer of acrylonitrile with a minor proportion of one or more other components which give it a moisture regain of 2% and a definite affinity for basic (cationic) dyes—this type of dye is particularly recommended for dyeing Courtelle since disperse dyes have a somewhat small affinity and can only be used for dyeing pale shades.

Properties

Courtelle has the low sp. gr. of 1·17 and has an off-white colour. It has the good tensile strength of 3·0 to 3·5 grams per denier which lowers to 2·5 to 3·0 grams on wetting. Courtelle fabrics have a considerably lower resistance to abrasion than have nylon and Terylene, but it wears better than viscose rayon.

Courtelle does not melt but it sticks to the iron if this attains 294° C. When mixed with wool Courtelle fibres hinder felting shrinkage of the mixture material. Claim is made for an exceedingly soft handle possessed by Courtelle pile fabrics. Like other acrylic fibres Courtelle is mothproof.

ZEFRAN

Little is so far known about the chemical composition of this new type of acrylic fibre, but it would appear to consist mainly of polyacrylonitrile molecules on which are grafted atomic groupings which make it slightly less hydrophobic. Consequently it has a moisture regain of 2·5% and an affinity for a wide range of dyes including azoic, vat, sulphur, pre-metallised, and direct cotton dyes so that it can be dyed by ordinary procedures. The makers of Zefran (the Dow Chemical Company in U.S.A.) describe it as a *nitrile-alloy* fibre.

The dry and wet tensile strengths of Zefran fibres are 3·5 and 3·1 grams per denier respectively. Fabrics made with it are stated to have good dimensional stability and permanent pleating properties, and also useful wash-and-wear characteristics.

Zefran fabrics stick to a hot iron at about 255° C and can be safely ironed up to 135° C.

DYNEL

Dynel is the staple fibre form of an acrylic fibre made from a copolymer containing 60% of vinyl chloride and 40% of acrylonitrile. It was originally introduced as an improved replacement of Vinyon and Vinyon HH which were earlier produced from a copolymer containing 88% of vinyl chloride and 12% of vinyl acetate but which suffered from the defect of softening at the very low temperature of 65° C, so that these early fibres could not be dyed in boiling aqueous liquors. The manufacture of Vinyon has been discontinued and Vinyon HH (a staple fibre) is now mainly used as a bonding fibre in the manufacture of non-woven fabrics. The use of acrylonitrile instead of vinyl acetate in the fibre-forming copolymer allows Dynel to resist softening until heated to 120° C or higher.

Manufacture

The copolymer (from which Dynel is made) has vinyl chloride, CH_2=CHCl, and acrylonitrile, CH_2=CHCN, as its sole components and has the molecular formula shown below:

$$- - -CH_2—CH—CH_2—CH—CH_2—CH- - -$$
$$\quad\quad\quad | \quad\quad\quad | \quad\quad\quad |$$
$$\quad\quad\quad Cl \quad\quad CN \quad\quad Cl$$

This copolymer has the advantage of being soluble in acetone so that the spinning solution is prepared with this solvent and is then dry spun into fibres which are highly stretched to increase their tensile strength. Wet spinning instead of dry spinning is also carried out. The resulting continuous fibres are then crimped and cut up to give short fibres of suitable length. Alternatively the fibres in the form of a tow may be cut up and then crimped.

Properties

A feature of Dynel is that it has the low moisture regain of 0·4% and that the fibres absorb so little water when wetted that their wet swelling is inappreciable. Hence the difficulties which have been encountered in dyeing them. The discovery of the cuprous-ion method of dyeing previously described has proved very helpful and allowed acid wool dyes and some direct cotton dyes to be applied satisfactorily to this type of synthetic fibre. Dye absorption can be aided by the use of dye-carriers and by employing high temperature + high pressure dyeing techniques.

The tensile strength of Dynel is 2·5 to 3·3 grams per denier in both the wet and dry states and the fibres have a high extensibility of up to 50%. Dynel is exceptionally resistant to attack by almost all the agents such as acids, alkalis, dry-cleaning solvents, insects, micro-organisms, etc. which can harm the natural fibres. Fabrics made of Dynel have good wash-and-wear characteristics.

Dynel fibres are off-white and must be bleached to obtain a better white.

Dynel fibres soften and shrink at about 130° C, but Dynel fabrics can be heat-set so as to be dimensionally stable up to temperatures approaching that of the heat-setting treatment. The setting of a Dynel fabric in boiling water can stabilise its size and shape for most uses to which it is likely to be put.

POLYVINYL AND POLYVINYLIDENE FIBRES

DARVAN

Darvan is a recently introduced fibre which is wet spun from a solution in dimethylformamide of a copolymer made of equal parts of vinylidene dicyanide, $CH_2{=}C(CN)_2$, and vinyl acetate, $CH_2{=}CHOCOCH_3$. It is the first dinitrile fibre to be made because vinylidene dicyanide (dinitrile) was not commercially available before 1947 when the fibre was first produced by the B. F. Goodrich Chemical Co. in U.S.A. Darvan, originally called Darlan, is now available only in staple fibre form.

The molecular formula for this new fibre-forming copolymer used in the manufacture of Darvan is:

$$- - -CH_2-C-CH_2-CH-CH_2-C- - -$$
$$\underset{(CN)_2}{\overset{\|}{\quad}} \quad \underset{O.COCH_3}{\overset{|}{\quad}} \underset{(CN)_2}{\overset{\|}{\quad}}$$

Properties

Among the more significant features of Darvan are its softness and high resistance to deterioration during outdoor exposure. It is exceptionally resistant to sunlight and dry heat. However, it has only medium tensile strength, 2·0 grams per denier dry and 1·7 grams wet. The fibres soften at about 170° C and have a sp. gr. of 1·18. Their moisture regain is 2 to 3% and Darvan fabrics shrink 1% in boiling water—the shrinkage is up to 15% in water at 120° C (under pressure) as might be expected.

Darvan has no practical affinity for direct cotton, acid wool, vat, premetallised, and chrome mordant dyes but it can be dyed in pale shades under ordinary conditions with disperse, cationic, and azoic dyes. For the production of deep shades it is necessary to use dye-carriers in the dyebath or to use high temperature, high pressure dyeing techniques (that is, with the dyeing temperature exceeding 100° C, say at 110° to 120° C).

Darvan is adversely affected by strong alkaline liquors.

An interesting feature of Darvan fibres is that their molecules are almost completely randomly distributed and show no crystallinity.

SARAN

Saran fibres are melt-spun from a copolymer containing about 85% of vinylidene chloride, $CH_2{=}CCl_2$, and 15% of vinyl chloride, $CH_2{=}CHCl$, into cold air which immediately solidifies the molten streams issuing from the spinneret so that they can be at once quenched in cold water; thereafter they are stretched to give them increased strength. Since Saran fibres are difficult to dye (their dyeing properties, such as they are, resemble those of Vinyon fibres) it is generally preferred to add coloured pigments to the copolymer melt and so spin coloured fibres directly.

The molecules of Saran fibres have the following formula:

$$- - -CH_2-CH-CH_2-C-CH_2-C-CH_2-CH- - -$$
$$\underset{Cl}{\overset{|}{\quad}} \quad \underset{Cl_2}{\overset{\|}{\quad}} \quad \underset{Cl_2}{\overset{|}{\quad}} \quad \underset{Cl}{\overset{|}{\quad}}$$

Properties

A significant feature of Saran fibres is their high sp. gr. of 1·75 and their exceptionally low moisture regain of 0·1%, which indicates their complete resistance to swelling in water and their reluctance to absorb dyes. The fibres are very sensitive to heat so that they lose about 30% of their strength when heated to 100° C (say in boiling water) and soften at about 120° C. It is not possible to hot iron Saran materials. These properties have prevented the wide use of Saran for the manufacture of wearing apparel but make it suitable for motor-car upholstery, filter cloths, and deck-chair coverings (Tygan deck-chair fabric is made of Saran).

Another significant property of Saran fibres is their low tensile strength of 1·8 grams per denier dry and wet. Saran does not burn.

RHOVYL

Rhovyl is the generic name given by the French Rhovyl Company to four closely related types of polyvinyl chloride fibres which are designated as Rhovyl, Thermovyl, Fibravyl, and Retractyl. All these fibres are dry spun from a solution of polyvinyl chloride having the formula:

$$- - -CH_2-CH-CH_2-CH-CH_2-CH- - -$$
$$\qquad\quad | \qquad\quad | \qquad\quad |$$
$$\qquad\quad Cl \qquad\quad Cl \qquad\quad Cl$$

in a mixture of acetone and carbon disulphide.

Properties

Rhovyl fibre is a highly stretched fibre with its molecules mainly aligned parallel to the fibre length. It has a tensile strength of up to 3 grams per denier and a sp. gr. of 1·4. It absorbs no moisture and its fibres do not swell in water, so that dyeing is difficult, and the only satisfactory dyeing method is to have a dye-carrier in the dyebath and use disperse dyes. However, the fibres are very sensitive to heat and they commence to soften and shrink at 70° C so that the temperature of dyeing must not be higher than this. Rhovyl definitely softens and decomposes at about 180° C. By contrast Rhovyl materials retain their original strength and flexibility at temperatures as low as −80° C.

Since Rhovyl fibres are very inert chemically and are not inflammable and resist attack by micro-organisms they can be used in the production of fabrics having industrial rather than textile uses.

G

Thermovyl fibres are similar to those of Rhovyl as described above but unlike these latter fibres have been heat-stabilised so that they do not materially shrink in boiling water. The stabilisation involves allowing the fibres to shrink at 100° C, and since this is counter to the stretching of the Rhovyl fibres during manufacture the Thermovyl fibres have only the low tensile strength of 0·9 grams per denier—they also have the very high extensibility of 160%. Thermovyl fibres do not shrink at 100° C.

Fibravyl is the staple fibre form of Rhovyl obtained by cutting up these latter continuous fibres to lengths appropriate to their use in admixture with cotton, wool, linen, or other fibres. Fibravyl fibres may also have given to them an artificial crimp. They shrink about 55% at 100° C.

Retractyl fibres have their molecules oriented (aligned parallel to each other and to the fibre length) about half-way between that of Rhovyl and Thermovyl fibres and they are in the form of staple fibre. They shrink 15 to 30% at 100° C.

PE-CE FIBRE

This fibre, wet spun from a solution in acetone of polyvinyl chloride which has been chlorinated, has only limited textile use although being non-inflammable it can be made into fireproof fabrics.

The essential properties are tabulated on p. 109.

Particular features are that it is non-absorbent towards moisture and is immune to any kind of attack by micro-organisms. It is highly sensitive to heat so that it softens and shrinks at temperatures exceeding about 75° C. The fibres have a sp. gr. of 1·39.

VINYLON

Vinylon is made in Japan from polyvinyl alcohol which in its turn is made by the alkaline hydrolysis of polyvinyl acetate. Polyvinyl alcohol is water-soluble, and by spinning a viscous aqueous solution of this polymer into water containing sodium sulphate to precipitate the extruded streams as solid filaments, Vinylon is made. The freshly formed filaments are stretched and after-treated with formaldehyde and dried at a high temperature to render them

water-insoluble. The molecules of Vinylon fibres have the following formula:

$$- - -CH_2-CH-CH_2-CH-CH_2-CH- - -$$
$$\qquad\quad | \qquad\quad | \qquad\quad |$$
$$\qquad\quad OH \qquad OH \qquad OH$$

Properties

Although polyvinyl alcohol is readily soluble in water and the
freshly spun fibres are strongly hydrophile, the stretching, drying,
and treatment with formaldehyde makes them hydrophobic and
insoluble so that fishing nets can be made from them. Yet their
residual hydrophile properties ensure that Vinylon materials can
be readily dyed with most types of dyes, including sulphur, vat,
azoic, direct cotton, and pre-metallised dyes, and by ordinary
dyeing methods.

The fibres have a sp. gr. of 1·26 and a moisture regain of about
5%. They soften at 200° C and melt at 220° C, resembling secondary acetate fibres in this respect. They have good resistance to
attack by acids and alkalis and also by all types of micro-organisms.

Other Japanese manufactured fibres based on polyvinyl alcohol
are Kuralon, Mewlon, and Vinylan, and it is believed that in these
the polyvinyl alcohol is acetylated to render it less soluble.

POLYOLEFINE FIBRES

Olefines are hydrocarbons mainly obtained from petroleum and
they are characterised by being unsaturated substances and capable
of polymerisation. So far only two olefines (both gases), ethylene
and propylene, having the following formulae:

$$CH_2{=}CH_2 \qquad\qquad CH_2{=}CH.CH_3$$
$$\text{Ethylene} \qquad\qquad\quad \text{Propylene}$$

have been found suitable for conversion into fibre-forming polyolefines, and considerable difficulty has been experienced in devising satisfactory methods for ensuring that these polyolefines are
linear—it is easy for the polymerisation to proceed in such a manner as to produce branched polyolefines which, as mentioned
earlier, do not yield fibres having satisfactory textile properties.

Manufacture

I.C.I. Ltd were pioneers in the polymerisation of ethylene. At
one time it was thought that the polyethylene produced had strictly

linear molecules but more recently it has been found that these molecules are to a considerable degree branched. However, the methods of polymerisation have now been much changed (in particular, modern methods do not employ the very high temperatures and pressures formerly used) so that polyethylene having more linear molecules is now available. At the same time great progress has been made in devising new catalysts for use in the polymerisation of propylene so as to ensure that linear polypropylene molecules are obtained suitable for conversion into fibres. Sufficient knowledge has now been obtained to show that it is possible to polymerise various olefines to give linear polyolefines capable of conversion into fibres having textile properties including an exceptionally high strength and resistance to abrasion. Polyethylene fibres have been for a few years in commercial production and now polypropylene fibres are being manufactured on a moderate scale. Important pioneer chemists in this field are Ziegler and Natta who have shown how to prepare the special catalysts which ensure the formation of linear molecules.

The polyolefine fibres so far produced are strongly hydrophobic and are thus very inert towards water. This will certainly raise difficulties in dyeing them but no doubt these will in due course be overcome. Temporarily such difficulties are avoided by adding a pigment to the fibre spinning melt so as to produce coloured fibres directly. At the present time polypropylene fibres are finding use as ropes which have the advantage of being so light that they float on water.

POLYETHYLENE FIBRES

COURLENE

Courlene fibres are obtained by the melt-spinning of polyethylene having the formula

$$- - -CH_2—CH_2—CH_2—CH_2—CH_2—CH_2- - -$$

and made by subjecting ethylene gas (obtained cheaply from petroleum) to high pressure at a high temperature in the presence of a catalyst. Polyethylene is a white wax-like solid and the fibres freshly spun from it at about $300°$ C are similar. By cold-drawing them to six times their original length their strength can be proportionally increased.

Properties

From a consideration of the above formula for polyethylene it will be seen that such straight molecules are amenable to very close packing within Courlene fibres so that there will be great difficulty for water and dyes to enter. Thus the moisture regain of Courlene is nil and no satisfactory easy method of dyeing is available. Coloured Courlene fibres are best made by adding a coloured pigment to the spinning melt.

A disadvantage of Courlene from the textile viewpoint is that the fibres soften at about 90° C and melt at 110° to 120° C. On the other hand, the fibres are not adversely affected by exposure to such low temperatures as −70° C.

Courlene is resistant to attack by strong acids and alkalis but it is degraded slowly in sunlight.

Very characteristic of Courlene fibres is the fact that they float in water since they have the exceptionally low sp. gr. of 0·92.

Courlene is a useful fibre for the manufacture of protective types of clothing and for upholstery fabrics. At present the industrial uses of Courlene exceed its textile uses but this position is not likely to continue.

REEVON

Reevon is the name of an American type of polyethylene fibre comparable in its general properties to the Courlene (Courtaulds) described above. A notable difference is that Reevon fibres have a much higher tensile strength and this can be from 3 to 8 grams per denier according to the grade.

TEFLON

A comparatively new polyolefine fibre which has unique resistance to high temperatures is Teflon. It is made from tetrafluoroethylene, $CF_2{=}CF_2$, which in its linear polymerised form has the formula:

$$- - -CF_2{-}CF_2{-}CF_2{-}CF_2{-}CF_2{-} - -$$

Manufacture

Polytetrafluoroethylene is insoluble in all solvents and it does not melt below 400° C and then only with rapid decomposition. Thus none of the usual methods for converting polytetrafluoroethylene into fibres by dry or wet spinning or by melt-spinning can be employed. The manufacturers of Teflon (E. I. du Pont de Nemours Co. Inc.) have overcome this difficulty by adopting an entirely new method of fibre production.

In the new method, the polytetrafluoroethylene is first converted into a highly divided form such that each particle is very much longer than thick. This is then extruded through relatively coarse orifices under conditions such that the particles are aligned parallel to the direction of extrusion and this ensures that they adhere together enough to give filaments of reasonable strength to allow their subsequent handling. These filaments just consist of discrete polytetrafluoroethylene ribbon-like particles tenaciously adhering to each other. Such filaments are then heated at about 385° C for a few seconds to produce sintering or an amalgamation of the particles; immediately thereafter the filaments are quenched in water and then are stretched to four times their original length. Thus are produced very strong clear filaments.

Properties

Outstanding properties of Teflon are its extreme resistance to high temperatures, its extreme hydrophobicity so that it is completely inert towards water, and its inertness to all reactive chemicals and organic solvents. Teflon fibres retain their strength at temperatures up to 200° C but lose their fibrous form at 327° C. However, the fibres have the comparatively low tensile strength of 1·6 grams per denier and yet have good resistance to abrasion. Teflon fibres are produced tan to brown in colour and are difficult to bleach to a reasonable white. They have a sp. gr. of 2·3.

The production of Teflon fibres is steadily being developed and improvements are expected. So far Teflon is finding many speciality uses apart from the making of wearing apparel, as for example, sewing threads, tapes, packing braids, and filtration cloths.

Miscellaneous Fibres

GLASS FIBRES

Glass fibres are made by allowing molten glass in an electric furnace to flow out and downwards through numerous small orifices at the bottom so that the emerging molten glass streams immediately solidify to filaments which are drawn away to be wound on bobbins at such a high rate that the filaments are stretched considerably. Before winding on the bobbins groups of filaments are collected into the form of thread which is appropriately lubricated. Continuous filament yarns are thus produced.

In an alternative procedure the issuing streams of molten glass are met by high pressure steam jets which both extenuate and break up the resulting filaments so that these can be collected in the form of a web or mat on a travelling conveyor belt or on a rotating drum—thus is produced the glass fibre which is much used for sound and heat insulating purposes.

Properties

Glass fibres are distinguished by their very high tensile strength of 6 to 7 grams per denier and their extreme resistance to deterioration by acids, alkalis, micro-organisms, water, and heat. Unfortunately the fibres are brittle, but they are sufficiently pliable, especially when fine, to enable them in yarn form to be woven and knitted into fabrics. Such fabrics are today being used with polyester resins to form laminated sheet material having exceptionally high strength and durability which warrants their use for the construction of the hulls of boats and yachts as well as other articles where high strength is essential.

Glass fibres have the high sp. gr. of 2·54 and although non-inflammable they commence to deteriorate when heated to about 315° C and this change continues up to the melting point of glass which is about 815° C.

Dyeing properties

It is a mistake to think that coloured glass fibres can be easily and satisfactorily made directly from coloured glass, for the simple reason that only pale coloured fibres can thus be produced and the colouring is not fast to washing. Coloured glass fibres have to be produced by dyeing processes and since glass fibres have no affinity for dyes they have first to be coated with a substance which adheres tenaciously to the fibre surface yet is strongly attractive to dyes.

Glass fibres are now being coloured by a Coronising process in which the fabric is first very strongly heated to burn off impurities and also give the fibres a crimp which confers crease-resistant properties to the fabric. Then follows the spreading over the fabric surface of a composition containing a suitable pigment and a resin binder for this pigment. After drying the fabric is further treated with an aqueous dispersion of a complex organo chromium–stearic acid compound and is finally dried at about 120° C, whereby the applied colouring is made fast to washing. Glass fibre fabrics can be printed with coloured patterns by a somewhat similar process but by a screen printing of the pigmented resin composition.

Electrical uses

Glass fibre fabrics and tapes are much used for electrical insulation purposes and are much superior in this use to shellac and other formerly employed alternatives. An important point is that when glass fibre insulation is used the space occupied by the insulation is much less than when other insulating materials are used.

ASBESTOS

Asbestos fibres are obtained by the longitudinal splitting of bundles of flexible crystals found in certain minerals and rocks and they consist of hydrated silicates of magnesia—*chrysotile* asbestos, which is the type of asbestos most amenable to spinning into yarn, has a chemical composition represented by the formula

$$3MgO.2SiO_2.2H_2O.$$

Other types may also contain small proportions of iron, alumina, and calcium. The splitting of the crystals can be carried on almost indefinitely so that asbestos fibres much finer than any textile fibre can be obtained if desired. The character of such fibres depends on the types of rock from which the crystal bundles are obtained. It would appear that individual fibres of chrysotile asbestos have a tubular structure.

The most important features of asbestos are its extreme resistance to high temperatures and its inertness to attack by most kinds of reactive chemicals; it is also resistant to weathering and attack by micro-organisms.

Yarns and fabric made from asbestos have many industrial uses where protection against heat and fire is required. Sometimes to assist the production of yarns and fabrics a suitable proportion of cotton or viscose rayon staple fibre is added to the asbestos fibre.

METALLIC AND METALLISED YARNS

Metallic yarns are made by various methods which include bonding metal (for example, aluminium) foil between two layers of plastic film and then cutting into very narrow strips (as narrow as 1/80th inch or less) which can be used as yarn before or after reinforcing with an ordinary yarn.

Metallised yarns are made by running glass, cotton, asbestos, nylon, viscose rayon, and even wool yarns through a vacuum chamber in which a metal such as aluminium or zinc is vaporised at a high temperature, say up to 1,300° C, so that the yarn becomes evenly coated with metal particles. In an alternative process the yarn (made of heat-resistant fibres such as glass or asbestos) is run rapidly through a bath of the molten metal.

Such metallic and metallised yarns can be used in weaving and knitting to produce highly decorative materials.

IDENTIFICATION OF TEXTILE FIBRES

In earlier days when almost all textile materials for domestic use were made from cotton, wool, linen, and silk, and regenerated cellulose and cellulose derivative artificial fibres, it was comparatively easy by use of staining and burning tests supplemented by microscopic examination and by a few other such simple tests to identify which of these fibres were present in fabrics and garments whether or not they were coloured. But in the meantime so many new fibres have come into use as a result of synthetic fibre manufacture that fibre identification has become much more complicated. The increasing use of fibre mixtures has added to the difficulties encountered.

At the present time there are at least fourteen different fundamental types of fibres—acetate, acrylic, modacrylic, nytril, olefin, polyester, rayon, polyamide (nylon), Saran, Spandex, cotton, linen, silk, and wool—and many of these have become available in modified forms. It is thus not considered satisfactory or suitable to describe here identification tests which could be relied on to indicate with certainty the type of fibre present in any textile material. It will be sufficient to state that identification requires the application of several tests based on the following:

1. Behaviour of the fibre towards heat and flame.

2. Microscopic examination of the fibre and also its cross-section.
3. Its behaviour and solubility in various acids and alkalis and organic solvents.
4. Its reaction to various colour-staining solutions including the proprietary *Shirlastain* (obtainable from Shirley Developments Ltd, Manchester, who willingly send free literature describing the full use of their product).
5. The melting point of the fibre.
6. Its moisture regain.
7. Its refractive index.
8. Its specific gravity, which is easily determined by noting in which liquid the fibre floats of a series of specially prepared liquids graded in respect of their density.

Questions for Chapter II

1. Distinguish between vegetable, animal, and man-made fibres by reference to their physical and chemical properties.
2. Describe the cultivation of cotton and indicate the subsequent stages by which it is brought into a form for delivery to yarn spinners.
3. How does the cotton fibre in bale form differ from the same fibres in a ripe cotton boll just about to open?
4. Describe types of abnormal cotton fibres.
5. What is cotton lint and for what purpose is it used?
6. Describe how caustic soda can be used to give cotton fibres an increased lustre, and the related discoveries of John Mercer and Horace Lowe.
7. Cotton is sometimes described as an inert fibre. Discuss how far this is true and give instances where cotton appears highly reactive.
8. Describe the cultivation of flax and how linen fibres can be obtained from it.
9. How does a linen fibre differ from a cotton fibre?
10. Describe the physical properties of hemp, jute, sisal, and ramie.
11. State how raw wool is obtained and describe the physical and chemical characteristics of this fibre.
12. What is the difference between cotton cellulose and wool keratin?
13. Describe the composite nature of a wool fibre by reference to its main structural parts. Indicate the importance of the epithelial scales.
14. How similar are the properties of wool and mohair fibres?

15. What is reclaimed wool and how is it freed from cellulose fibres and other cellulose impurities?

16. Describe the shrinking of wool fabrics when washed with reference to relaxation and felting.

17. Indicate a fundamental difference between cotton and wool in respect of their behaviour towards acids and alkalis and also to hypochlorite bleaching liquors.

18. What fibres are indicated by: shoddy, mungo, and alpaca?

19. A wool garment bears the label—*all-wool*. Do you consider this to be completely satisfactory as describing the quality of the garment?

20. Describe the cultivation of silkworms and the manner in which raw silk thread is ultimately obtained. What is the effect of a boiling soap solution on raw silk thread?

21. How does a silk thread differ from cotton and wool in respect of its physical form and chemical composition?

22. How did Louis Pasteur by his researches on micro-organisms assist the manufacture of silk?

23. Describe how raw silk is converted into threads suitable for weaving and knitting. Compare tram and organzine silk threads. What is Schappe silk?

24. Compare the behaviour of cotton, wool, and silk threads as regards their burning.

25. What is wild silk? How does it differ in physical form and general properties from cultivated silk?

26. Describe the early circumstances under which the first man-made fibres were discovered. What contributions in this field were made by Count Hilaire de Chardonnet, Cross and Bevan, Topham, Drs Henri and Camille Dreyfus?

27. Describe the manufacture of viscose rayon from cotton or wood pulp cellulose. What are alkali-cellulose and cellulose xanthate?

28. What is the function of the 'coagulation bath' in the manufacture of viscose rayon? Indicate the purpose of each ingredient.

29. Indicate the importance of stretching during viscose rayon manufacture. Correlate the resulting changes of molecular structure to the changes of physical properties.

30. What are the moisture regains of cotton and viscose rayon? Discuss the reasons for the difference between them.

31. What is the colour of viscose rayon as it leaves the spinning machine and how is this subsequently removed?

32. Sketch the cross-section of an ordinary viscose rayon fibre and discuss any connection between this and the fibre properties.

33. What is the *skin* of a viscose rayon fibre? Discuss its importance.

34. Describe the difference between the 'continuous filament' and

'staple fibre' forms of viscose rayon. What is the object of cutting up the longer fibres into shorter ones?

35. Describe the manufacture of cuprammonium rayon. How does it differ from viscose rayon?

36. Describe how acetate rayon came to be made in England. How does this type of rayon differ from viscose rayon?

37. Describe the differences between ordinary (secondary) acetate and triacetate fibres. Indicate how these fibres differ from cotton in respect of their chemical and dyeing properties.

38. What are Tricel, Arnel and Dicel? In which countries are these fibres made?

39. How are ordinary cellulose acetate and cellulose triacetate rayons manufactured? What is the ripening stage and what is its importance?

40. What do you understand is the difference between dry- and wet-spinning processes as applied to man-made fibres?

41. Name three important properties of ordinary acetate rayon in which it differs fundamentally from cotton and wool.

42. If you wished to dye a mixture fabric in two different colours would you use a cotton + viscose rayon or a cotton + acetate or a viscose rayon + acetate fabric?

43. Describe the manufacture of Fortisan fibres and indicate how they differ in physical properties from ordinary acetate fibres.

44. How would you raise the safe ironing temperature of triacetate fibre materials? Could you obtain the same improvement by a similar treatment of ordinary acetate materials?

45. Discuss how triacetate fibre garments and fabric are amenable to permanent pleating.

46. Compare the dyeing properties of wool, viscose rayon, and triacetate fibres.

47. What do you understand by a regenerated cellulose and a regenerated protein fibre? Indicate by reference to the fibre properties how these fibres differ from the original cellulose and protein raw materials used in their manufacture.

48. What are the fibres Fibrolane, Lanital, Aralac, and Ardil? Indicate the raw protein substances used for the manufacture of regenerated protein fibres. Note two main disadvantages of these fibres.

49. Describe the manufacture of alginate fibres and give their more important properties.

50. What do you understand by the term—synthetic fibre? Who was Carothers and what important discoveries did he make?

51. Discuss the molecular structure of a synthetic fibre. What are the amorphous and crystalline regions of a fibre?

52. Discuss the different ways in which polymers having the long linear molecules necessary for fibre formation can be made.

Properties of the more important Natural and Man-made Fibres

NATURAL FIBRES

Fibre	Chemical Type	Strength, Grams/denier	Extensibility at Break, %	Spec. Gravity	Moisture Regain, %	Behaviour at High Temperatures	Resistance to Micro-organisms	Dyeing Properties
Cotton	Natural cellulose	2·0–4·1	5·5–9·5	1·52	8·5	Scorches and burns without melting	Attacked when damp. Mothproof	Dyed with direct cotton, vat, sulphur, azoic, reactive, and oxidation dyes
Linen	Natural cellulose	5·5–6·5	2·8–3·4	1·50	12·0	As cotton	As cotton	As cotton
Wool	Natural protein	1·29–1·60	30–43	1·33	18·0	Chars without melting. Burns with characteristic odour like burning horn	Attacked when damp. Attacked by moth	Dyed with acid, mordant, pre-metallised, basic, neutral dyeing direct dyes
Silk (degummed)	Natural protein	4·3–5·3	23–31	1·35	12·0	As wool—chars to give a hard bead	Attacked under damp conditions. Mothproof	Dyed with most dyes
Jute	Natural cellulose	3·3–3·8	1·7–1·9	1·48	13·7	As cotton	As cotton	As cotton but also with basic and acid wool dyes

MAN-MADE REGENERATED CELLULOSE AND CELLULOSE DERIVATIVE FIBRES

Fibre	Chemical Type	Strength, Grams/denier	Extensibility at Break, %	Spec. Gravity	Moisture Regain, %	Behaviour at High Temperatures	Resistance to Micro-organisms	Dyeing Properties
Viscose rayon	Regenerated cellulose	1·8–2·4	12–20	1·51	12·5	Chars without melting. Burns. Loses strength at 300° F with decomposition	Attacked when damp. Mothproof	As for cotton
ditto (high tenacity)	ditto	3·6–4·0	10–17	1·52	12·5	As ordinary viscose rayon	As ordinary viscose rayon	ditto
Vincel (Courtauld's new polynosic fibre)	Special regenerated cellulose fibre with properties similar to cotton	3·5–4·0	15	—	11·8	As ordinary viscose rayon	As ordinary viscose rayon	ditto
Cuprammonium rayon	Regenerated cellulose	1·7–2·3	10–17	1·53	12·5	As ordinary viscose rayon	As ordinary viscose rayon	ditto
Cellulose acetate (ordinary)	Secondary cellulose acetate (54% acetyl)	1·1–1·4	23–30	1·32	6·0	Softens at 400–450° F. Safe ironing temperature about 300° F. Burns forming a black hard bead	Resistant. Mothproof	Disperse dyes and selected azoic dyes
ditto (high tenacity)	ditto	3·9	5·5	1·33	6·0	Softens at 400° F and otherwise as ordinary cellulose acetate fibres	ditto	ditto
Cellulose triacetate	Cellulose triacetate (62·5% acetyl)	1·3	22–28	1·30	3·2 (after heat setting, 2·7)	Softens at 480° F. Melts at 572° F. Safe ironing temperature 374° F which is raised to 455° F by a heat treatment	ditto	ditto
Fortisan (highly stretched and saponified ordinary cellulose acetate)	Regenerated cellulose	6–7	5–6	1·51	12·0	Similar to cotton	As cotton	As for cotton

SYNTHETIC FIBRES

Fibre	Chemical Type	Strength, Grams/denier	Extensibility at Break, %	Spec. Gravity	Moisture Regain, %	Behaviour at High Temperatures	Resistance to Micro-organisms	Dyeing Properties
Nylon 6.6	Polyamide	4·5–5·5	20–25	1·14	4·5	Safe ironing temperature 356° F. Sticks to hot iron at 445° F. Melts at 482° F. Burns with fusion; does not smoulder	Resistant. Mothproof	Disperse and neutral dyeing pre-metallised dyes; acid and direct dyes by special methods and use of dye-carriers
Nylon 6.6 (high tenacity)	Polyamide	6·0–8·5	15–18	1·14	4·2	ditto	Resistant. Mothproof	ditto
Nylon 6	Polycaprolactam	4·5–5·0	24–40	1·14	3·5–5·0	Softening point 340–355° F. Melting point 419–426° F	Resistant. Mothproof	ditto
Terylene (Dacron is similar)	Polyester	4·5–5·5	15–25	1·38	0·4	Sticks to hot iron at 445° F. Burns and melts	Resistant. Mothproof	Difficult to dye. Disperse dyes at high dyeing temperatures and with aid of dye-carriers. Azoic dyes
Kodel	Polyester	2·5–3·0		1·22	0·4	Safe ironing temperature 410° F. Melts at 555° F.	Resistant. Mothproof	Disperse and azoic dyes using dye carriers for deep shades
Acrilan	Acrylic	2·0–2·7	36–40	1·17	1·6	Softening point 455° F. Sticks to hot iron at 475° F. Burns and melts	Resistant. Mothproof	Disperse, acid, basic, chrome mordant, pre-metallised neutral dyeing dyes, azoic dyes
Creslan	Acrylic	3·3	33	1·18	1·3	Sticks to hot iron at 450° F	Resistant. Mothproof	Most types of dye except direct cotton dyes
Orlon	Acrylic	2·4–4·7	20–28	1·14–1·17	1·5	Safe ironing temperature 275° F. Sticking temperature 455° F. Burns and smoulders	Resistant. Mothproof	Difficult to dye. Dyed with cationic, disperse, acid dyes using 'cuprous-ion' technique, and some vat and sulphur dyes
Courtelle	Acrylic	3·0–3·6	40–45	1·15	1·3	Safe ironing temperature 310° F. Burns and smoulders	Resistant. Mothproof	Disperse and cationic dyes
Vinyon HH	Copolymer of 88/12 vinylchloride + vinylacetate	3·4	22	1·35	0·5	Softens at 150–160° F. Melts at 260° F	Resistant. Mothproof	Disperse dyes
Vinyon N (Dynel)	Copolymer of 60/40 vinylchloride + acrylonitrile	2·5–3·3	30–42	1·30	0·4	Burns with difficulty and does not smoulder. Softening temperature 300–325° F	Resistant. Mothproof	Disperse dyes. Also acid wool dyes by using the 'cuprous-ion' technique
Fibre BHS (new Courtauld's fibre)	Acrylic	3·5–4·0	18–20	—	Low	Completely flameproof	Resistant. Mothproof	Most classes of dyes
Zefran	Copolymer of 60/40 vinylidine chloride + acrylonitrile	3–4	30	1·19	1·5	Safe ironing temperature 275° F. Sticks to hot iron at 490° F	Resistant. Mothproof	Dyed with cationic, vat, sulphur, azoic, and neutral-dyeing pre-metallised dyes
Darvan	Copolymer of 50/50 vinylidene cyanide + vinylacetate	2·0–2·1	25–35	1·20	2·0–3·0	Burns as cotton. Safe ironing temperature 350° F	Resistant. Mothproof	Azoic, cationic, and disperse dyes at high temperatures
Saran	Polyvinylidene chloride	1·8	15–25	1·75	0·1	Very difficult to ignite. Softens at 250° F but loses strength in boiling water	Resistant. Mothproof	Difficult to dye. Best spin-dyed
Verel	Copolymer of mainly acrylonitrile and vinyl- and vinylidene chloride	2·5–2·8	33–35	1·37	3·5–4·0	Safe ironing temperature 300° F. Flameproof	Resistant. Mothproof	Dyed easily with disperse, cationic, basic, and neutral-dyeing pre-metallised dyes at temperatures not exceeding 100° C
Thermovyl (heat stabilised)	Polyvinyl chloride	2·8–3·0	150–180	1·4	0·1	Softens and shrinks at 212° F. Difficult to ignite	Resistant. Mothproof	Difficult to dye. Best spin-dyed
Rhovyl and its staple form Fibravyl (both are stretched forms of Thermovyl)	ditto	2·8–3·0	14–20	1·4	0·1	Softens and shrinks at 140–165° F. Difficult to ignite	ditto ditto	ditto ditto
Vinylon	Polyvinyl alcohol	5·2–7·2	10	1·26–1·30	4·5–5·0	Softens at 390° F and melts at 430° F	Resistant. Mothproof	Dyed with most dyes
Fibrolane	Regenerated casein	1·1	50	1·31	18	Burns as wool	Attacked when damp. Attacked by moth but less than wool	As for wool
Alginate rayon	Calcium alginate	1·2	10–14	1·75	21	Burns but does not smoulder		Basic and neutral-dyeing pre-metallised dyes
Fibreglass	Glass	6·5–9·0	3–4	2·5–2·7	0	Non-inflammable. Loses strength at 600° F and softens at 1,500° F	Resistant. Mothproof	Dyed by a special 'coronising' process in which a chrome-mordant is used
Ulstron (I.C.I. Ltd raw fibre)	Polypropylene	8–9	18–22	0·91	0·15	Softens at 305° F. Melts at 330° F	Resistant. Mothproof	Very difficult to dye
Courlene	Polyethylene	2–3	40	0·96	0	Softens at 194° F. Melts at 248° F.	Resistant. Mothproof	Very difficult to dye. Best spin-dyed
Teflon	Polytetrafluoroethylene	1·6	13	2·3	0	Non-inflammable. Not adversely affected up to 550° F	Resistant. Mothproof	Very difficult to dye

53. Describe the main differences in respect of the polymers from which polyamide, polyester, and acrylic fibres are made.

54. What are the differences between a monomer, polymer (sometimes termed homopolymer), and copolymer? By reference to some synthetic fibres indicate how *copolymers* can in some instances give fibres superior to those obtainable from a *polymer*.

55. Describe melt-spinning by reference to nylon. What are the essential differences between wet, dry, and melt-spinning? What factors influence the choice of a spinning method? In your answer make reference to the spinning of Dynel, nylon, Courtelle, and Acrilan.

56. What is the difference between nylon 6 and nylon 6,6?

57. Describe by reference to nylon 6,6 and Perlon two basically different methods for manufacturing a polyamide fibre.

58. Describe some difficulties you would expect to encounter in converting polyacrylonitrile into a synthetic fibre and indicate some special properties of the resulting fibres.

59. What do you understand by 'cold-drawing' and 'hot-drawing'? What is the importance of this stage in synthetic fibre manufacture?

60. What advantage has the staple fibre form over the continuous filament form of a synthetic fibre?

61. Describe the manufacture of Terylene and of Rilsan.

62. What is Dacron? How is it related to Terylene? Describe the circumstances surrounding the discovery of Terylene.

63. Why has every synthetic fibre a natural tendency to contract in length and what conditions are favourable to such contraction?

64. What do you understand by the term—acrylic fibre?

65. Orlon consisting of 100% polyacrylonitrile is a fibre which is difficult to dye. Why is this? Describe progress which has been made in making fibres related chemically to Orlon but more amenable to dyeing.

66. What are the differences between Acrilan and Kodel fibres?

67. Describe the main differences between hydrophile and hydrophobic fibres.

68. Classify the following fibres according as they are hydrophile or hydrophobic—cotton, nylon, Acrilan, Orlon, Rilsan, silk, Creslan, wool, mercerised cotton, hemp, Perlon, nylon 6, Courtelle, and linen. Which of these fibres would you expect to be easily dyeable with direct cotton dyes and with disperse dyes?

69. Describe the main differences between nylon and Rhovyl fibres. In what way does the latter fibre compare with Saran?

70. State which synthetic fibres are best suited for the manufacture of industrial and outdoor fabrics.

71. What is polyvinyl chloride? For what synthetic fibres is it used?

72. Name a Japanese synthetic fibre of considerable importance but mainly in Japan. How is it made?

73. Discuss polyolefine fibres and their present importance and future significance.

74. What is Teflon and what difficulties are experienced in the manufacture of this type of fibre?

75. Describe the manufacture of glass fibres and compare their properties with those of cotton as regards conversion into yarns and fabrics.

76. Discuss the differences and similarities of natural and man-made fibres in relation to their chemical composition and their uses in the production of fabrics and garments.

77. Describe recent progress as regards discovering and producing improved synthetic fibres.

78. Compare the advantages and disadvantages of hydrophile and hydrophobic fibres from the viewpoint of textile manufacture.

79. Illustrate with the aid of drawings the normal appearance of the different fibres and give their cross-sections.

80. How does the melting or softening temperature of a fibre depend on its molecular structure? List the various fibres and state against each its behaviour on being heated to a high temperature.

81. The different fibres have different densities. List these fibres with their densities. Why is fibre density important from the viewpoint of yarn and fabric manufacture?

CHAPTER III

Fibre Conversion into Yarns and Fabrics

In the previous chapter description has been given of the various textile fibres which are now in current use, but it is seldom that loose fibres are used as such. The textile materials commonly found in general and domestic use are often in the form of yarn but much more often as woven and knitted fabrics with a minor proportion of non-woven fabrics in which the fibres are either felted together or bound together with the aid of suitable adhesives or binders. It is quite an interesting story that covers the methods for making yarns and fabrics. Here it can only be told briefly.

YARN

If a length of knitting wool representing a typical yarn be cautiously untwisted it will be found to consist either of a single yarn or of two or more similar single yarns twisted together. If two or more yarns are found twisted together then it will be a 'folded' or 'multi-ply' yarn and may be two-ply, three-ply, etc., according to the number of yarns twisted or folded together.

Use of twist in yarn

Now let a single yarn be similarly untwisted and usually it will be seen to consist of individual fibres which have apparently been straightened and brought together more or less parallel to each other, and the resulting loose yarn then twisted so as to cause the fibres to grip each other and so be less liable to slide over each other when the two ends of the yarn are gently and progressively pulled apart. If the fibres do slide over each other in this pulling, there comes a point at which the yarn has become so thin that the remaining few fibres slide over each other and the yarn comes into two parts. It cannot accurately be said that the yarn has broken in this process of being pulled apart into two separate lengths since no fibre has been broken—the severance of the yarn has resulted entirely from the fibres sliding over and separating from each other.

This is obviously better observed with a yarn made of short rather than long fibres.

If the single yarn is used as it is, or perhaps better, if it is given more twist and the pulling apart of the two ends is again repeated, then quite a different result is obtained. Because of the high degree of twist the fibres are unable to slide over each other except with great difficulty, for they grip each other firmly. So if the pulling force is increased there comes a point at which the yarn separates into two parts by an actual breaking at some point of all the fibres there present.

The above experiment tells much about the nature and structure of yarns which are currently produced either for weaving or knitting purposes. Thus with a single yarn the strength of the yarn will be dependent on the force required to break all the fibres at any part of it if the yarn twist is so great that it entirely prevents any sliding of the fibres over each other, but it will be dependent only on the much smaller force required to cause the fibres to slide over each other if the yarn twist is so small that there is practically no grip between the fibres.

Properties of yarn determined by twist

In a similar manner much the same considerations apply in a multi-ply yarn if the two or more single yarns present are only slightly or highly twisted (often referred to as soft and hard twist) together.

From all that has been stated about the behaviour of a yarn it will be evident that for the production of a single yarn it is necessary to comb the loose fibres more or less parallel to each other and then twist them together—the strength of the yarn will be proportional up to a certain point to the degree of twist so imparted. It can happen that with excessive twist the yarn can become progressively weaker.

There is yet a further feature of the above yarn which can give useful information. It will be noticed that the yarn substantially free from twist is very soft while with the introduction of twist the yarn acquires a firmer handle until it becomes somewhat wire-like. Thus strength and softness in a yarn are incompatible properties, for the one has to be sacrificed for the other. The structure of any particular yarn will thus be in the nature of a compromise—in making a soft handling yarn less twist will be used, up to the point at which the yarn strength falls below a value which cannot be accepted as satisfactory.

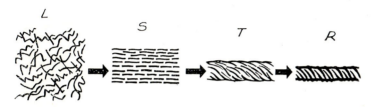

FIG. 24. Showing the principal stages by which loose fibres are converted into thread or yarn. The loose fibre *L* is first opened out and simultaneously partially freed from loose impurities while the fibres are straightened and brought more parallel to each other in the form of a sliver *S* which is substantially free from twist. Thereafter several slivers are mixed and together drawn out or drafted while twist is introduced during this attenuation to give the sliver the strength to pass through such mechanical treatment. When the sliver has been sufficiently attenuated as at *T* it is further drafted and given a greater degree of twist so that the resulting thread *R* is strong enough to be used for weaving or knitting purposes. At every stage from loose fibre to finished yarn every opportunity is taken to remove impurities and immature or imperfect fibres and to ensure that the resulting yarn consists of fibres as uniform as possible in respect of their physical characteristics.

Yet one other feature can be observed. If the fully twisted and the almost untwisted yarns be pulled equally tight and compared it will be seen that the untwisted yarn appears to be more lustrous than the highly twisted one. This illustrates a general rule that the more parallel are the fibres to each other and the more they are aligned in the direction of the yarn length the more lustrous will the yarn appear, and vice versa.

Woollen and worsted yarns

This is a convenient point for stating the main difference between woollen and worsted yarns. In the former the relatively short wool fibres are not arranged parallel to each other so that the yarn has not its maximum lustre, and it is somewhat fuzzy so that fabrics woven from it lack a clean-cut appearance. In worsted yarns the longer wool fibres have been especially combed to be parallel to each other so that the yarn has most of the lustre possible and is non-fuzzy, so that fabrics made from it have a clear-cut appearance. Comparison of woollen and worsted yarns and fabrics will

H

always clearly show how important can be the degree to which the individual fibres are arranged parallel or otherwise.

FIG. 25. Showing the fuzzy character of a woollen yarn (above) and the clear-cut appearance of a worsted yarn (below) which produce woven fabrics having the corresponding characteristics.

By courtesy of The International Wool Secretariat

Influence of fibre length in yarn

From the description of the various types of fibres in Chapter 2 it will have been noticed that textile fibres may, according to their type, range from a length of say $\frac{1}{2}$ inch to several inches, and that with silk and the artificial fibres these may in fact be of a hundred or more yards long. Fibre length plays an important part in yarn structure and properties; fibre thickness plays a part but it is less important than fibre length. If the fibres are short then the sliding of the fibres over each other within a yarn could more easily result in yarn breakage (not fibre breakage) than if the fibres are long. Long fibres can thus give stronger yarns.

MANUFACTURE OF YARN

It will be realised that the exact conditions for manufacturing yarn from raw fibres must always be modified to suit the type of fibre. However, present methods of yarn manufacture are largely based on those which have gradually been developed over at least two centuries for the production of cotton and wool yarns, and when new fibres are discovered attempts are usually made to use these same methods after appropriate modification. So for the purpose of indicating the essential features of yarn manufacture, attention will be confined to the spinning of cotton and wool yarns.

The spinning of yarn from cotton and wool was for many centuries carried on as a home industry in which the hand-propelled Jersey spinning wheel was most favoured. A similar Brunswick wheel was foot-propelled. But at the beginning of the eighteenth century various inventors such as Arkwright, Paul, Wyatt, Kay, Strutt, Hargreaves, and Crompton succeeded in devising purely mechanical methods for spinning yarn more rapidly and also of more uniform quality. These inventions were necessary since at that time yarn production lagged behind its weaving into fabric and thus created a bottleneck in the manufacture of fabric.

PREPARATORY AND SPINNING OPERATIONS

The production of cotton, woollen and worsted yarns involves a large number of preparatory operations before the final spinning stage, and they are set out below in a summarised form, but it must be realised that they are subject to various modifications arising from special circumstances.

In several of the following stages of preparation and spinning cotton (also wool) it is necessary that the fibres should be oiled so as to slide more freely over each other during their mechanical manipulation. It is generally desirable that the lubricating oil used shall be capable of being readily washed out from the yarn and the fabrics made from it so as not to interfere with subsequent dyeing and finishing treatments.

Cotton yarn

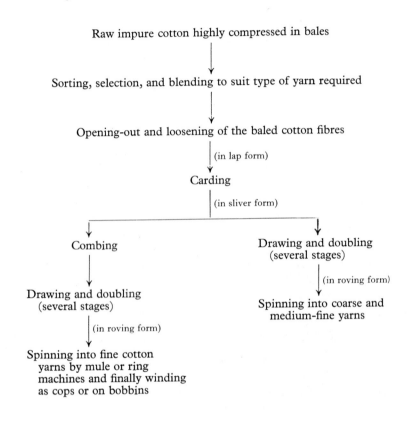

Raw impure cotton highly compressed in bales

↓

Sorting, selection, and blending to suit type of yarn required

↓

Opening-out and loosening of the baled cotton fibres

(in lap form)
↓

Carding

(in sliver form)

Combing

↓

Drawing and doubling
(several stages)

(in roving form)
↓

Spinning into fine cotton
yarns by mule or ring
machines and finally winding
as cops or on bobbins

Drawing and doubling
(several stages)

(in roving form)
↓

Spinning into coarse and
medium-fine yarns

Woollen and worsted yarns

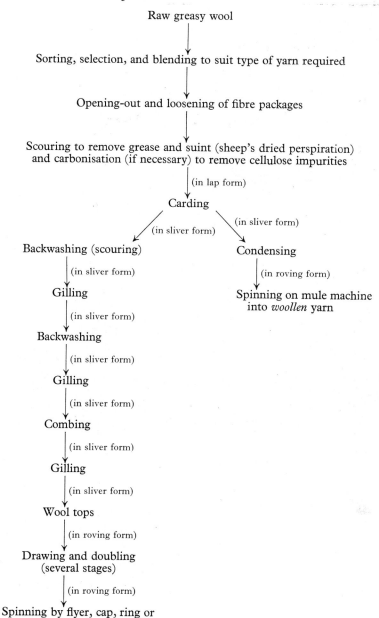

Raw greasy wool

↓

Sorting, selection, and blending to suit type of yarn required

↓

Opening-out and loosening of fibre packages

↓

Scouring to remove grease and suint (sheep's dried perspiration) and carbonisation (if necessary) to remove cellulose impurities

| (in lap form)

Carding

(in sliver form) ↙   ↘ (in sliver form)

Backwashing (scouring)   Condensing

| (in sliver form) | (in roving form)

Gilling   Spinning on mule machine into *woollen* yarn

| (in sliver form)

Backwashing

| (in sliver form)

Gilling

| (in sliver form)

Combing

| (in sliver form)

Gilling

| (in sliver form)

Wool tops

| (in roving form)

Drawing and doubling (several stages)

| (in roving form)

Spinning by flyer, cap, ring or mule machine into *worsted* yarn

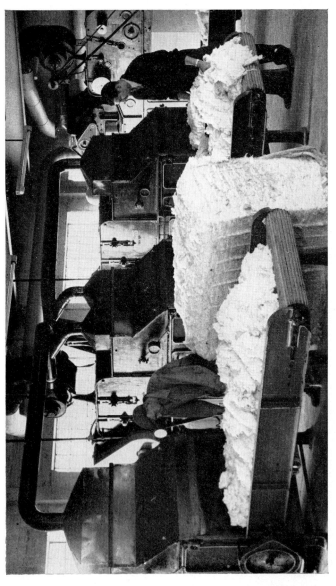

FIG. 26. Showing bales of raw cotton being fed by hand into a bale-breaking machine—the first stage in a sequence of operations by which raw cotton is converted into yarn. The raw cotton is often much matted so that it requires to be opened out; it also contains many impurities such as sand and cotton plant leaf and seed which must be extracted. In passing through the bale-breaking machine the cotton encounters sharp spikes which pluck out tufts of it to convert it into a soft fluffy mass, while the heavy impurities are thrown out to fall through a grid. By feeding into the machine cotton taken from two or more bales simultaneously it is possible to effect a mixing of cotton if desired to secure a more uniform grade of cotton.

FIG. 27. Showing the 'drawing' or 'drafting' or attenuation of a cotton 'roving' (a thick bundle of fibres more or less parallel to each other which has been prepared in a number of stages from the loose fibre) as one of the intermediate stages towards the preparation of yarn. The drafting is effected as the roving passes between pairs of rollers of which the back pair rotate more slowly than the front pair. This drafting is continued until the roving is suitably attenuated to be ready for twisting into yarn which is strong because of the twist imparted to it. The drafting effect is shown by the thickness of the roving at the back of the drawing machine in comparison with its thickness at the front after having passed through the drafting rollers.

By courtesy of The Cotton Board (Manchester)

Notes on the above preparatory and spinning operations

1. Cotton and wool fibres are found to be more amenable to mechanical manipulation when warm and suitably damp. Spinning mills are thus kept warm and the air is maintained with an optimum

moisture content by use of special humidifying apparatus. When very dry fibres are manipulated (especially the synthetic fibres) they accumulate static electricity so as to repel each other and sometimes to cling to surrounding objects, thus making it difficult to control them while passing through the various machines. Hence the need for humidifying spinning mills.

2. As regards *purification* of the fibres to aid their conversion into yarn, it is to be noted that while both cotton and wool are mechanically freed from gross impurities such as earth, twigs, stalks, etc. in the preparatory processes where there is opportunity to beat or shake the fibres and draw air through them, thus blowing out these impurities, it is usual for the raw wool to contain upwards of 40 to 50% of greasy and other impurities so that this kind of mechanical purification is not sufficient. Thus raw wool (not cotton) must first be scoured to remove these impurities. Sometimes further purification by carbonisation is required.

Raw wool scouring

This purification can be achieved in various ways but that commonly practised is to propel the loose wool slowly in succession through two or three long shallow tanks filled with a warm soap liquor; in passing from one tank to the next the excess liquor is squeezed from the wool by a mangle. By this treatment the wool is freed from the wax, oily, and protein impurities by a process in which the suint helps to emulsify the wax and other impurities so that these pass from the wool into the detergent liquor and the wool leaves the last tank (usually termed a bowl) substantially clean.

Another system of purifying wool is to solvent extract it with an organic solvent such as trichloroethylene (non-inflammable) but this is only used to a small degree. Yet another system found satisfactory but not widely carried out consists of freezing the wool at $-20°$ C so as to make the wax and other impurities brittle and suitable for removal by a treatment in which the wool is mechanically beaten and the powdered impurities then blown away by air pressure.

Wool carbonisation

Sometimes the wool contains impurities in the form of cellulosic parts of the bushes and plants where the sheep have been grazing and these will not be removed by the alkaline soap scouring

Fɪɢ. 28. In the production of worsted yarns it is important that the shorter wool fibres should be removed and the remaining longer ones straightened and made more nearly parallel to each other. This is achieved by combing the wool slivers in a Noble combing machine (other types of combing machines are also used) as here shown. After combing the slivers are further attenuated and finally twisted to produce yarn.

By courtesy of The International Wool Secretariat

described above. Such wool is purified by carbonisation—a process in which the wool is impregnated with a weak solution of sulphuric acid, dried, and then baked by passage through a suitably heated chamber. Under these conditions the drying of the acid into the cellulose impurities causes them to become friable (the wool remains substantially unaffected) so that the wool can then be led through a special type of willeying machine in which it is crushed and shaken free from the thereby powdered impurities.

3. In all the preparatory processes up to the spinning stage every opportunity is taken to mix the fibres in whatever form they may be—lap, sliver, or roving—so as to ensure that the yarn ultimately spun has a uniform composition throughout its length. It has to be remembered that cotton and wool fibres, from whatever source they are obtained, differ from each other individually just as do the people forming a nation. Each cotton boll contains several thousands of fibres but these are all slightly different, say in respect of their length, thickness, internal structure, etc., although these variations may be within close limits. The wool fibres from various parts of a sheep also vary in the same manner. It is only by very thorough mixing that a uniform yarn can be obtained.

The opportunity for fibre mixing occurs in those operations when the lap, sliver or roving of fibres is being extenuated (drafted or drawn), for then several rovings, for instance, can be combined and then extenuated to give one roving, having the same weight of fibre per unit length as each of the rovings brought into combination. Thus if four rovings are combined then they will together be drawn to four times their individual length in the resulting single roving and because of this there will be better mixing of the fibres. Such fibre mixing occurs in the opening-out, the carding, drawing, and gilling and combing operations. A limited amount of drawing and fibre mixing can take place in the spinning operation and actually such drawing is an essential part of mule spinning.

4. The *carding* operation is essentially one of combing and opening out of the fibres accompanied by the removal of gross impurities which have escaped earlier removal. Carding also serves to remove the shorter weaker fibres whose presence in the final yarn would be undesirable.

In *cotton carding* the fibre is presented in lap form by means of a small 'licker-in' roller to a rotating large diameter roller whose surface is covered uniformly with a dense fabric through which short wires having sharp pointed ends protrude. Under these conditions the wire points comb or teaze out fibres from the lap so that the roller surface then carries forward a fairly uniform layer of fibres which lie more or less parallel to each other and are considerably more separated than in the lap. On the other side of the machine the fibres are teazed off by 'touching' contact with a so-called doffing-roller covered with similar wire points to give a lap of carded fibres which may have only about 1/50th of the thickness of the original lap, and this new highly extenuated lap (now called a sliver) is gently coiled into narrow cylindrical containers for further processing. But between the licker-in and the doffing-rollers the thin layer of fibres lying on the surface of the rapidly rotating large diameter carding roller is combed or teazed by a slowly moving closely positioned band carrying parallel narrow strips covered with wire points, and this action of the so-called 'flat card' effectively breaks down any remaining matted fibres and at the same time takes off light impurities such as leaf fragments, motes, and short immature fibres. The carding process proper thus takes place between the large carding roller and the flat card.

In carding the fibres are certainly brought together so as to be more parallel in the resulting sliver, but it is not the object of carding to effect this parallelism. Actually after carding the slivers are coiled and further combined so that much of this parallelism is lost. The primary objects of carding are to produce sliver in which the fibres are better spaced and from which undesirable impurities and weak and short fibres have been removed.

The *carding of wool* is similarly carried out using machines differently constructed but with their action depending on the wire carding described above. In carding wool for the spinning of fine worsted yarn steps are taken to retain the parallelism of the carded fibres as much as possible, since the essential feature of worsted yarn is that its constituent fibres lie closely together and parallel to each other except in so far as this parallelism is disturbed by the yarn twist needed to give high yarn strength. Of course these steps are not required in the carding which precedes the spinning of woollen yarns in which fibre parallelism is particularly absent.

5. *Combing* of the carded sliver is only necessary for the spinning of fine cotton yarns and worsted yarn, since this is an operation whose essential object is to straighten the fibres and make them

more parallel to each other. Combing also removes any short fibres, and these, termed *noils* in the case of wool, are collected for use in making woollen yarn. The yarns made with noils can be used for carpets, especially if they are of a lustrous type of wool.

Four main types of combing machine are in use—the Heilman, Noble, French, and Lister combs—each having its own special uses and also its own advantages and disadvantages.

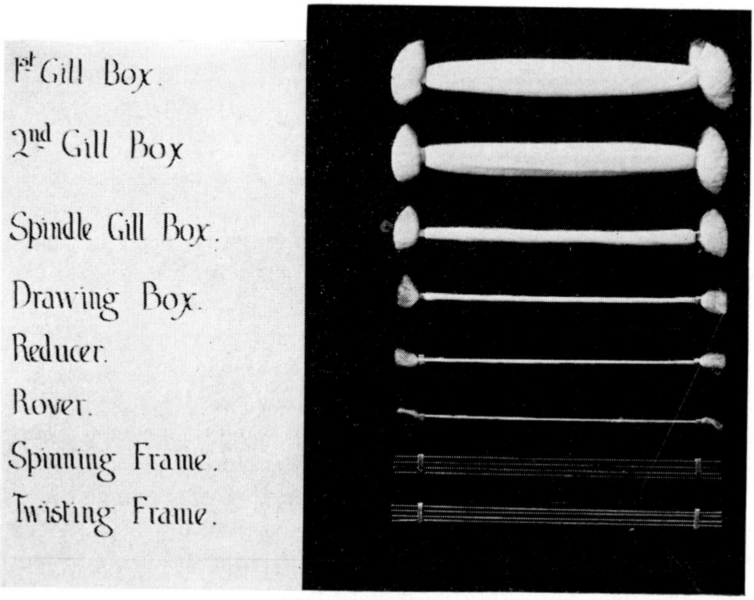

1st Gill Box.

2nd Gill Box

Spindle Gill Box.

Drawing Box.

Reducer.

Rover.

Spinning Frame.

Twisting Frame.

Fig. 29. Showing the stages by which combed slivers of wool are progressively attenuated up to the final stage in which suitably twisted yarn is produced.

By courtesy of The International Wool Secretariat

6. *Gilling* is carried out on a machine which allows the fibres to be combed by means of moving rows of fine spikes. This operation both straightens and frees the fibres from coarse impurities and in general it continues the carding process in preparing the fibres for combing with one or other of the different types of combs mentioned above.

7. *Backwashing* is an operation which is carried out on wool in sliver form to remove impurities such as grease, oil, dirt, etc. which may be residual from the original wool or have been introduced

by the preparatory processes themselves. It also straightens the wool fibres after carding and thus assists the subsequent gilling and combing. In backwashing the wool in sliver form is led through a detergent liquor containing soap or other detergent and is then mangled and led over a number of rotating steam-heated drying cylinders to dry it.

8. Wool in the form of *tops* is a standardised form of wool which has passed through numerous preparatory treatments and a final combing. Wool tops are formed as large balls (about one foot in diameter) by suitably winding many yards of combed wool sliver, which latter has been brought into the form of a kind of loose twistless rope of about 1 inch thick. Tops are bought and sold as such by spinners who will then (with or without first dyeing them in top form) convert them into worsted yarn. To aid spinning, the top will have been previously oiled so that the fibres may more easily pass through the drawing and spinning operations.

9. The term *doubling* implies fibre mixing. It refers to the bringing together of several laps or slivers or rovings of fibres, which is followed by the drawing or extenuation of the resulting combinations, thus effecting simultaneously a greater parallelism of the fibres and a more uniform fibre mixture.

10. In *drawing* or *drafting* operations the fibre material is extenuated or drawn out in length, thus reducing its thickness. This is almost universally achieved by leading, say, a roving through two pairs of rollers spaced a suitable distance apart—in each pair the bottom roller is positively rotated and by reason of the pressure between the two rollers the upper roller also rotates and the roving is propelled forward. It is arranged that the the surface speed of the second pair of rollers is greater than that of the first pair, and so the roving moving between the two pairs of rollers is subject to a stretch which is greater as the difference of the surface speeds is greater. The conditions are arranged so that the roving does not break under this stretch but the fibres slide over each other and the roving thus becomes longer but thinner to accommodate this movement of the fibres. Usually a third pair of rollers is placed between the other pair and driven at an intermediate speed—the purpose of this third pair is to support the moving roving and prevent its breaking. Prevention of breaking is also obtained by slightly twisting the roving, but not so much as to prevent fibre slippage. The distances between the three pairs of rollers must be

FIG. 30. Showing the first bowl (tank) and part of the second bowl of a 5-bowl wool washing machine. The loose raw wool to be washed is fed into the entry end of the first bowl *A* by the hopper-feeder *B* and is immediately immersed in the washing liquor (usually a soap liquor which may contain some soda ash to make it more effective in removing the grease and other impurities from the wool). Thereafter the Rake or Harrow types of forks (the latter are used when the wool is especially liable to felt or mat as the result of any rough movement through the washing liquor) impel the wool forward to the end of the bowl where it is evenly carried to and through the mangle, thus pressing out excess dirty washing liquor and passing into the second bowl *C* where the now partly purified wool receives a second similar washing treatment, and so on to the fifth bowl where it is washed with water. After a final mangling it emerges fully purified so as to be ready for drying by passage on a continuously moving brattice through a large chamber where it is dried by circulating hot air.

Each washing bowl has a perforated false bottom to allow solid impurities to pass through and settle on the narrowed bottom as a sludge which can be automatically removed. Since fresh water enters the fifth bowl and passes counter-current through the other bowls and fresh amounts of soap and other detergent are periodically added the washing process can go on continuously.

It is important that the wool moves smoothly with the least disturbance apart from opening out to allow free access of the washing liquor—otherwise felting may occur. The hopper-feeder also opens out the wool and effects a partial removal of heavy solid impurities.

By a combination of cam and crank the Harrow forks as a group drop down into the loose wool, move forward about 1 foot, lift clear of the wool and then return by a backward movement to drop again and repeat their propelling action.

By courtesy of Petrie & McNaught Ltd and the Regina Combing Co. Ltd adjusted in accordance with the average length of the fibres in the roving. It is by this expedient that the roving becomes extended in length. The same principle is used to extend laps and slivers of fibres.

In reducing slivers and rovings in preparation for yarn spinning it is obviously desirable to reduce the number of drawings as much as possible. It would, for example, be very economical if, say, a cotton roving could be reduced to a degree of fineness suitable for immediate spinning by just one drawing instead of by the many drawings needed actually. But if the number of drawings is too drastically reduced then the extenuation of the roving will be uneven and the yarn ultimately spun from it will be equally uneven, quite apart from the high number of breakages which will occur during spinning. However, the present trend in yarn preparation for yarn spinning is to reduce the number of drawing operations.

11. The four main types of *spinning machine* are the mule (invented by Crompton), flyer (Arkwright), cap (Danforth), and ring (Thorp) machines.

VARIOUS TYPES OF YARN

The character of the yarn can considerably modify or influence the nature of the fabric into which it is made, and so while there have been created in past years a number of standard types of yarns suitable for conversion into standard types of fabric, novelty yarns and fabrics are frequently produced to make a special appeal to the users of textile goods. The properties required in a knitting yarn are much different from those of a weaving yarn. It is thus easy to understand that there are now being produced some hundreds of different types of yarn. These yarns will differ in respect of the fibre or fibre mixture on which they are based, in their fineness or coarseness, their smoothness or roughness, their lustre, their softness of handle, their strength, and their colour, etc. In recent years so-called special *textured* or *bulky* yarns have become very popular and their production has become possible because of the unique thermoplastic properties of the new synthetic fibres such as nylon, Orlon, Terylene, etc.

'Textured' yarns

There are various types of textured yarns which have now become available for weaving and knitting into fabrics under branded names such as Agilon, Banlon, Taslan, etc. Some types are characterised specially by their bulkiness so that they are useful for the production of fabrics and garments required to have a very soft handle, while others have a coiled spring nature so that they can be highly stretched yet return to their original length immediately on release of the stretching force. These so-called 'stretch' yarns are particularly used for articles which are required to be close-fitting such as men's socks.

Manufacture of high-bulk and stretch yarns

The bulky yarns of the Taslan type are made by running a synthetic fibre yarn, say of nylon, between two pairs of rollers spaced a short distance apart and with the second pair running more slowly than the first pair so that the yarn tends to sag between them. On leaving the first pair of rollers the yarn is subject to a strong hot blast of air issuing from a fine jet which is pointed into the yarn and so has the effect of separating the individual fibres there present and almost free from twist. As a result the yarn becomes bulky, with each filament having heat-set small loops closely but irregularly spaced, and unless the yarn is highly stretched under high temperature conditions sufficient to soften the filaments it retains its bulkiness, as for example during weaving and knitting and the after-processing (dyeing and finishing).

Agilon yarns are made by running ordinary nylon yarns over a hot knife-edge in such a way that they become crimped (wavy) and this gives them a considerable degree of elasticity such that they can be used as stretch yarns.

Banlon yarn has both high bulk and good stretchability. It is made by a treatment in which the yarn is subject to high temperature steaming while passing through a closed box with the yarn in a highly crimped and folded state as produced by its tight packing therein. The steam sets the crimps in the yarn to give it stretchability and since the yarn is compressed lengthwise in the box it simultaneously acquires a loose bulky structure which is also heat-set.

Another much used method for giving thermoplastic synthetic fibre yarns a bulky character is that of highly twisting say a nylon yarn and heat-setting the twist and then untwisting it to zero twist or further into the opposite direction of twist. When left free the yarn partly back-twists to a point at which the two twists balance and the result is a considerable increase of bulkiness. This method can be varied by doubling the heat-set highly twisted yarn with another yarn of suitable twist and direction of twist before un-twisting—this gives the resulting bulky yarn more stability in subsequent handling.

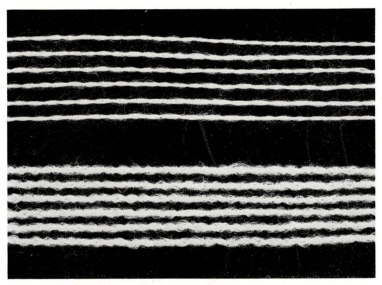

FIG. 31. Longitudinal view of ordinary and 'high-bulked' Courtelle (Courtaulds) yarns. The bulked type of yarn is produced by a special twisting process such that the fibres in the yarn become permanently more loosely packed to give yarn softness such as is desired in knitted materials.

By courtesy of Courtaulds Ltd

These special yarns are now being developed for the production of many special types of fabrics and garments.

Coloured yarns

Whenever possible, the introduction of colour into a yarn is left to a late stage in its production. Preferably yarns are dyed rather than spun from fibres which have already been dyed. This pre-ference arises from the convenience of leaving the choice of colour to the last moment in view of constantly changing requirements, but it also arises because it is most economical and suitable to dye yarn rather than loose fibre—loose fibre can become highly entangled

I

in dyeing so as to hinder the parallelisation of the fibres as required in the production of yarn and also the individual fibres may suffer changes which hinder their easy mechanical manipulation in the various stages involved in yarn spinning.

Spin-dyed yarns

In spite of the above generalisation it is true that large amounts of man-made fibres are produced in coloured form (a range of at least twenty standard shades is generally available for any particular type of fibre) by adding coloured pigments to the spinning solution or melt. Generally, by this use of pigments instead of dyes it is possible to produce coloured fibres and yarns having the maximum fastness properties; they are often designated 'spin-dyed' yarns.

Coloured wool yarns

Quite a considerable amount of wool yarn is made from dyed loose wool. Special shades of yarn can be obtained by mixing loose wools of different colours before conversion into yarn. Here it may be recalled that wool fibres are liable to become matted together during wet processing owing to the felting properties possessed by wool. Because of this the greatest care must be taken in the dyeing of loose wool to prevent such felting, since tightly entangled wool fibres can cause much difficulty in yarn spinning.

Hand knitting wool yarns are frequently given a special treatment to reduce their tendency to felt so that articles made from them are shrink-resistant and in washing hold their original shape and dimensions. A number of different anti-felt treatments are available and are described in Chapter IV.

Mercerised cotton yarn

Cotton yarn is frequently *mercerised* to give it permanently increased lustre. Usually the yarn is processed in skein form. The skeins pass through a machine where they are held stretched between pairs of rollers. While so held the yarn can be in succession treated with a caustic soda solution of about 50 to 55 Tw. (say 20–25%), and then hot and cold washing water to remove all the residual alkali. The rollers automatically move slightly inwards to assist the skeins of yarn upon them to become saturated with the mercerising liquor and then outwards to stretch them to their original length; the skeins are held stretched during removal of the mercerising liquor by washing. It is necessary to maintain the yarn stretched and by an amount that will finally leave the skeins at about their original size in order that an increase of lustre may be obtained. If the yarn is allowed to contract (the mercerising liquor will cause this unless prevented) no increase results.

Folded and multi-ply yarns

The yarns as produced by the spinning machine are single and consist of a single bundle of fibres twisted together to give the required strength. From these it is possible to produce two-, three-, four-fold and even higher multi-ply yarns by twisting the corresponding number of single yarns together. In this way it is possible to prepare a large number of different types of multi-ply yarns having special uses. Thus one or more of the yarns twisted together may be coloured or may be made from a different type of fibre. In another variation of this principle one of the yarns may have thick and thin places so that a fancy type of uneven multi-ply yarn may be produced such as may be suitable for weaving into fabric having an irregular but attractive appearance.

Yarns for particular purposes

It is usual to adjust the character of a yarn either by modification of the spinning operation or by subsequent treatment so that it may best satisfy the purposes for which it is used. Thus in a woven fabric the warp yarns will generally be considerably stronger than the weft yarns because in weaving the warp yarns are subject to most stress. In America the weft yarns are often referred to as 'filling' yarns and this suggests that they play a subsidiary part in the fabric. In the same way, yarns to be used in knitting are usually substantially different from those employed for weaving. In many instances the knitting yarn is required to be softer and more bulky. It is mainly by means of fibre selection and the amount of twist given to the yarn in spinning that these special requirements can be met, but it may be recalled that, as earlier mentioned, worsted yarns are distinguished from woollen yarns in that the former contain fibres which are largely parallel to each other, while the latter type of yarn has its constituent fibres randomly distributed.

Yarn specification

Yarns are made in a wide range of thickness according to the purpose for which they are required, that is, some are fine and others coarse. Also the multi-ply yarns consist of two or more single yarns folded or twisted together. It is thus necessary to have some system for closely defining or specifying these various yarns so that all those concerned with their manufacture and use and also their buying and selling may know exactly the characteristics of the yarn under consideration. It is necessary to be able to place a specification label on any specimen of yarn which can be understood by anyone textile-minded. Primarily such specification indicates either the weight of a given length or the length of a given weight of the yarn—both methods of specification are employed, the former for real silk and the man-made fibres and the latter for the older natural fibres such as cotton, wool, linen, etc.

Such a specification of a yarn is usually spoken of as being its *count* but in the case of real silk and man-made fibre yarns the term *denier* is usually employed instead of *count*.

Owing to the haphazard way in which textile industries have been developed in different countries there are different methods of specification (all within the method described above) and some of them are given below:

Count by weight per given length of yarn

Real silk and man-made fibres   The number of grams per 9,000 metres of yarn.

Thus a yarn having a *count* of 15 weighs 15 grams per 9,000 metres. It is more usual, as noted above, to refer to this yarn as being of 15 *denier* or as being a 15 *denier* yarn. Most ladies' nylon stockings today are made with yarns of 15 or 30 denier so that the latter is twice as thick or coarse as the former.

Count by length per given weight of yarn

Cotton	The number of skeins each of 840 yards in 1 lb		
Linen, hemp, and ramie	,,	300	,,
Spun silk	,,	840	,,
Worsted yarn	,,	560	,,
Woollen yarn (Yorkshire)	,,	256	,,
,, (Hawick—Scotland)	,,	300	,,
,, (Galashiels—Scotland)	,,	200	,,
,, (Alloa—Scotland)	,,	480	,,
,, (West of England)	,,	320	,,

Note: Spun real silk yarn is made from waste silk and therefore consists of short fibres (it is thus unlike the yarn made by twisting together the very long continuous silk filaments directly drawn from the silk cocoons without breakage and whose *count* as described above is expressed as *denier*) and because it is thus closer in type to cotton yarns whose constituent fibres are short its count is similarly determined.

There is a fundamental difference between these two systems of specifying yarns. By the first (weight per given length) the higher the count (or denier) the *coarser* is the yarn but by the latter (length per given weight) the higher the count the *finer* is the yarn.

In recent years a new method for specifying yarns has been introduced with the purpose of effecting simplification and allowing its universal use—it is foreseen that eventually this method will displace the various methods described above. This is known as the Tex system and by this the count of a yarn or any other length of fibres in bundle form (for example, roving) is the number of grams which 1,000 metres of the yarn weigh.

Since all textile fibres absorb moisture from the surrounding air it is necessary in determining the count of a yarn to take into account its moisture content. The various fibres absorb moisture in proportion to the temperature and especially the humidity of the surrounding air and it is now universally recognised that when the various types of yarns are in contact with air under average conditions which are specified as 68° F and 65% Relative Humidity they have the following moisture contents which are usually referred to as their Moisture Regains:

Fibre	*Officially recognised Moisture Regain*
Cotton, ordinary	$8\frac{1}{2}\%$
Cotton, mercerised	$8\frac{1}{2}$
Viscose rayon	11
Worsted yarn	$18\frac{1}{4}$
Silk	11
Acetate rayon	6

Note: Actually these official values which are used in determining the count of a yarn for commercial purposes do not agree with the moisture regains which are normally obtained—7, 11, 13, 15, 10, and 6% respectively.

Thus in measuring the count of any yarn it is first left for two or three hours in a closed chamber in which the air is maintained at 68° F and 65% Relative Humidity, that is, until the yarn has either lost or gained moisture to become in equilibrium with this surrounding air. It is then in a fit state to have its count measured by winding off a suitable length of the yarn and weighing it under conditions such that its moisture regain is not meanwhile allowed to change.

Multi-ply or folded yarns are usually indicated thus: 2/16's or 3/12's, etc. where the yarns referred to are made by twisting together two yarns each of 16's count and three yarns each of 12's count so as to produce 2-ply and 3-ply yarns respectively which are really the equal in coarseness to single yarns of 32's and 36's respectively.

It is also necessary in many instances to specify whether the fibres in a yarn are right- or left-hand twisted and the number of twists per linear inch.

FABRICS

The two main types of fabric are produced by weaving and knitting, and the differences between woven and knitted fabrics are fundamental. In the former type of fabric two sets of yarns are employed—the warp (running lengthwise in the fabric) and the weft (running across the fabric)—and these are interlaced with each other at right angles so that the fabric is not easily deformed and tends to retain in use its original dimensions. In a simple form of knitted fabric only one yarn is used and in the knitting operation this is formed into courses or rows of special loops or stitches in such a manner that each course of stitches is linked to the preceding course. A break of the yarn in any stitch leads to a loosening of the fabric structure not only in its own course but also on several courses linked directly or indirectly to this course. The nature of a knitted fabric is such that it can be much more easily distorted in any direction by stretching or contraction than can a woven fabric. Thus while men's outer garments are best made from woven fabric because it is generally desirable that they should maintain their shape and 'give' only to a moderate extent in accommodating the movements of the body, underwear garments are better made from knitted material since this can the more easily accommodate considerable body movement yet always fit closely and snugly.

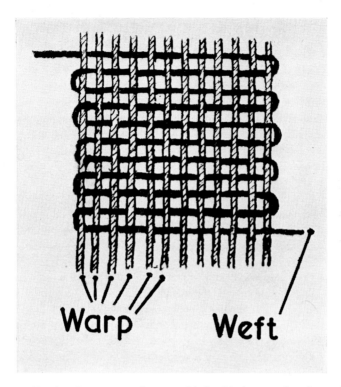

FIG. 32. Showing the structure of a woven fabric with the warp threads running lengthwise and the weft threads widthwise. It is usual for the warp threads to be stronger than the weft threads, so that in using woven fabric in the production of articles of clothing it is advisable to arrange that the fabric is cut to allow the warp threads to take any strains which are likely to be placed upon the clothing under the conditions of use.

By courtesy of The Cotton Board (Manchester)

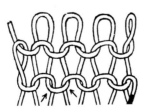

FIG. 33. Structure of a knitted fabric, showing how the loops are pulled through and depend on one another, in marked contrast to the effect produced by weaving.

Fabric elasticity

Both types of fabric can have their stretch properties modified to suit their use. Thus a woven fabric can have its warp and/or weft yarns very closely or loosely packed—the more closely are the yarns packed the more rigid is the fabric. Similarly, a knitted fabric can be made rigid by closely packing with small stitches. An alternative method for stiffening a knitted fabric is to introduce an additional yarn which can be inserted in such a way that it links together the courses additionally to the linkage through the stitches.

Ladies' hose and 'laddering'

Ladies' nylon and rayon stockings are knitted with a single yarn so that the courses hang on each other and it is because of this that they *ladder* so easily. If one stitch breaks at any point then the two ends of the yarn thus made free are so smooth that they readily slide into the adjacent stitches (one on either side of the broken stitch) and then into the next stitches for some distance in the same course of stitches. Then if the stocking is pulled lengthwise the stitch in the next course immediately below the first broken stitch has no upper stitch to hold on to and so collapses to leave a gap. Thereupon the stitch immediately below this second collapsed stitch similarly collapses to leave a gap and so on right down the stocking, leaving a gap or ladder for a considerable length.

Prevention of laddering

It is otherwise with a stocking made of a single cotton or wool yarn which is hairy, having fibre ends protruding from it. When the first stitch breaks the two free yarn ends commence to move into the adjacent stitches as described above with a nylon stocking. But because the cotton or wool yarn is hairy the protruding fibres become caught in the adjacent stitches, thus arresting any further movement of the free yarn ends and so the progressive collapse of the knitted structure along the courses and downwards through successive courses does not take place and no ladder is produced beyond the first broken stitch.

FIG. 34. Showing the beaming of warp yarns so as to be in a suitable form for use as the warp of a woven fabric. Up to 500 separate yarns drawn from the same number of specially wound cones or other forms of yarn package are brought together side by side through suitable guides so as to form a flat 'sheet' and finally are wound on so-called 'warper's beams' as shown. If a coloured pattern fabric is to be woven, various coloured yarns suitably spaced in relation to each other may be beamed—in this way coloured stripes throughout the length of the fabric will result. If differently coloured weft yarns are also used in the weaving then coloured check patterns can be obtained. It is usual, after beaming, to run the 'sheet' of yarn through a sizing composition and then over hot cylinders to dry the yarn. This sizing is to give the warp yarn smoothness and increased strength to withstand the stresses of weaving.

By courtesy of The Cotton Board (Manchester)

WOVEN FABRICS

Woven fabrics are universally manufactured with looms which have during the past fifty years been brought to a high degree of perfection. Earlier types of looms required considerable attention by operatives but nowadays automatic looms are favoured since much of this labour can be dispensed with.

The weaving of a fabric involves the following sequence of essential operations.

How a loom works

Firstly all the warp yarns (the fabric may be say 36 inches wide with 60 or more warp yarns laid side by side for each 1 inch of width) are drawn together (each from a separate bobbin of yarn—many such bobbins are conveniently arranged on a framework or creel) so as to be evenly wound side by side on a so-called *warper's beam* (roller) which is then placed at the back of the loom. It is then arranged that all these separate yarns, still lying side by side as a 'sheet' of yarn, pass through to the front of the loom where they are given a few turns round another roller which will eventually draw on to itself the fabric as fast as this is woven. The weft yarn, carried in a small shuttle at present temporarily stationary on one side of the loom, is now rapidly propelled to and fro across the loom and by means of two sets of harness carrying healds it is ensured that the shuttle passes over selected warp yarns and under the others each time that it moves across the loom. This movement of the shuttle under and over selected warp yarns determines how the weft yarn interlaces the warp yarns and thus establishes the kind of fabric being woven. For instance, the pattern of interlacing may be regularly over and under successive warp yarns, thus producing a simple plain fabric. On the other hand, the weft yarn may be caused to pass under one warp yarn, then over the next three warp yarns, under the next, and so on to produce another type. There are a large number of such variations of the interlacing pattern to produce a corresponding number of different types of fabrics such as satin, twill, poplin, etc.

Automatic looms

The shuttle holds only a limited amount of weft yarn and so this must be periodically replenished. Actually the yarn is wound on a small pirn and this is held by the shuttle. So with the older type of

Fig. 35. A much-used ordinary type of loom often referred to as a Lancashire Loom. It is for weaving plain and simple variations (checks and stripes) of plain fabrics. The weaver (back of loom) is required to stop the loom as becomes necessary when the weft thread 'runs out' and replenish by placing a fresh pirn of weft thread in the shuttle. Automatic devices are present to stop the loom if the weft thread accidentally breaks—in this way less spoilt fabric is produced. The woven fabric is shown wound in the front roller.

By courtesy of The Cotton Board (Manchester)

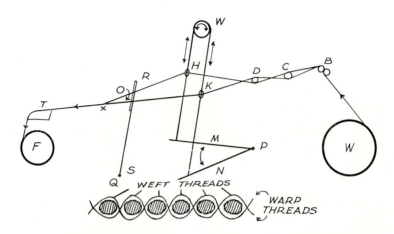

FIG. 36. How plain woven fabric is made with a loom. *W* is the warper's beam which carries all the warp threads (up to say 1,000) side by side. In their passage through the loom these are converted at *X* into fabric which is then wound on the roller *F*. In the simplest case of weaving the warp threads are divided into two groups and this separation commences at the backrest *B* whence each group passes over and under back and front lease rods *C* and *D*. Then one group passes through a set of healds *H* (one thread through each heald) and the other group similarly through another set of healds *K*. The two groups of warp threads then converge from the healds to *X* at which they are converted into fabric. *R* is the reed which may be likened to a horizontal comb—the warp threads pass through it and are thus kept evenly in place and evenly spaced. This reed is fastened to the sley sword *S*, which is pivoted at *Q* so that as required it can swing to and from position *X* after the insertion of each weft thread, as a result of the passage of the shuttle across the loom within the space or shed at *O* created by the converging two groups of warp threads. This to and fro movement is to beat-up the freshly inserted weft thread against the previously inserted weft thread which latter is now part of the fabric—such beating-up ensures that the weft threads are evenly spaced throughout to yield a uniform fabric. After each passage of the shuttle across the loom and the resulting insertion of a weft thread the healds *H* and *K* are reversed by a raising or lowering of the treadles *M* and *N* which are pivoted at *P* so that alternately one group of warp threads is uppermost and the other lower in the shed. The fundamental operations of weaving are thus seen to be *shedding* (forming the space *O*), *picking* (inserting the weft thread by passage of the shuttle carrying the weft yarn), and *beating-up* the freshly inserted weft yarn to ensure uniform spacing of the weft threads—these three operations are repeated in succession until the desired length of fabric has been woven. The structure of the fabric is shown at (*a*).

FIG. 37. An automatic loom which allows more looms to be supervised by each weaver since, unlike the Lancashire Loom, it need not be stopped for replenishing the weft during the whole of the weaving. The loom is provided with a battery of pirns of weft thread *W* and just before the pirn of weft thread in the shuttle in use becomes exhausted, a mechanism comes into operation whereby while the shuttle is directly under the battery of pirns the exhausted pirn in the shuttle is ejected and its place is taken by a full pirn from the battery.

By courtesy of The Cotton Board (Manchester)

F<small>IG</small>. 38. Showing a Jacquard loom which is used for weaving fabrics such as curtains, tapestries, upholstery cloths, etc. which have an elaborate pattern such as can only be produced by changing the intersection of the warp threads with the weft threads whilst the fabric is being woven. These changes are effected by suitably lifting selected warp threads after each passage of the shuttle carrying the weft thread across the loom, and this selected lifting is automatically controlled by the perforated cards C (the perforations are in accord with the pattern) which in their turn control the numerous cords P (one cord to each warp thread) which actually lift the warp threads. The assembly of cords and attachments is called a 'harness'.

By courtesy of The Cotton Board (Manchester)

loom the attendant operative had to take out the empty pirn from the shuttle and insert a full one. The modern automatic loom now has a device at the side of the loom which does this replenishing with scarcely any attention of the operative, who can now look after a considerably larger number of looms.

Jacquard device for pattern weaving

With the simple type of loom the interlacing of the warp yarns by the weft yarn can only be varied within moderate limits so that the types of fabric which can be woven are correspondingly restricted. But by having attached to the loom a so-called Jacquard device it is possible automatically to move each warp yarn independently of the others and this allows the interlacing to be varied to a much greater degree and without stopping the loom. With such a device it is possible to weave fabric having various kinds of patterns due to this greater scope in varying the manner of interlacing the warp yarns by the weft yarn.

Coloured pattern weaving

Since it is easily possible to have differently coloured warp yarns suitably distributed among non-coloured yarns on the warper's beam while it is also possible to change the colour in the weft as desired by using, one at a time, differently coloured pirns of weft yarn, so does the loom allow colour patterned fabrics to be produced. However, the greater proportion of fabric woven is with non-coloured yarns so that the resulting fabric can afterwards be dyed to any required shade or be printed to any desired pattern.

The character of woven fabrics may also be varied by using special yarns in the warp and/or weft. Thus the warp yarn may be of one type of fibre, say acetate rayon or wool, while the weft yarn may be of another, say cotton or nylon. The special yarn may also be one of the 'slub' type, intentionally having thick and thin places along its length so as to produce a fabric with an attractive uneven surface. Otherwise the warp yarns may be uniformly thin and the weft be thick, thus allowing the production of a so-called repp fabric.

Crepe fabrics

Quite a distinct and always popular type of fabric is a crepe fabric. This may be a *warp* or a *weft* crepe fabric according as the special highly twisted yarns which produce the cockled or crepe appearance are present in the warp or the weft with plain yarns of ordinary twist in the weft or warp respectively.

A *warp crepe* fabric is woven so as to have a plain weft through-out but the highly twisted warp yarns are arranged so that pairs of these having right-hand twist alternate right across the fabric with pairs of yarns having left-hand twist. It is a special character-istic of highly twisted yarns that when entered into boiling water (preferably containing soap to act as a fibre lubricant) they tend strongly to untwist. But if the ends are held (as in the selvedges of a fabric) so that untwisting is prevented, then the yarns snarl or form small loops, thus attaining a more stable state. The loops form to the right or left according to the direction of twist in the crepe yarn. Thus when a crepe fabric produced as described above is entered into a boiling soap liquor the snarling of the yarns takes place and a cockled surface is produced—the desired crepe appear-ance. It is important that this creping be carried out with the fabric free from creases or folds since these would become per-manently set and spoil the appearance of the fabric. Very large

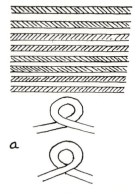

FIG. 39. Showing the arrangement of alternating pairs of right-hand twisted and left-hand twisted yarns in a crepe fabric (loom-state). When such fabric is entered into a hot or boiling soap liquor the high twist causes the yarns to shrink in length and endeavour to untwist, but because the ends of these yarns are not free ordinary untwisting is not possible and the untwisting forces are relieved by the formation of innumerable kinks as shown at (*a*). These kinks form in opposite directions according to the type of twist. Thus as a result of the hot soap treatment the surface of the fabric acquires a roughness which is attractive and characteristic of a crepe fabric. It is important that the kinks formed should be uniform in size and evenly distributed, otherwise the fabric will have an objectionable irregular appearance.

FIG. 40. Showing the weaving of ribbon using multi-shuttle looms. Each ribbon is woven separately.

By courtesy of Messrs Berisfords Ltd

K

amounts of such crepe fabric containing viscose rayon and acetate rayon yarns are being produced—it is usual for the viscose rayon to be the crepe yarn since acetate rayon yarns do not lend themselves to creping so satisfactorily.

Ribbons

Ribbons are made on looms which allow several separate ribbons to be woven side by side. In recent years with the availability of thermoplastic synthetic fibres it has become possible in one operation to cut several ribbons from a woven fabric (say of nylon,

FIG. 41. Showing ribbons being produced by slitting woven nylon fabric into narrow widths—the cutting knives are hot so that the edges of each ribbon produced are fused to prevent any subsequent unravelling. This method of ribbon production is more rapid and economical than weaving each ribbon separately but has limitations.

By courtesy of Messrs Berisfords Ltd

Dynel, etc.) using hot cutting knives which in addition to cutting the fabric also fuse the cut edges so that these edges in the resulting ribbons do not fray in ordinary use.

As earlier explained, knitted fabrics are constructed of rows (courses) of stitches, each row hanging on the previous row, and there are many types of knitting machines which can rapidly produce such fabric. These machines use one or other of two main types of needle—one having a spring beard and the other a latch. In the knitting machine a large number of these needles are arranged evenly spaced, sometimes in a straight line and sometimes around a circle. If a fabric is being knitted on a straight line or bar machine it will have two selvedges, but unlike the selvedges of a woven fabric they will curl up or roll in when free to do so. The fabric from a circular knitting machine will be tubular without any selvedge.

Flat and circular knitted fabrics

Large amounts of flat-knit fabric are produced with straight bar knitting machines for suitably cutting and then seaming to give various types of garments. The circular knitted fabric is largely used for underwear and often can be made into the necessary shapes with but little cutting. It is possible to use knitting machines provided with automatic control so that the diameter of the tubular fabric can be varied as the knitting proceeds and thus allow the fabric to be directly shaped as required for the garment to be made from it.

Hose and half hose

Men's socks and ladies' stockings are knitted on special machines which are largely automatic and allow complete socks or stockings to be produced without an operative being required to attend to the knitting of special tops, the heels, feet, and toes. If a fully-fashioned stocking is required instead of one in which the leg is seamless and which is only given some shaping by suitably varying the tightness of stitch from the top (welt) to the heel, then use must be made of a fully-fashioned knitting machine. This automatically produces a flat open fabric, which, when the free selvedges are sewn together, gives a stocking conforming closely in shape to that of a lady's leg and foot. It is easy to recognise a fully-fashioned stocking by its shape and also by the seams, which are not present in a circular knitted seamless stocking.

FIG. 42. Showing a machine which allows the simultaneous knitting of several fully fashioned outerwear garments.

By courtesy of The Bentley Engineering Co. Ltd

Purl or rib knitwear

Although most knitted fabrics have a high degree of elasticity so that when pulled out of shape they tend to return to their original shape, it is often desirable that the fabric should be relatively stiffer in structure than is possible with ordinary knitting, that is with the new loops or stitches always pulled through the old ones from front to back. This special characteristic is obtained by knitting a course as just described and then knitting the next course with the new loops being pulled through the old loops in the opposite direction, that is from back to front. By knitting alternate courses in this way the well-known *purl* or *rib* knitwear is produced and it has the extra stiffness and elasticity required.

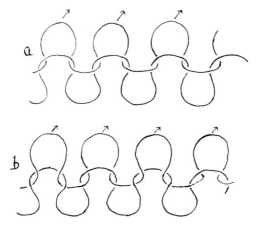

FIG. 43. Showing the difference between (*a*) plain and (*b*) purl knitting. In plain knitting a fresh course is made by pulling new loops through the loops of the previous course all in the same direction, that is, from front to back. In purl knitting the new loops are pulled through alternately, that is, from front to back and back to front. Purl knitted fabrics have much greater extensibility and elasticity than plain knitted fabrics and it is for this reason that parts of garments (for example, the top or welt of a man's sock) which are required to stretch and so better fit the body are purl knitted. The terminology is different for hand knitting, where stocking stitch and rib are obtained by turning the fabric round after each row.

Non-ladder knitwear

The laddering of ladies' stockings referred to earlier can occur in all plain knitted fabrics in which a single and very smooth yarn is employed—it results because with such knitted structure any broken stitch can spread very easily. As pointed out, if the yarn is hairy and has protruding fibres it is less easy for the breakdown to spread and so the hole produced remains in one place. Many attempts have been made to impregnate the stockings with a resin or other composition which will stick the stitches together or make the yarn rougher and in this way localise any broken stitch. These are generally unsatisfactory since if really effective so much resin composition has to be used that the handle of the stocking and its smoothness are impaired.

It is possible to knit such stockings by a modified knitting method and produce stockings that do not ladder, but these lack the sheer appearance that is so generally desired and ladies do not seem to demand them. Actually non-ladder fabrics can be and are being knitted in large amounts. In these, additional yarns are introduced in the knitting process with the idea of locking the knitwear structure and so preventing laddering. But most of the non-ladder fabrics are considerably thicker and less sheer than a lady's stocking and they are used for articles of clothing which are not particularly required to be sheer. The demand for excessive sheerness and transparency in ladies' stockings is the root cause of their tendency to ladder.

Plated knitwear

In a special type of knitting using two or more yarns simultaneously it is possible to ensure that one of these yarns appears more on one side of the fabric than the other. Thus using cotton and wool yarns it can be arranged that the front of the fabric appears to be made of cotton with the back made of wool. Such fabrics are known as *plated* fabrics. By plating in knitting, fabrics can be produced having a different feel on each side. For instance, a stocking or other article of underwear made with cotton on the front and wool on the back will have a brighter appearance but because of the predominance of wool on the underside will have a warm feel in wear. By plating colour effects can also be obtained which differ on the two sides of the fabrics.

Capabilities of knitting machines

On the whole fabric can be knitted faster than it can be produced by weaving. Hence the incentive to make better use of knitting methods for the production of fabrics of all kinds. The drawback of the knitted fabric as compared with a woven one is that the knitted fabric is less rigid. But modern finishing methods coupled with new improvements in knitting machines should in due course remedy this disadvantage. Certainly knitting machines have in recent years been modified so as to allow an extraordinarily high rate of knitting.

NON-WOVEN FABRICS

Three main types of non-woven fabric are now being produced and deserve mention here. They are felts, laces and nets, and bonded fibre fabrics, and they differ widely from each other.

Felted fabrics

Felted fabrics are made from wool. Loose wool fibres are passed through a so-called carding machine similar to the type of machine which is used to prepare wool fibres for spinning into woollen yarn, but in this case the loose wool leaving the machine is in the form of a lap or web. A number of such laps are superimposed so as ultimately to give a felt of the required thickness. The thick lap, now called a *bat*, is 'hardened' or consolidated by placing it between upper and lower cast-iron plates so that while the wool is being steamed and the two plates are pressed together the upper plate is given a reciprocating motion. Under these conditions the wool fibres are both pressed and rubbed together while in a hot moist state favourable to felting (a permanent closing-up or entanglement of the fibres) and this is continued until the resulting partly felted bats are strong enough to withstand the next treatments. These comprise impregnation with a soap liquor (soap lubricated wool fibres felt more easily) and then subjection in a special machine to continuous and all-over pounding until the resulting felted bat is of the desired uniform density. Finally the felt material thus produced is washed free from soap, optionally dyed, and dried. It can then be finished, as for example by brushing up the surface and leaving it as such, or the lightly brushed surface can be sheared and pressed to leave a soft and smooth surface. The strength of such a fabric is entirely dependent on the degree to which the entangled or felted wool fibres hold together. Since the finished felt consists of wool fibre laps superimposed and the felting proceeds laterally more easily than vertically these laps may not be too strongly joined together, so that it is easier to separate the felted fabric into layers than it is to break up the fabric by pulling it in length or width.

Felts of this kind find considerable use for industrial purposes, as for instance to give sound and heat insulation. They may also be used as underlays for carpets to give increased resilience and for silencing pads under typewriters.

Laces and nets

Laces may be considered to be ornamented nets while the nets themselves are mesh fabrics in which the weft threads do not simply interlace the warp threads (as in a woven fabric) but are twisted around them and move across the fabric in a diagonal direction instead of at right angles to the warp threads (as in a woven fabric). The ornamentation of the net can be simple or elaborate and may be effected with the use of a number of different threads made from different fibres and sometimes of different colours.

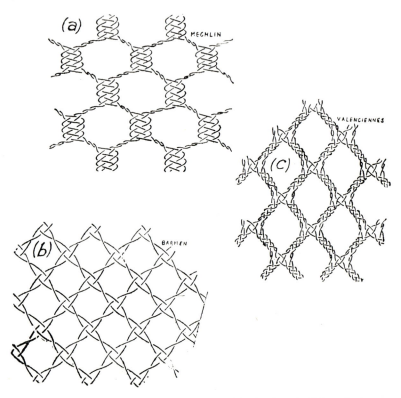

FIG. 44. Showing types of lace structures with the threads differently inter-laced—(*a*) Mechlin, (*b*) Barmen and (*c*) Valenciennes laces.

By courtesy of The Textile Institute (Manchester)

The earliest samples of lace have been found in Egypt. In the Middle Ages lace was made by hand throughout Europe and some beautiful samples of it have been preserved. Lace-making as a home industry was early extensively practised in Britain. The art appears to have been introduced into England in the middle of the sixteenth century by lace-makers from the Low Countries on the Continent who had fled from religious persecution, and it became well established, particularly in Bedford, Buckinghamshire, and Northamptonshire.

Lace is now made mainly around Galston in Scotland and around Nottingham and Tiverton in England. Formerly all laces and nets were hand-made but now are machine-made following the invention by Heathcoat of a machine for making bobbin nets.

Bonded-fibre fabrics

The production of felts depends on the use of wool, since this is the one suitable textile fibre which has the power to felt and give the fibre entanglement which is necessary for holding a layer of random mixed fibres together. But wool is a comparatively expensive fibre and is not so readily available as are some other non-felting fibres, particularly cotton and viscose rayon. Hence the incentive to devise methods for manufacturing non-woven fabrics akin to felts from non-felting fibres.

Gradually over the years experience has shown that quite a useful type of non-woven fabric can be made by preparing laps or webs of loose fibre such as cotton or viscose rayon staple fibre in which there is uniformly distributed an adhesive substance which at the appropriate stage can be caused to bond the fibres together and so yield a kind of artificial felt. The question is—what is the best method of bonding the fibres together?

Methods of bonding

At first bonding was secured by spraying over the fibres while they were being brought together in the form of a lap, or at some other stage, a solution of a gum or a synthetic resin; then at a later stage while the lap of fibres was being suitably compressed subjecting it to a raised temperature sufficient to produce a permanent bonding at spaced points throughout the fibres. By space bonding in this way a porous flexible non-woven fabric could be produced without the objectionable board-like handle and stiffness which would result from a uniform all-over bonding. However, it is not easy to ensure such space bonding using an adhesive substance in this way and so an improved method of bonding has become available.

It has already been pointed out in describing the various types of textile fibres that some of these, for instance Vinyon, Thermovyl, acetate, and Dynel fibres, have relatively low softening and melting points—some of them have melting points at or below 100° C. When these fibres are heated to an appropriate temperature they become tacky and if pressed against another fibre they adhere to it tenaciously on cooling. On this behaviour a very convenient and satisfactory method for making bonded-fibre fabrics has been developed.

Bonding with aid of thermoplastic fibres

In this new method the main bulk of loose fibres not sensitive to a high temperature are intimately mixed with a suitable proportion of those fibres (cut up in short lengths to favour their admixture with the other fibres) which are heat-sensitive and which melt at a temperature not far removed from 100° C. The mixture of fibres is then made into a suitably thick layer and subjected to heat and pressure which causes the small proportion of heat-sensitive fibres to soften and melt and bond together at spaced intervals the heat-insensitive fibres. Because it is easy to mix the two types of fibres together evenly, the fibre bonding can be uniformly spaced. Thus by mixing together say 80 parts of cotton with 20 parts of Vinyon (softening temperature 52° C and melting point 135° C) and then subjecting layers of the mixed fibres to a suitable temperature and pressure, a stable reasonably strong nonwoven fabric can be produced which will withstand a considerable amount of wear under the circumstances which usually pertain to articles made from such fabric.

Fibre criss-crossing

At this stage it must be pointed out that the way in which the lap of loose fibres is prepared has a large influence on the strength and other properties of the resulting non-woven fabric. In one way of making the fabric the loose fibre mixture is passed through a machine in which a blast of air effectively mixes the fibres and then enables them to be collected on a moving mesh belt or brattice in the form of a lap characterised by the fact that the fibres are distributed at random and in no particular direction. If several such laps are superimposed and fibre bonding then effected, the resulting non-woven fabric is equally strong in the length and the width directions. On the other hand if the loose fibre mixture is run through a carding machine whereby the fibres become aligned mainly in the length direction of the resulting loose fibre lap, then the resulting non-woven fabric is stronger in its length than in its width. Yet if the laps from the carding machine are superimposed by laying each lap at right angles to the one beneath it and the resulting composite lap is converted into non-woven fabric this is equally strong in length and width.

At the present time quite a large amount of non-woven fabric is being manufactured along the lines indicated above and this production is being steadily increased as many new uses are being found for fabric so made without incurring the expense of spinning yarns and then weaving or knitting these into fabric form.

Laminated fabrics

Mention must be made of just one more special type of fabric which is made by amalgamating two or more layers of woven fabric. It is obvious that one method for producing multi-layer fabrics of this kind is to coat one of the fabrics with a suitable adhesive, superimpose a second fabric, and then press the two fabrics together under conditions such that they become firmly united by the adhesive. A modern method for achieving the same object is ingenious and quite different from that mentioned above, since it uses no adhesive as such. The method is to weave one or both fabrics so that they contain a proportion of heat-sensitive threads evenly distributed. The fabrics are then superimposed and subjected to heat and pressure to melt the heat-sensitive threads and allow them to be squeezed among the other threads and act as an adhesive. This effect can be accentuated by first spraying the fabrics with an organic solvent which will cause the heat-sensitive threads to soften more readily. 'Trubenised' fabrics are made in this way.

Foam-back fabrics

A new development in the manufacture of fabric is to apply to the back of a woven or knitted fabric a very thin layer of synthetic foam sheeting. A suitable adhesive is often used for this purpose, but there is the alternative method of applying a high temperature to one side of the foam sheeting so as just to make it tacky and then pressing it against the fabric and thus securing good bonding.

Foam-back fabrics are being used for wearing apparel and the presence of the foam layer confers greater warmth and induces the garment to retain its shape better during wear.

Fibre density

In these days when light-weight wearing apparel is much favoured the density of a textile fibre is important. Fibres of low density lend themselves more than those more dense to the production of bulkier yarns which in their turn allow the knitting and weaving of fabrics having an apparently more dense texture—such fibres give greater 'coverage' in a fabric.

Questions for Chapter III

1. Describe the essential physical characteristics of a textile fibre and indicate the importance of these in the spinning of a yarn.
2. Outline the essential features of yarn spinning. How are multi-ply yarns made?
3. How do woollen yarns differ from worsted yarns?
4. What importance has fibre length and thickness in the production of yarns?
5. Why are cotton yarns spun directly from raw cotton whereas raw wool generally has to be purified before spinning into yarn?
6. What do you understand by the preparatory processes for yarn spinning? How do these processes differ for cotton and wool yarns? Give reasons for the differences.
7. Describe the operation of carding and state the objects of this preparatory process.
8. What is meant by the terms drawing and doubling in relation to yarn spinning?
9. Describe the processes through which raw wool passes so that it may ultimately be formed into a top.
10. Name four different types of yarn spinning machines. Which of these was invented by Crompton and for what was it once used?
11. Point out at what stages in the preparatory treatment of raw cotton and wool fibres for spinning into yarn a purification of the fibres is effected.
12. Why is it easier to produce synthetic fibre rather than cotton or wool yarns?
13. Name as many inventors as you can who have made important contributions to the spinning of yarn. Briefly indicate the particular contribution of each of them.

14. What do you understand by 'static electricity'? Indicate how it can cause difficulties in the mechanical manipulation of fibres and yarns.

15. Discuss the influence of temperature and air humidity on the conversion of fibres into yarn.

16. What advantages can be obtained in yarn spinning by the use of synthetic fibres? Are there any disadvantages and if so what are they?

17. Indicate the importance of twist in yarn production. What is a crepe yarn? Describe its use in the production of crepe fabrics.

18. What are high-bulk yarns and how are they made?

19. Most synthetic fibres are thermoplastic. Indicate some important consequences arising from this.

20. What is mercerised cotton yarn? How is it produced and in what important properties does it differ from non-mercerised cotton yarn?

21. How is yarn converted into fabric? Indicate the main structural differences between woven and knitted fabrics. How do these differences influence their utilisation as textile materials?

22. What are the essential constructional and operational features of the loom by which fabrics are woven?

23. What is the difference between plain and purl knitting? Sketch the stitches in these knitted fabrics.

24. What do you understand by circular-knitted and fully-fashioned ladies' hose?

25. How do smooth-fibre ladies' hose ladder? How can this laddering be prevented?

26. What precautions have to be taken in wet processing a crepe fabric to develop its crepe appearance? Discuss the formation of un-wanted permanent creases in such fabrics.

27. What are plated knitted materials and what advantages can they have over ordinary knitwear?

28. Describe the production of non-woven fabrics. Indicate their advantages and disadvantages. Point out different methods of fibre-bonding.

29. How does the structure of a lace material differ from that of a woven fabric?

30. How are 'trubenised' fabrics made?

31. Describe the principles which underlie the manufacture of felted fabrics such as blankets and hats.

CHAPTER IV

Processing of Yarns and Fabrics to Meet Users' Requirements—Bleaching, Dyes, Dyeing, and Printing

Yarns and fabrics as they leave the yarn spinner and the fabric weaver and knitter are seldom in a condition to offer directly to those who wish to use them. In the first place they contain many impurities which give them a harsh, lustreless, and discoloured character which is quite unacceptable. This state arises from the fact that not only are the yarns and fabrics usually made from the raw impure fibres but there are frequently added to the fibres and to the yarns substances to facilitate their passage through the various machines which have to be employed. For example, fibre lubrication is an important necessity and this can involve the addition to the fibres of vegetable and mineral oils which may be yellowish to brown and also have an undesirable odour. Even in the case of raw wool which is so impure that it has to be scoured before spinning into yarn, special oils have to be added before spinning to take the place of the natural wool grease lubricant which has been scoured out of the wool in its purification. Again raw silk is frequently made directly into yarn and fabric and then it is found that the silk-gum present confers harshness and often a yellow colour. Thus such silk materials have to be purified (de-gummed) before the inherent softness and lustre of de-gummed silk is obtained.

Even when the yarns and fabrics have been purified they may not yet be acceptable to their users. Usually they must be bleached to a good white or be dyed or printed to give them a colour appeal. And when the yarns and fabrics have thus been improved they have further to be treated (finished) to give them desired properties of handle, lustre, resistance to shrinkage in washing, resistance to creasing, wash-and-wear or drip-dry characteristics, etc. Furthermore, the yarns and fabrics must have their structure and appearance regularised, that is, the yarn and fabric distortion produced in dyeing and finishing operations must be corrected by bringing the fabric to a uniform width with the threads straightened.

Finally the yarns and fabrics must be brought to specified lengths and be packaged and labelled suitably for offering to the user.

All this varied processing to make the initially manufactured yarn and fabric suitable for passing on to the user is usually comprised in operations designated *dyeing and finishing*, although it includes others such as bleaching and printing. The essential features of textile processing normally included in dyeing and finishing will now be dealt with.

Bleaching

Bleaching is carried out either to produce goods which can be sold as white materials or to bring yarns and fabrics into a satisfactory condition so that they can be dyed or printed. In either case the bleaching process must be devised so that it is suitable for the type of fibre involved and so that it results in the permanent removal or destruction of the impurities present. Generally it is not difficult to devise a bleaching treatment which will destroy the impurities, but it is more difficult to ensure that this object is achieved without at the same time harming the textile material being bleached. It is an unfortunate fact that most of the bleaching agents employed can attack both fibre and impurities simultaneously, so it is up to the bleacher to conduct the processing under conditions such that the impurities are attacked first, thus leaving the fibres substantially unharmed, or, if harmed, to a degree which can be tolerated.

A bleaching process has to be adapted to suit the character of the textile material, that is, consideration must be paid to the type of fibre and the nature of the impurities. Thus different bleaching methods are employed for cellulose, protein, and synthetic fibres.

Cellulose fibres are resistant to alkalis but sensitive to acids, protein fibres are sensitive to alkalis and resistant to acids. Synthetic fibres, partly because of their hydrophobic nature, are difficult to bleach. These are important facts which guide the bleacher in his selection of bleaching processes.

BLEACHING OF COTTON
AND OTHER CELLULOSE FIBRE GOODS

Rayon goods

Firstly it will be recognised that man-made regenerated cellulose and cellulose derivative fibres such as viscose and cuprammonium rayons and cellulose acetate rayon have a very good white colour as manufactured and it is seldom necessary to bleach them to make them white. However, if any whitening is required they can best be treated with a cold solution of sodium hypochlorite (the action of this is accelerated by slight acidification) or with a hot (not boiling) moderately alkaline solution of hydrogen peroxide under much the same conditions as will be described for cotton later.

Cotton and linen

Linen and cotton can be bleached by similar methods, since these fibres contain similar impurities, although cotton is purer than linen. The main impurities are natural waxes, pectins, minerals, and some protein substances. In the spinning of yarns oily fibre lubricants may be added and for weaving fabric the warp yarns will be strengthened and protected against abrasion in the loom by a pre-sizing with a composition which will contain starch, possibly a synthetic polymer (for example, polyvinyl alcohol), and an antiseptic to guard against mildew incidence if the warp yarn or fabric is stored under damp conditions. These additional impurities have to be removed in the bleaching.

Kiering and bleaching

These natural cellulose fibres, either loose or in yarn or fabric form, are bleached in two stages. In the first the textile material is boiled with a 1 to 2% solution of sodium carbonate or caustic soda or a mixture of these, according to the type of material, within a closed or open large steel container termed a *kier*, for several hours; if the kier is closed the contents may be heated under pressure to a temperature exceeding 100° C. The material is then thoroughly washed and it is at this stage substantially free from most impurities except the natural colouring matters. This colour is removed to produce white textile material in the second stage, in which the goods are treated cold with a dilute solution of sodium hypochlorite which may be alkaline or slightly acid, or they may be steeped for a few hours in a hot (40° C) hydrogen peroxide liquor of 2-volume strength also containing some sodium silicate (or a suitable proprietary oxalate compound) which acts as a stabiliser and ensures that all the oxidising power is exerted in destroying the natural colouring matters. If the peroxide bleaching

Fig. 45. A kier for the purification of cotton fabric by boiling with a detergent alkaline liquor. The kier consists of a vertical steel cylinder provided with a false perforated bottom, an outside tubular heater for the liquor, and on top an automatic fabric piler. In operation, fabric in rope form is drawn over a rotating winch so as to fall downwards through a funnel and trunk pipe into the kier, while at the same time the alkaline liquor is pumped into the funnel to commence its impregnation of the fabric. The trunk as part of the automatic piling device is given a combined rotary and oscillatory movement which piles the fabric uniformly layer by layer within the kier from the perforated false bottom up-wards until it is full. The kier cover is then closed securely. At this stage the alkaline liquor passes downwards through the layers of fabric (it is essential that the uniform piling allows an even distribution of the liquor so that all parts of the fabric are equally treated) and then through the false bottom, which is directly connected to a pump so that the liquor is continuously pumped up-wards through the heater to be raised to boiling point or any other desired temperature for return to the top of the kier, when it again percolates through the fabric. In this way the liquor is continuously re-circulated for several hours and until purification of the fabric is complete. The kier is then opened and the fabric drawn out to be washed free from the dirty kier liquor in, say, a roller washing machine. The liquor used in the kier is usually a 1 to 2% solution of caustic soda or soda ash to which may be added a detergent.

By courtesy of Mather & Platt Ltd

L

liquor is too acid it is ineffective and if too alkaline it prematurely decomposes to liberate oxygen gas which is wasted; thus the liquor should be of pH about 9 to 10. Usually not all the hydrogen peroxide is used up in such a bleaching operation, so it is possible to replenish by an addition of hydrogen peroxide and adjust the alkalinity and add fresh stabiliser to enable the residual bleach liquor to be used for a second, third, and perhaps fourth time. It has been observed that a fresh peroxide bleaching liquor is often not so effective and stable as a re-used liquor.

Continuous bleaching methods

Such bleaching treatment can be carried out batchwise or by the use of special plant (this is much favoured in America) which allows yarn or fabric to be completely purified in a continuous manner, that is, it can enter the plant at one end to pass through a

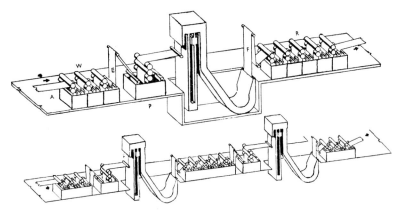

Fig. 46. Showing plant for the continuous scouring and bleaching of cotton fabric in open width. The top-half plant is for scouring the fabric. It is washed in section *W* and impregnated with a 3% solution of caustic soda before entering the top of the J-box where it is first heated to about 100° C and then folded down so as to occupy within it about one hour, until it emerges with the impurities loosened and solubilised by the action of the hot caustic soda so that these are removed in the final washing section *R*. The large fabric capacity of the J-box allows this period of one hour although the fabric may be passing through the whole plant at the rate of 100 yards per minute. The lower-half plant allows the fabric to be treated with hot caustic soda as in the top-half plant, but after the washing it passes through a second J-box after having been first impregnated with hydrogen peroxide solution. It is thus bleached to a good white requiring only the final washing.

By courtesy of E. I. Du Pont De Nemours & Co., U.S.A.

caustic alkali boil and then through a hydrogen peroxide bleach, and emerge purified and bleached at the other end.

New solvent extraction process

Since the kiering or alkali-boiling of cotton is mainly for the purpose of removing the natural waxes and oils by a process of saponification and emulsification, it could well be asked—would not a solvent extraction of the cotton with some organic solvent achieve this more efficiently and rapidly? The answer is Yes, but the use of such a solvent is liable to be costly and could introduce a fire risk. However, quite recently I.C.I. Ltd have introduced a solvent extraction process superior to others which have been previously proposed and have not proved commercially successful.

In the new process of I.C.I. Ltd the cotton fabric is run continuously through a vessel containing boiling trichloroethylene (this is non-inflammable), then through a mangle, and then through a vessel containing boiling water which immediately evaporates ('flashes-off') residual solvent so that the fabric can then be washed, hot soaped, washed again, and dried. The waxes are removed by the trichloroethylene and the fabric is left so that it can then be bleached in the usual manner with a hypochlorite or hydrogen peroxide, to give a white cotton fabric which has the same high absorbency and purity as one which has been thoroughly kiered and hypochlorite bleached. Suitable plant for carrying out solvent extraction and bleaching of cotton fabric by this method has been designed and it includes the recovery and purification of most of the trichloroethylene carried forward by the fabric so that it can be re-used, with a considerable saving in trichloroethylene cost. The period of treatment in the trichloroethylene is only a few seconds.

Mild bleaching processes

When it is known that the textile material contains but little impurity, or when the cotton or linen is in admixture with regenerated cellulose or cellulose derivative man-made fibres, which are somewhat fragile in the wet state and are more reactive to hot alkalis and to oxidising agents of the hypochlorite and peroxide type, the kiering can be replaced by a milder treatment. In this the starch impurities are removed by treatment with a liquor which contains a starch-liquefying enzyme followed by a hot scouring in a moderately alkaline soap liquor.

If the bleaching is satisfactorily carried out, then the cotton or other fibre material should not only be left white (this white should not yellow during subsequent storage) but it should be highly absorbent towards aqueous liquors such as will later be employed in dyeing and finishing operations. At one time it was considered that such desired absorbency could only be obtained by complete removal of the natural waxes and fats from the fibres but it is now known that a fair proportion of these water-repellent impurities can be left in the fibres yet allow the desired high absorbency. It would appear that absorbency is influenced by fibre structure as well as by the presence or absence of waxes and fats.

Singeing

It is necessary to point out here that yarn and fabric purification may not be the first treatment. If the textile material is hairy then it may be desirable to singe off the protruding fibre ends by running the yarn or fabric over an elongated gas flame or close to the surface of a red-hot curved metal plate. The speed of the yarn or fabric has to be adjusted so that while the fibre ends are burnt off the body of the yarn or fabric is left unharmed. Immediately after leaving the gas flame or hot plate the yarn or fabric must be run through a trough of water to quench any adhering burning fibres. The fabric leaving the quenching trough can at once pass through a machine where it is impregnated with the starch-liquefying enzyme liquor and then be piled in a tile-lined cistern for a few hours to allow the enzyme to make the starch impurities soluble and thus enable them to be washed out of the fabric quite easily.

BLEACHING OF WOOL AND SILK

Before bleaching wool and silk materials to secure a good permanent white it is usually necessary to scour them thoroughly, using a warm soap liquor to which some ammonia may be added to increase the efficiency of the treatment. Sodium carbonate is sometimes used instead of ammonia but the latter is preferred in that it cannot damage the wool so much.

Preliminary purification treatments

Continuous machines for scouring wool yarn in skein form are available and they comprise two or more long shallow tanks filled with a warm, slightly alkaline soap liquor. The wool skeins are conveyed at a steady rate through the detergent liquor in each tank by a moving brattice and the skeins are mangled as they pass from one tank to the next.

Wool fabric can also be degreased in a continuous manner by use of the I.C.I. trichloroethylene process as previously described for cotton fabric.

Raw silk materials may have to be de-gummed, and this is effected by boiling them for an hour or so in a 1% solution of soap which dissolves the silk-gum leaving the silk fibres separate from each other and much softer in handle and with an increased lustre.

Bleaching processes

It is not advisable to attempt the bleaching of these protein fibres with a hypochlorite liquor, since the chlorine adversely affects them and may make them yellow and harsh in handle while at the same time lowering their strength and durability. Nylon, although a synthetic fibre, contains amide—NH—CO— groups such as are also present in protein fibres, and so this fibre should not be bleached with a hypochlorite as for cellulose fibres.

Protein fibres, particularly wool and silk, are most satisfactorily bleached by steeping for a few hours in a hot 2-volume hydrogen peroxide solution which also (as described above) contains a small amount of an alkali to bring the pH to 9 to 10, and also a stabiliser such as sodium silicate. When the required degree of whiteness is obtained the bleached goods are thoroughly washed.

Comparison of hypochlorite and peroxide bleaching

It may be noted here that bleaching with hydrogen peroxide is generally simpler than the corresponding bleaching with a hypochlorite liquor for the reason that it is only necessary to wash with water afterwards. In hypochlorite bleaching there is a tendency for the textile material to retain active chlorine, and this is objectionable, so that the bleached goods are finally preferably given an anti-chlor treatment—this involves a treatment with a dilute solution of sodium bisulphite or sulphite to destroy the active chlorine, followed by a thorough washing.

Bleaching with sulphur dioxide

Wool yarn and fabric are sometimes bleached by hanging from overhead wood poles within a closed chamber filled with the fumes from burning sulphur, that is, sulphur dioxide (the process is known as 'stoving'). In the simplest type of plant for this purpose, a heap of sulphur is ignited on the floor of the chamber in one corner and as this burns it fills the chamber with sulphur dioxide. Wool greedily absorbs this gas and in the process becomes whitened. It is usual to leave the wool in the chamber overnight.

It is unfortunate that the white obtained in this way with the aid of sulphur dioxide is not permanent, since the original yellowish colour of the wool tends to return during subsequent storage and use. It is for this reason that wool bleachers prefer to bleach with hydrogen peroxide, which yields a permanent white.

BLEACHING OF SYNTHETIC FIBRES

The synthetic fibres do not always respond satisfactorily to bleaching with hypochlorite or hydrogen peroxide liquors, and in any case, because of their protein character, nylon fibres should not be bleached with a hypochlorite or any other liquor containing active chlorine. Actually it is difficult to secure a good white on synthetic fibres without degrading them to some degree. Experience has shown that a useful degree of whitening can be obtained by treatment with a hot liquor containing acidified sodium *chlorite* having the formula $NaClO_2$, in distinction from $NaOCl$ which is the formula for sodium *hypochlorite*.

Acidified solutions of sodium chlorite are also capable of bleaching cellulose fibres and to some extent they are employed for this purpose on the large scale. But such bleaching liquors are highly corrosive to the bleaching plant and can liberate chlorine dioxide which is harmful to the operatives. Otherwise sodium chlorite is a good bleaching agent for cotton since it can be applied to give a good white and yet less adversely affect the cotton than does sodium hypochlorite.

OPTICAL BLEACHING
OR FLUORESCENT WHITENING AGENTS

From the above description of the usual methods for bleaching textile materials it is seen that considerable care has to be taken to avoid damaging the fibres, and it is difficult to envisage any method for destroying impurities in a textile material by chemical means (these must employ agents which are acid or alkaline or which have oxidising or reducing power) which will not produce at least some degree of impoverishment of the fibres. Hence the importance of a discovery made by the German chemist Krais about 1929 that a considerable degree of whitening of a half- or incompletely bleached textile material could be achieved simply by depositing within the fibres a substance capable of emitting a bluish fluorescence.

Blueing to improve whiteness

It is well known that slightly off-white fabrics can have their whiteness improved by impregnation with a blueing agent—ultramarine and blue vat dye dispersions have long been used for this purpose. The theory behind this blueing to improve a yellowish white is that the yellow of the fabric together with the red and blue of the reddish blue of the blueing agent give, in combination, grey, and a greyish white appears a better white than does a yellowish white. To the extent that the resulting white is greyish it definitely is not the most pure white that can be produced.

Fluorescent blueing

Krais's discovery has resulted in the preparation of a number of substances which themselves are white but which in ultra-violet light emit a reddish to green blue fluorescence (daylight contains sufficient ultra-violet light to stimulate this fluorescence). Many of these substances have an affinity for cellulose and protein fibres and so can be applied to them from aqueous solution in much the same way as a dye. Thus if one of these substances is applied to yellowish cotton this material is made whiter because the substance itself emits white light and because the yellowish appearance is masked by the blue fluorescence. Thus an excellent white can be produced which is not possible to obtain by adding to the fabric an ordinary blueing agent. But there is obtained by the use of a fluorescent blueing agent another most important advantage. It is that the improved whiteness is obtained without damaging the textile material in any way. Thus today these so-called optical bleaching or fluorescent whitening agents are being increasingly employed to give textile materials an excellent white without incurring any fibre damage. It is not satisfactory to avoid a preliminary chemical bleaching treatment but it is most convenient and satisfactory to bleach chemically as far as possible without incurring fibre damage and then to give the added whiteness by impregnation with a fluorescent whitening agent.

Soap powders which bleach

Manufacturers of soap powders and other detergent compositions often add to these a fluorescent whitening agent so that textile materials washed at home absorb the fluorescent whitening agent from the washing liquor and thus gain in whiteness. However, it must be noted that these new whitening agents do not clean textile materials—they only mask any dirty impurities left in the fabrics or garments after washing.

Optical bleaching agents are now available which have a good affinity for synthetic fibres and these are of considerable help in producing nylon, Orlon, Terylene, etc. materials with a better whiteness than can be obtained by chemical bleaching methods.

Disadvantages of fluorescent whitening agents

While these new fluorescent whitening agents are of themselves a good white they will commence to turn a white fabric off-white if too much of them is applied. It is partly because of this that it is not practicable to make a really dirty fabric white by applying to it a sufficiently large amount of one or other of these agents—as more and more is applied there comes a point at which the off-white produced by the high concentration of whitening agent counterbalances the whitening effect due to its fluorescence.

Dyes

Before describing the dyeing and printing of textile materials it is convenient and useful here to deal with the dyes themselves, since their properties determine to a large degree how they can be applied to give even and satisfactory fast shades.

HISTORICAL

For several centuries natural dyes were available and have been used. Such dyes have had to be extracted from such materials as leaves and bark and so could not be obtained with the degree of purity necessary to good control in their application. The discovery of the first so-called coal tar dye by Perkin in 1856 showed how dyes could be synthetically made from the benzene, naphthalene, anthracene, and other constituents of coal gas tar. From this beginning has been built up a dyemaking industry which is now able to supply thousands of dyes in a high state of purity, to meet the modern demands of a dyeing industry which is able to produce coloured textiles of infinite variety yet with the colours having a degree of fastness and brilliance suitable for the uses to which they are likely to be put.

Perkin's first coal tar dye

Perkin's first dye would now be classed as a basic dye; it was mauve and was found useful for dyeing silk, although it was at the time also used as a postage stamp colouring matter. Actually the dye resulted from an unsuccessful experiment intended to give quinine, and it was only because Perkin resisted the temptation to throw away the tarry and apparently useless product and found that a mauve colouring matter could be extracted from it that the way was pointed by which other similar colouring matters could be made. Within a few years of this discovery many chemists in Britain and on the Continent were feverishly following the path first indicated by Perkin and discovering quite a large number of dyes all made by the chemical treatment in different ways of the many ingredients extractable from coal tar.

Griess' diazo reaction

Many different methods were discovered for making coal tar dyes, and one of the most fruitful and interesting was made by Peter Griess while working as chemist to a brewing firm at Burton-on-Trent. Briefly, this method, which yields so-called azo dyes, consists of converting a coal tar product into a diazo compound by treatment with nitrous acid and then coupling this with one or more other components to give dyes. The diazo reaction is capable of almost infinite exploitation in this way, and since the time of Griess hundreds of thousands of azo (also related disazo and trisazo) dyes have been made to allow a selection of a limited number having the most useful properties.

Dye production and selection

In course of time with new dyes being continuously discovered in several countries the coal tar industry was built up, with the result that many dyes became available for the dyeing of textile materials of all kinds. As new dyes were discovered so a decision could be made as to whether they could better replace those already available—the incentive always existing was the production of dyes capable either of more easy application or of giving shades of improved fastness to light, washing, etc. The discovery of new dyes and the deciding of what to do with them—discard or use according to whether they are better or not than existing dyes—continues in just the same way today. For every new dye taken into use it is probable that a thousand or perhaps ten thousand are discarded as perhaps being good but not good enough.

CLASSIFICATION OF DYES

It is possible to classify all these dyes (there are about 3,000 now in daily use) according to their chemical composition and also according to the methods by which they are applied and to which types of fibre they are most applicable. All three classifications are used, but the following is most used, and although not entirely one or the other of those just mentioned it proves very satisfactory to those engaged in the dyeing of textiles.

1. Direct cotton dyes
2. Acid wool dyes
3. Basic and cationic dyes
4. Sulphur dyes
5. Vat and solubilised vat dyes
6. Disperse dyes
7. Insoluble azoic dyes
8. Dyes produced on the fibre by oxidation
9. Dyes produced on the fibre by diazotising and developing
10. Mordant wool dyes
11. Reactive dyes
12. Pre-metallised dyes
13. Pigment dyes

The following is a brief description of these dyes, also indicating the essential features of their method of application to textile materials and their usefulness.

DIRECT COTTON DYES

Many of these dyes are made by use of the Peter Griess diazo reaction, and as their name indicates they can be applied to cotton and other cellulose fibres from a simple aqueous solution also containing assistants to promote uniform and complete dye absorption from the dye liquor. In applying direct cotton dyes it is usual to enter the textile goods into the dye liquor cold or warm and then gradually increase the temperature to the boil and keep at this temperature for about one hour. The addition of common salt or Glauber's salt towards the end of the dyeing operation promotes dye absorption and the more complete exhaustion of the dye liquor. Dyeing at the boil also aids even dyeing and the more thorough penetration of the dye into the fibres. The dye liquor should be neutral or alkaline but not acid.

Direct dyes can give bright shades having very good fastness to light with only good fastness to washing or vice versa; only a few of these dyes can give shades having very good fastness to both.

While these dyes are of most importance for the dyeing of cotton, some of them can be used for dyeing protein fibres such as wool and silk.

ACID WOOL DYES

These comprise diazo dyes but also many other dyes made by various means other than the diazo reaction. They are characterised by being easily applicable to wool and silk or other protein fibre from a boiling dye liquor, which in addition to the dye also contains Glauber's salt to promote level dyeing, and sulphuric, acetic, or formic acid to promote dye absorption by the fibre, just as common salt is used for a similar purpose in the dyeing of cellulose fibres with direct cotton dyes. Many of these dyes give very bright shades. They vary as regards the fastness of shade which can be produced by means of them but on the whole they are only of moderate fastness (on wool) to washing and especially if the washing liquor is slightly alkaline. Acid wool dyes can however give shades of excellent fastness to light. From the viewpoint of fastness acid wool dyes are on about the same level as direct cotton dyes.

Affinity for various fibres

Acid wool dyes are mainly used for wool and silk. At one time they were thought to be useless for nylon and other synthetic fibres but recently methods have been discovered for applying them to nylon and Orlon (that is, to polyamide and acrylic fibres) and this has made a welcome addition to the limited number of dyes which can be satisfactorily applied to hydrophobic fibres. The new methods used include the cuprous-ion dyeing process, the use of dye-carriers in the dye liquor to loosen the fibre structure and make it more accessible to dye penetration, and the use of dyeing temperatures exceeding the usual boiling point (100° C) so that the fibre structure is similarly loosened.

Acid wool dyes have no useful affinity for cellulose fibres and usually if a mixture of cotton and wool is dyed with an acid wool dye the cotton will be left white; in a similar way in dyeing with a direct cotton dye in neutral or alkaline conditions it will be the wool that is left white.

Application to nylon

In dyeing wool with acid wool dyes it is possible to use almost any mixture of dyes in the same dyebath, yet no one dye present will interfere with the absorption of the other dyes. On the other hand, if a mixture of the same dyes is applied to nylon it is possible that one or more of the dyes will be absorbed preferentially and so give a shade different from that produced on wool where no preferential absorption of any one dye occurs. This preferential dye absorption can make the dyeing of nylon goods to a required shade difficult, since according to the temperature and other conditions of dyeing so will the preference vary. This special behaviour of acid wool dyes in the dyeing of nylon arises from the fact that nylon unlike wool has a strictly limited capacity for absorbing these dyes so that the nylon fibres soon become saturated with dye.

BASIC DYES

Most of the coal tar dyes discovered shortly after the pioneering work of Perkin were basic dyes. They are usually exceptionally brilliant, and because of this they have in the past been much employed for dyeing cotton materials for export to foreign countries where highly coloured textile materials are much prized.

Mordanting to aid dye absorption

Basic dyes have no direct affinity for cellulose fibres, so that these have first to be treated with tannic acid and then with antimony salts whereby antimony tannate is deposited within the fibres (tannic acid has a natural affinity for cellulose fibres while it forms with antimony salts a white insoluble antimony tannate). This so-called mordant within the fibres attracts basic dyes to them when the cellulose material is worked in an aqueous solution of the basic dye, also containing a small proportion of acetic or other acid to maintain the basic dye in solution. The colouring matter ultimately left in the dyed cotton is a complex chemical compound of dye, tannic acid, and antimony salts. Certain sulphurised phenols have also been found to combine strongly with basic dyes and a number of proprietary mordants of this type are now available to assist the dyeing of cellulose fibres with basic dyes.

In the presence of urea and with the aid of a steaming treatment viscose rayon materials can be dyed with basic dyes to give shades of useful fastness to washing.

Basic dyes are useful for the dyeing of wool and silk and they are applied directly under slightly acid conditions.

Although basic dyes give such brilliant shades these (on cotton and to a less degree on wool and silk) suffer from the great disadvantage of fading very rapidly in sunlight. Various after-treatments of the dyed cotton (or other cellulose fibre) have been proposed but have only been moderately successful. It is under moist conditions that sunlight is most destructive to basic dyes and so in some tropical countries which have dry climates cotton goods coloured with basic dyes resist fading surprisingly well.

CATIONIC DYES

Although basic dyes have tended in recent years to be less and less used, a recent surprising discovery that they give shades of very good fastness to light and washing on acrylic fibres has again brought them into favour. Several dyemakers are now producing special ranges of basic dyes (in *base* rather than *salt* form) which are being used for the dyeing of Orlon, Dynel, Acrilan, and similar fibres. They have the big advantage of requiring only a simple method of application and they have much assisted the dyeing of acrylic fibres which have in the past given much trouble to dyers because of their poor dye absorptive properties. Basic dyes for acrylic fibres are now usually designated *cationic* dyes.

SULPHUR DYES

These dyes are obtained from a variety of coal tar products by treatment with sulphur or sulphides, and as a class they can be most satisfactorily applied to cellulose fibres under alkaline reducing conditions to give dullish shades which have very good fastness to washing and sometimes also to light. The range of shades obtainable by these dyes is limited. Black sulphur dyes are especially useful as affording a means for dyeing cheaply good fast black shades on cotton particularly.

Conditions of application

Sulphur dyes are insoluble in water, so for their application to cotton it is necessary to use a dyebath containing a reducing agent, generally sodium sulphide and a small proportion of sodium carbonate to maintain the dyebath alkaline. The sodium sulphide reduces the sulphur dye to a leuco form which is soluble in dilute alkali, and in this form it has an affinity for cellulose fibres—the presence of common salt in the dye liquor promotes its more complete exhaustion of dye. Dyeing is carried out at the boil and at the end of the dyeing operation the absorbed dye is in its leuco form. Thus the dyed material then has to be treated with an oxidising liquor containing hydrogen peroxide or sodium bichromate to convert the dye back to its original insoluble state. With the dye thus deposited insoluble within the fibres it can be understood why the shade should be fast to washing.

Application to wool

Sulphur dyes are not applied to wool materials because the alkaline dyeing conditions required can adversely affect the alkali-sensitive wool fibres. However, some special processes have been devised to allow the dyeing of wool with sulphur dyes in which a reduced amount of alkali is used, but they are only used to a moderate extent.

Sulphur dyes are not generally useful for the dyeing of synthetic fibres.

VAT DYES

This class of dye is generally known to comprise the fastest dyes known—they can give shades of excellent fastness to washing, light, perspiration, bleaching, etc. Such dyes were not discovered until the beginning of the present century and many of them are made from the anthraquinone that in its turn is made from the anthracene obtained from coal tar.

Application

Vat dyes resemble sulphur dyes in that they are insoluble in water but are amenable by reduction to give a leuco form which is soluble in dilute alkaline solution (some vat dyes—the *indigoid* vat dyes—are satisfied with a weak alkali such as sodium carbonate or even ammonia, but others—the *anthraquinone* vat dyes which contain the fastest dyes—require a caustic alkali such as caustic soda or potash) and which has a strong affinity for cellulose fibres. Thus in dyeing, say, cotton with a vat dye, this has to be brought into solution by treatment with caustic soda and sodium hydrosulphite (or similar strong reducing agent but not the sodium sulphide employed for reducing sulphur dyes) and then applied either at room temperature or up to 60° C according to the particular dye being applied. Some vat dyes require more alkali than others and so for vat dyeing the dyes are applied by one or other of three methods depending on the optimum dyeing temperature and the amount of caustic soda which should be present. After the vat dye has been absorbed into the cotton in its leuco state there must follow a wash and then an oxidising treatment with hydrogen peroxide or sodium bichromate to restore the vat dye to its original insoluble fully oxidised state. A final hot soaping helps to do this and also to aggregate the vat dye particles within the fibres to a degree which gives the dyeing increased fastness to light.

Vat dyes are not much applied to wool and silk because the strongly alkaline dyeing conditions required can harm the fibres.

Indigoid vat dyes

It may be recalled that indigo is a natural vat dye and that it has inspired dye chemists to ascertain its chemical composition and then make it synthetically. With the introduction of synthetic indigo the cultivation of the indigo plant for its dye content has practically ceased. Dye chemists have since their discovery of the chemical nature of indigo been able to make many other dyes similar to but chemically different from the natural indigo, and all these new synthetic dyes related in chemical composition to indigo are classed as *indigoid* dyes. They comprise yellow, red, and blue dyes, and so constitute a very useful group of vat dyes which are applicable under milder alkaline conditions than the anthraquinone group of vat dyes.

Solubilised vat dyes

Some twenty or more years ago it was discovered that the leuco (reduced) forms of indigoid and anthraquinone vat dyes could be converted into sulphuric acid esters whose sodium salts were water-soluble, and applicable to both cellulose and protein (wool and silk) fibres. After dyeing with these solubilised vat dyes the textile material simply required to be oxidised for restoration of the dye to its original water-insoluble form. This has proved for many purposes a very convenient method for applying vat dyes where it is not desirable to use the caustic soda + sodium hydrosulphite process.

Solubilised anthraquinone and indigoid vat dyes of this kind are typically represented by the *Soledon* and *Indigosol* ranges of dyes.

It is to be noted that these solubilised dyes have only a moderate affinity for cellulose fibres, so that the dyeing method often consists of impregnating the yarn or fabric with a solution of the Soledon or Indigosol dye and then, with or without intermediate drying, developing the final shade by an oxidation treatment. On the other hand, these dyes have an affinity for protein fibres and can be applied to wool and silk as for an acid wool dye and then finally be oxidised on the fibre.

So far, the vat and solubilised vat dyes are only of moderate importance in the dyeing of synthetic fibres.

DISPERSE DYES

Until the introduction of acetate rayon about 1920, almost all the dyes in use for application to the hydrophile natural fibres cotton, wool, silk, linen, etc. and early man-made regenerated cellulose fibres such as viscose and cuprammonium rayons, were required to be water-soluble or to be capable, at the time of dyeing, of conversion into a temporary water-soluble form. But early experience in the dyeing of this new acetate rayon showed that the fibres resisted absorption of water-soluble substances while they readily absorbed those which were insoluble in water. Thus it was with only a few of the dyes then readily available and in common use that acetate rayon goods could be dyed. It was obvious that new dyes would have to be made for the colouring of this particular type of man-made fibre.

Historical

Ellis early found that coloured organic compounds insoluble in water were readily absorbed by acetate rayon if they were presented in the form of aqueous dispersions prepared by fine grinding and the aid of dispersing substances, particularly sulphonated ricinoleic acid (sulphonated castor oil). In this way he was able to prepare a range of so-called S.R.A. dyes. The success of these indicated the path for preparing other dyes all characterised by consisting of dispersions of water-insoluble colouring matters. Hitherto it had been necessary to introduce sulphonic acid, carboxylic acid, and other water-solubilising groups into the molecules of dyes to make them water-soluble; now, for the making of the new dyes, the presence in the dye molecule of such water-solubilising groups had to be avoided.

Special dyeing conditions

The new dyes were at that time often referred to as *acetate* dyes but more recently they have come to be called *disperse* dyes. They are really water-insoluble coloured organic compounds which are absorbed by acetate fibres by a process of the dye dissolving in the fibre, and it is necessary that when applied to acetate fibres the dye particles be extremely small so that when attracted to the surface of each fibre they and the fibre make mutual contact over a relatively large area, which is favourable to their rapid absorption.

A number of disperse dyes are of a type which contain amino (NH_2) groups capable of diazotisation and thus are capable of coupling with a suitable component to give a more complex dye. Deep black and navy blue shades are more satisfactorily produced in this way than by applying the complex dye in its dispersed form.

Although the presence of a sulphonic acid group (SO_3H) in a disperse dye would prevent its absorption by acetate rayon, it is possible to have a carboxylic acid group (COOH) without completely preventing absorption. Thus a range of water-soluble disperse dyes is available, but they are not so well absorbed as the insoluble disperse dyes.

M

Disperse dyes have been found very useful for dyeing most types of synthetic fibres, and they have the valuable property of giving level shades even when there are present in the material being dyed unequally drawn or stretched yarns (dye absorptive power is lowered by the stretching of a synthetic fibre yarn during manufacture). Acid wool dyes will reveal these yarn differences clearly by dyeing to a deeper shade on the less stretched yarns. By the use of dye-carriers or of high temperature dyeing conditions all synthetic fibres, including the reluctant Terylene and Rhovyl fibres, can be made amenable to dyeing with disperse dyes.

Properties of disperse dyes

Since disperse dyes contain no sulphonic or carboxylic acid groups they are liable at high temperatures to sublime from the dyed fibres—thus all those disperse dyes which dyemakers offer must first have been tested to show whether or not they are satisfactory from this viewpoint. Some disperse dyes on acetate (including triacetate) rayon but not on synthetic fibres suffer a peculiar drastic type of fading when exposed to the acid reducing vapours which are liberated by burning coal gas, but which may also be present in the atmosphere of industrial towns (especially during the damp winter months). Thus gasfading can cause blue shades to become reddish and even grey. Several aminoanthraquinone disperse dyes are liable to this gasfading and they should not be used if it is at all possible to obtain the desired shade by the use of any other dye. However a number of proprietary anti-gasfading agents have been made available which if applied to the dyed material give a certain degree of protection against this type of fading. Among these may be mentioned diphenylethylene diamine, methyl benzylamine, Tumescal D (diphenyl) (I.C.I.), triethanolamine, and zinc oxide.

INSOLUBLE AZOIC DYES

Dyes of this group are water-insoluble and they are not applied as such but are actually formed from their components within the fibres. These dyes are employed more especially for the colouring of cellulose fibre goods in shades having the highest degree of fastness to light and washing, and in this respect of fastness they are often equal to vat dye shades. The process of dyeing an insoluble azoic dye is based on the Griess diazo reaction.

Application

The components of an insoluble azoic dye are a base having at least one diazotisable amino (NH_2) group in its molecule and a coupling component which is usually a phenol or naphthol. In the form of dyeing practised some seventy years ago cotton fabric was impregnated with an alkaline solution of beta-naphthol, dried, and then treated with a solution of diazotised paranitraniline, when immediately a deep bright red shade developed in the fabric as the result of formation within the fibres of an insoluble pigment by coupling of the beta-naphthol with the diazotised para-nitraniline, thus:

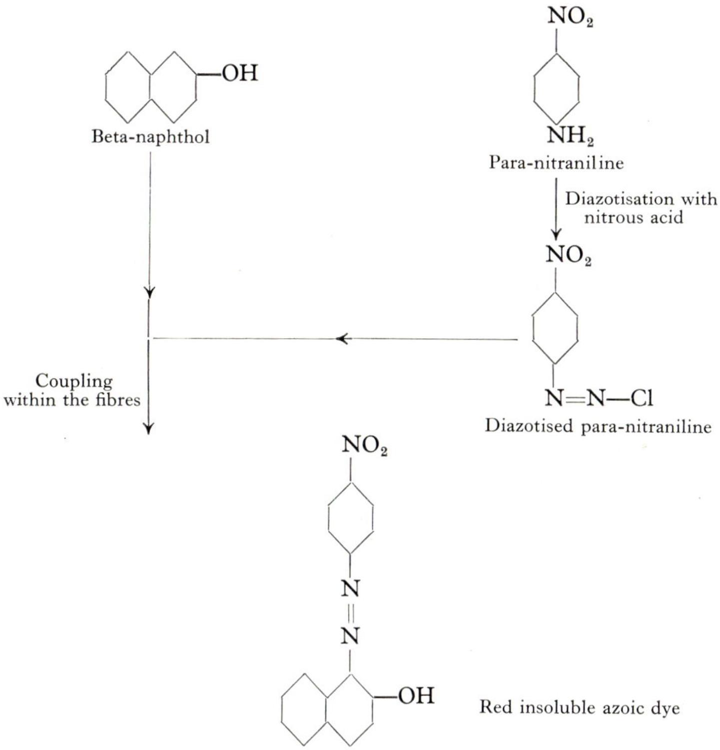

Beta-naphthol —OH

NO_2

NH_2
Para-nitraniline

Diazotisation with nitrous acid

NO_2

N=N—Cl
Diazotised para-nitraniline

Coupling within the fibres

NO_2

N
‖
N

—OH   Red insoluble azoic dye

By using different combinations of the limited number of bases and phenol and naphthol coupling components then available, cotton fabric could be dyed to a limited number of shades (mostly red to scarlet and orange) having very good fastness to washing and possibly to light.

Use of improved naphthol coupling components

Later it was found much better to use instead of beta- or alpha-naphthol an anilide or other similar derivative of beta-oxynaphthoic acid which had then become available. Not only could shades of improved fastness be obtained but many other newly discovered bases capable of diazotisation and coupling with these new components could be used to secure quite a wide range of shades including blue and black. So at the present time these new naphthols and diazotisable bases are almost always used for the dyeing of insoluble azoic dyes. It is an advantage of the newer naphthols that most of them have an affinity for cellulose fibres, whereas the earlier used beta-naphthol completely lacked this affinity. This substantive nature of the new naphthols hinders their bleeding out of the fabric into the diazo solution before the coupling of naphthol and diazotised base is complete.

Use of stabilised diazotised bases

In recent years it has been found possible to prepare the diazotised base in a temporarily stabilised form so that the dyer and printer need not prepare the diazotised base himself but can purchase it from a dyemaker and then at any desired moment bring it into the active form by heating or acidification or by simple dissolution in water. Also, stabilised mixtures of naphthol and diazotised base can be prepared so that after their printing on fabric the formation of azoic dye can be induced by a steaming treatment.

The insoluble azoic dyes have proved useful in the dyeing of Terylene and some of the other synthetic fibres including triacetate, nylon, and Creslan.

The difference between the formerly employed beta-naphthol and the now universally employed naphthols is indicated by the following formulae:

Beta-naphthol

Anilide of beta-oxynaphthoic acid

OXIDATION DYES

These are very limited in number, the one most used being the so-called *Aniline Black*. By oxidation under certain conditions aniline yields an insoluble black pigment and this reaction has for many years been used in the dyeing of cotton and viscose rayon fabrics but not those of wool. The dyeing process consists of impregnating say cotton fabric with a liquor containing aniline, hydrochloric acid, sodium chlorate (the oxidant), and a catalyst such as copper chloride or sodium ferrocyanide, then partially drying by running the fabric over a number of hot cylinders, then heating in a moist atmosphere as achieved for example by running the fabric through a chamber heated inside by live steam and steam pipes, so that oxidation of the aniline takes place and the fabric emerges a black shade. Then follows a run through a hot liquor containing sodium bichromate to complete the oxidation and secure a full, deep and fast black shade. In this dyeing process the acid present can weaken the fabric being dyed, but by careful adjustment of the conditions it is possible to keep the fibre damage below 10%, which is an acceptable value.

The attractiveness of Aniline Black dyeing is that the shade has very good all-round fastness (except to bleaching with hypochlorite) and that a continuous process can be employed so that cotton fabric can be run through the dyeing plant at say 20 to 30 yards per minute to come out at the far end fully dyed.

An improved process

It has been found that if part of the aniline is replaced by a similar substance known as para-aminodiphenylamine the oxidation will proceed much more smoothly and completely yet under milder oxidation conditions to allow the production of black fabric considerably less weakened.

DIAZOTISING AND DEVELOPING DYES

These are direct cotton dyes which contain a free amino (NH_2) group so that after their application to cellulose fibre goods they can be treated with nitrous acid (usually this is obtained by mixing sulphuric acid with sodium nitrite in the treating liquor) to diazotise the amino group so that the resulting diazotised dye can then couple in the fibre with the naphthol applied thereafter. By this coupling of a naphthol (or other coupling component) to the dye already present in the fibres there results a more complex dye which may be somewhat different in shade but desirably have a much greater fastness to washing. This method of dyeing can be used to produce wash-fast shades not so obtainable by the simple application of a direct cotton dye—such shades are navy blue, deep bottle green, and maroon.

It may be mentioned here that the resulting dyeings of this kind are generally more easily reduced to white by treatment with sodium hydrosulphite than the original dye applied, and this can be of assistance in discharge printing processes to be described later.

MORDANT WOOL DYES

A number of colouring matters are not completely satisfactorily applicable to wool unless there is present in the wool a substance, termed a mordant, which has an affinity for both the wool and the dye. Various metal salts serve as useful mordants for wool, but of these sodium and potassium bichromates are most satisfactory. The dyes which are applied with the aid of a chrome mordant are termed chrome mordant dyes and it is possible to apply these by three different methods.

In the first (*chrome mordant*) method, the wool is heated in a bichromate solution whereby a chrome oxide becomes fixed in the wool so that this can then in a separate liquor be dyed with the chrome mordant dye. In the second (*after-chrome*) method, the wool is first dyed with the chrome mordant dye and is afterwards treated with the bichromate.

The third (*metachrome*) method enables both dye and bichromate to be applied at the same time and it depends on the fact that no appreciable combination occurs between the bichromate and the wool or the dye under alkaline conditions, but this holds only for a limited number of dyes. So in this method the dyebath is prepared with ammonia, ammonium sulphate, sodium or potassium bichromate, and the dye, and the wool is worked in this with the temperature being raised to boiling point. Gradually the dye is absorbed by the wool and the bath tends to become acid with the loss of ammonia, and at the same time this change enables chrome oxide to be absorbed by the wool so that simultaneously the wool, dye, and chrome oxide become combined with the result that the wool fibres are dyed. There are a number of variations of this so-called *metachrome* method of dyeing. It is a method much favoured so far as dyes suitable for it are available.

But however the bichrome and dye are applied the resulting shades are of excellent fastness to washing, and mordant wool dyes are generally used instead of acid wool dyes whenever really good washing fastness is required.

REACTIVE DYES

This type of dye has only recently been introduced more or less independently by three different dyemakers, and such dyes are likely to prove of great value to dyers of all types of material in the near future. The five ranges of reactive dyes now available are the Procions (I.C.I.), the Remazols (Hoechst A.G.), the Cibacrons (CIBA), the Reactones (Geigy), and the Drimarenes (Sandoz).

These dyes are characterised by containing in their molecules reactive atoms or atomic groups capable of entering into chemical reaction with an hydroxyl (OH) group present in a cellulose fibre such as cotton or a regenerated cellulose rayon, and with an amino (NH_2) group such as may be present in a protein or regenerated protein fibre which includes wool. As a result of such reaction the dye becomes chemically combined with the fibre. It is generally necessary for a weak alkali to be present for the dye to combine chemically with a cellulose fibre, and this combination may be represented thus:

$$Dye—Cl \quad + \quad Cell—OH$$

Reactive dye with one reactive chlorine atom (Procion or Cibacron dye)

Cellulose fibre

Alkali such as sodium carbonate to combine with the hydrochloric acid liberated

$$Cell—O—Dye \quad + \quad HCl$$

Dye combined with cellulose fibre   Hydrochloric acid

$$Dye—SO_2—CH_2CH_2OSO_3H \ + \ Cell—OH$$

Reactive dye with one reactive vinyl sulphon group (Remazol dye)

Alkali to combine with the sulphuric acid liberated

$$Cell—O—CH_2 . CH_2 . SO_2—Dye \ + \quad H_2SO_4$$

Dye combined with cellulose fibre   Sulphuric acid

It is to be noted that whether a Remazol or a Procion or Cibacron dye is used it becomes chemically united to the cellulose fibre by an oxygen atom, that is, by an *ether* type of linkage. Cellulose ether compounds are known to be very stable.

Since the dye becomes chemically united to the cellulose fibres it is practically impossible to wash the dye from the dyed cotton or other cellulose fibre material. These reactive dyes thus have the great advantage of giving colourings very fast to washing and it is possible also for them to be very fast to light.

Since the water of the dyebath consists of molecules each containing a hydroxyl group according to the formula for water, (H—OH), it is evident that during dyeing the reactive dye can also enter into reaction with the water. This does in fact take place so that a new water-soluble dye is simultaneously formed thus:

$$\text{Procion} \quad \text{Dye—Cl} \qquad\qquad\qquad + \text{H.OH}$$
$$\text{Remazol} \quad \text{or Dye—SO}_2\text{CH}_2\text{CH}_2\text{OSO}_3\text{H} \qquad \text{Water}$$
$$\downarrow$$
$$\text{Dye—OH}$$
$$\text{or Dye—SO}_2\text{CH}_2\text{CH}_2\text{OH}$$
$$\text{Water-soluble new dye}$$

Fortunately the conditions of dyeing can be controlled so that this unwanted reaction occurs only to a small degree. Because the new dye thus formed has no affinity for the cellulose fibres and is water-soluble it can be readily washed out completely after the end of the dyeing operation, but of course such new dye represents a loss of reactive dye.

Reactive dyes have now been found useful for the dyeing of wool and also nylon. They give dyeings of good fastness on the latter fibre and this fastness is found with quite pale shades—something unusual.

New types of reactive dyes are now being found which have reactive groups other than those mentioned above.

In the Procion and Cibacron dyes the reactive chlorine atoms are attached in the dye molecule to a special atomic grouping known as a triazine nucleus. Recently it has been discovered that a pyrimidine nucleus with attached chlorine atoms can be present instead of the triazine nucleus and so a new range of reactive dyes has become available.

PRE-METALLISED DYES

Early types

In earlier days a number of selected direct cotton dyes were applied to cotton or other cellulose fibre and the resulting dyeing after-treated with a solution of a metal salt such as one of copper, nickel, or chromium with the object of improving the fastness of the dyeing to washing and sometimes also to light. This improvement resulted from a combination of the dye in the fibre with the applied metal. This stimulated research to discover how such a dye could be pre-treated with the metal salt yet remain in a form which would allow it to be applied as a direct cotton dye to cellulose and also protein fibres. Success was obtained and it resulted in the introduction of the Neolan (CIBA) and Palatine Fast (I.G. Farbenindustrie, A.G.) dyes which are of the *pre-metallised* class of dye.

Application

It appears that in treating the dye with say a chromium salt the chromium atom enters into a special kind of chemical combination with the dye so that it ceases to give its ordinary reactions—the dye + metal is a *chelated* or *co-ordinated* type of compound. Such pre-metallised dyes are water-soluble and have an affinity for both cellulose and protein (wool) fibres so that they can be applied to these fibres from an acid dyebath in much the same way as an acid wool dye, but to give shades having very good fastness properties. However, these early discovered ranges of pre-metallised dyes require a high proportion of sulphuric acid in the dyebath (about double that required in dyeing wool with an ordinary acid wool dye) and so the dyeing process is liable to harm cellulose and even wool fibres.

New, more useful types

Recently the way has been found to form similar dyes with about one-half as much metal in combination with the dye and so new ranges of pre-metallised dyes have become available, for example, the Cibalans (CIBA). The special useful feature of these new dyes is that they can be applied to wool from a neutral or only slightly acid dyebath to give shades which have a high degree of fastness to washing and to light. These dyes can thus be used to replace the older Neolan and Palatine Fast type of pre-metallised dye and also the chrome mordant methods for dyeing wool (including the meta-chrome process) and thus with a simplified dyeing procedure which requires the use of but a small proportion of acid towards the end of the dyeing process it is possible to produce fast bright shades on wool.

In applying these new pre-metallised dyes it is important to commence the dyeing under carefully controlled conditions of slight acidity or alkalinity in order to prevent an uneven 'strike' of the dye on the textile material, since it is difficult to level out any such unevenness during the remainder of the dyeing period. Special agents have been discovered for addition to the dyebath to assist the production of level shades by retarding dye absorption.

These new pre-metallised dyes have now been found most useful for the dyeing of nylon and other polyamide fibres, since even when applied to produce pale or pastel shades these have good fastness properties—it is found with other dyes that pale shades are not so fast as medium and deep shades.

The various ranges of these new pre-metallised dyes applicable under neutral dyeing conditions are now being rapidly expanded to meet an increasing demand by dyers for these useful dyes.

PIGMENT DYES

There are available a comparatively small number of pigments such as carbon black, iron oxide, cadmium sulphide, Prussian Blue, ultramarine, and also some insoluble dyes (mostly of the insoluble azoic type) which because they are insoluble in water cannot ordinarily be applied to textile materials by dyeing methods. Yet several of these pigments are exceptionally stable and if they could be fixed on fabrics would give colourings of excellent fastness to light and washing and other adverse influences.

Application

In earlier days such pigments were applied by printing methods in which the fabric was printed with a paste containing the pigment and a gum, resin, casein, or other natural binder which in the printing process became insoluble. Thus the colouring fastness depended on the tenacity with which the binder adhered to the fabric surface. Much of the printing thus carried out was not of the highest quality because of the lack of satisfactory binders. But in recent years with the introduction of synthetic resins of the urea–formaldehyde and other types it has been found very convenient to use these in pigment printing, for they allow the pigment to be anchored in the fabric much more firmly and satisfactorily than hitherto.

Today pigments are used to a considerable extent for the production of coloured patterns on textile materials and the colours usually have excellent fastness. It is a marked advantage of the coloured patterns now being produced with the aid of synthetic resins that the colour does not easily rub off the fabric on to adjacent materials.

DYE SELECTION FOR DYEING THE DIFFERENT FIBRES

Responsibility for dye choice

Before commencing to dye any given type of textile material the dyer has to decide which dyes he shall apply, and this choice is governed by a few major considerations. In the first place his choice must include only those dyes which can be satisfactorily applied to the kind of fibre of which the yarn, fabric, or garment is made. Secondly he must give due consideration to the general colour fastness required and also to any special requirements of fastness depending on the use to which the dyed material will be put. Finally his dye selection must take into account the cost of the dyes and of their application, since if he has a wide choice of dyes he will tend to use those which are cheapest. The choice of dyes may be easy or difficult and it is not a matter which can be casually considered, for if he is a commission dyer he will later be held responsible for the satisfactory behaviour of the dyed goods and perhaps have to pay compensation for any defects. The commission dyer, that is one who does not make or own the textile materials but only undertakes for a stipulated payment to convert them into coloured materials, is always under some kind of risk for a considerable period after the materials have been dyed and returned to their owner—the goods may not be used until several months later and it is then that faults and defects may become revealed which could not be seen immediately after dyeing.

The choice of dyes may be fairly easy when the textile material consists of one type of fibre only. It becomes more difficult when there are two or more fibres in admixture and in this case a very difficult choice may be involved if special fastness requirements are insisted on.

It is not possible here to consider all the details concerning such a choice of dyes, but it is possible and useful to indicate below a rough classification of dyes according to the fibres to which they can be satisfactorily applied.

Fibre	*Types of dyes applicable*
Cotton	Direct cotton dyes. Diazotising and developing dyes. Vat dyes. Sulphur dyes. Reactive dyes. Oxidation dyes. Insoluble azoic dyes. Basic dyes. Pre-metallised dyes.
Wool	Acid wool dyes. Selected direct cotton dyes. Basic dyes. Selected sulphur dyes under special conditions. Reactive dyes. Mordant wool dyes. Pre-metallised dyes.
Linen	As for cotton.
Regenerated cellulose fibres (viscose and cuprammonium rayons)	As for cotton.
Di- and Tri-acetate fibres	Disperse dyes.
Silk	Direct cotton dyes. Acid wool dyes. Mordant wool dyes. Insoluble azoic dyes. Vat dyes. Selected diazotised and developing dyes. Selected sulphur dyes under special conditions. Basic dyes. (Silk is unique in the large number of different types of dyes which can be applied to it.)
Polyamide fibres	Disperse dyes. Selected acid wool, direct cotton dyes, and pre-metallised dyes under special conditions. Vat dyes. Wool mordant dyes. Insoluble azoic dyes. Neutral dyeing pre-metallised dyes. Reactive dyes.
Polyester fibres	Disperse dyes. Insoluble azoic dyes. Vat dyes under special conditions.
Acrylic fibres	Disperse dyes. Cationic dyes. Insoluble azoic dyes. Acid wool dyes. Vat dyes. Sulphur dyes. Pre-metallised dyes. Direct cotton dyes. (The

acrylic fibres vary among themselves in their dyeing properties and for any particular acrylic fibre it will be necessary to select from the dyes mentioned above.)

Wool + a cellulose fibre   Union dyes to secure a solid shade with both fibres equally dyed (union dyes are a mixture of direct cotton dyes and neutral dyeing acid wool dyes). Some direct cotton dyes alone give the same shade on both cotton and wool.

PRINCIPLES OF DYE MIXING

In dyeing textile materials it is seldom possible to produce the shades demanded by the use of single dyes—it is usual to employ a mixture of two or three dyes but not often more than four. In using such mixtures the dyer makes use of the Newtonian theory of colour which is based on regarding all colours apart from black and white as being compounded of three pure colours—red, yellow, and blue. The brightness of such colours can be modified by addition of white or black.

In compounding dye mixtures to secure any desired shade the dyer makes use of the following colour relationships:

Primary colours

Red   Yellow   Blue

Secondary colours (mixtures of two of the above primary colours)

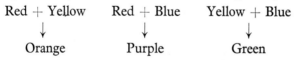

Red + Yellow   Red + Blue   Yellow + Blue

Orange   Purple   Green

Tertiary colours (mixtures of three of the above primary colours with one in excess)

Red + Yellow + Blue (excess) *or* Green + Purple = Grey
Red + Yellow (excess) + Blue *or* Green + Orange = Olive
Red (excess) + Yellow + Blue *or* Orange + Purple = Brown

No dyes are available which have exactly the red, yellow, and blue shades required by the Newtonian theory, so in general dyeing practice it is necessary for the dyer to take this into account in preparing his dye mixtures.

THE PRINCIPLES OF TEXTILE COLOURING

Two main methods for colouring textile materials are recognised—*dyeing* and *printing*. There is a third method used to a considerable extent, but it does not fall within the scope of the ordinary dyer since it involves adding a pigment to the fibre-forming polymer prior to its extrusion by a dry, wet, or melt-spinning technique into man-made fibres which are thus already coloured at this early stage in their manufacture and utilisation. These so-called *spin-dyed* fibres are readily available in a limited number of standard shades having excellent fastness properties. They are convenient to use in weaving and knitting for producing colour patterns with the remainder of the fabric left white.

Dyeing and printing methods

The difference between dyeing and printing is essentially that by dyeing yarns, fabrics and garments are coloured throughout to the same colour, whereas by printing the textile material is given a coloured design or pattern such as coloured flowers on a white ground or white spots on a coloured ground. It is possible by dyeing to produce fabric having a coloured pattern if two or more different types of fibre are present in the fabric (say, a fabric woven according to a pattern with cotton and wool yarns) for then in a one- or two-stage dyeing operation dyes can be applied which will be absorbed only by the fibre for which they have an affinity. Thus with a two-fibre fabric a two-colour pattern can be produced; it is possible but more difficult to dye in three different colours a three-fibre fabric. But in any case the co-operation of the fabric manufacturer is required and there are definite limitations to the kinds of pattern which can be produced in a fabric by weaving and knitting methods. By contrast, a fabric can be printed with a pattern containing a large number of different colours, say up to sixteen, and the pattern itself can be very clearly delineated.

DYEING TECHNIQUES

Although textile materials may be dyed in different forms, as for example loose fibre, yarn, fabrics, garments, hose and half hose, etc., there are certain fundamental principles underlying the dyeing of all these various types of goods, and much of the equipment employed is today standardised.

In dyeing operations the object is generally to colour the textile goods all over and to ensure that the colouring is uniform and that it matches exactly the shade specified. Further useful requirements are that the dye applied penetrates the material thoroughly so that not only the inside but also the outside fibres are equally dyed, and it is also desirable that each fibre shall ultimately be left with the dye uniformly distributed throughout its substance and not be largely confined to its outer surface. If these requirements are satisfied then the dyed material will have the maximum fastness which the dyes applied permit.

Dyeing processes

In the dyeing operation itself the dye is usually applied in the form of an aqueous solution, and this must be brought into uniform contact with the textile material so that the dye can pass from it into the fibres. There are two main methods employed for achieving this. In the first method the textile material is continuously moved relatively to a more or less stationary dye liquor or the dye liquor is moved continuously relatively to the textile material. In these circumstances all parts of the dye liquor are brought evenly in contact with the textile material throughout the dyeing operation, and uniform dye absorption by the textile material takes place while the dye liquor continuously and evenly becomes exhausted of dye. In the second method of dyeing, the textile material (usually fabric) is impregnated evenly with the dye liquor with the aid of a so-called padding mangle and is then subjected to a high temperature (about 100° C), as for example by drying while running over heated rotating cylinders and then steaming while running through a closed chamber; or it may be steamed in this manner without the intermediate drying. Under these conditions the dye passes from the dye liquor into the fibres, and if the dye liquor is initially evenly padded into the fabric and remains evenly distributed during the high temperature treatment, then an evenly dyed fabric results. The steaming or other high temperature treatment is necessary to fix the dye in the fibres in such a manner that it afterwards resists easy removal by washing—if there is no steaming then the dye will wash out easily and almost completely by simple washing with water.

Dyeing machinery

Appropriate dyeing machinery is available for carrying out the dyeing techniques mentioned above. The equipment available for dyeing by the second method often allows dyeing to be carried out in a continuous manner so that loom-state fabric suitably purified and made absorbent for dyeing is led in at one end to emerge at the other completely dyed—many thousand yards of fabric may thus be dyed to the same shade in the course of the day. When dyeing by the first method it is usual to dye relatively small amounts of textile material at the one time, say 500 yards of fabric or 200 lb of yarn or a load of 100 lb of garments.

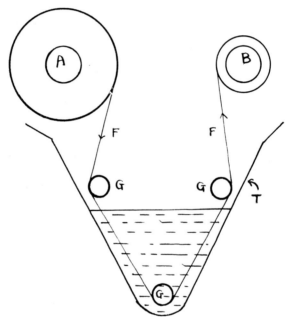

FIG. 47. Showing the essential features of a jigger dyeing machine for the dyeing of woven fabric in open width. The jigger consists of a trough T for containing the dye liquor and it is provided with means for heating this liquor as desired. G are guiding rollers which freely rotate. Rollers A and B are so-called 'batching rollers'. At the commencement of dyeing all the fabric is neatly 'batched' or rolled on roller A. Then roller B is rotated so that the fabric F is drawn downwards through the dye liquor to be wound on roller B. Then roller A is rotated so as to draw the fabric back through the dye liquor and re-wind it on roller A. With each passage through the dye liquor the fabric picks up dye and so the backwards and forwards operation is repeated until the fabric has acquired the desired shade—additions of dye can be made from time to time as required. About 500 yards of fabric are dyed at once. An important advantage of the jigger is that the fabric being dyed is always in open width and so does not become creased.

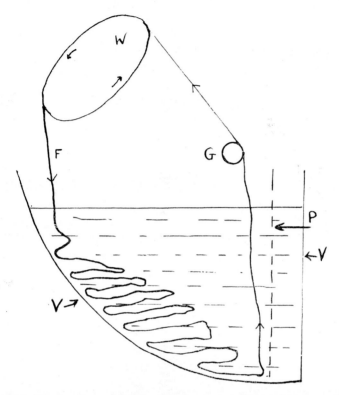

FIG. 48. Showing the essential features of a winch dyeing machine as used for the dyeing of both woven and knitted fabrics. The machine is shown in cross-section so that only one piece of fabric (made endless by temporarily sewing its two ends together) is shown, but the width of such a machine may allow ten or more such fabrics to be dyed simultaneously side by side, being kept in their relative positions by a row of guiding pegs. The machine comprises a dye liquor vat V having at the front a perforated partition P to make a small vertical chamber into which dye can be added from time to time and be washed through the partition into the main bulk of dye liquor—this ensures its even distribution. It also comprises a guiding roller G and a rotating circular or elliptical winch W which continuously pulls the fabric F out of the dye liquor at the front of the machine to fold it down at the back, thus ensuring an even exposure of the fabric to the dye liquor. During dyeing the fabric is usually in rope form and so may acquire permanent creases if it is of a type susceptible to such creasing. For most of the time the fabric is immersed in the dye liquor in a slack condition and this is favourable to dye penetration which might be difficult if the fabric is very tightly woven or knitted. It is to be noted that in dyeing fabric in a jigger dyeing machine (Fig. 47) the fabric is pulled from one batching roller to the other and for most of the dyeing period is out of the dye liquor tightly wound on one or other of the batching rollers.

N

Fig. 49. Showing the dyeing of yarn in the form of skeins. An overhead frame carries a number of horizontal parallel rods from which the skeins are suspended, while to maintain them regularly spaced and evenly hanging a rod is placed within the lower end of each skein. In dyeing the frame is lowered into a rectangular tank containing the dye liquor and this, by means of a pump, is then continuously circulated through the skeins. Means are provided to reverse the direction of dye liquor flow periodically so that even dyeing may be ensured. Arrangements are also provided to heat the dye liquor as desired. When the required shade has been obtained the spent dye liquor is run off and replaced by water to rinse the skeins. The frame can then be raised and moved to allow the skeins to be taken off the rods and hydroextracted and subsequently dried.

By courtesy of The Longclose Engineering Co. Ltd

FIG. 50. Showing machines used for dyeing yarn wound in the form of cheeses and cones. In such machines the yarn is first wound evenly on perforated stainless steel tubular centres (these may be bobbins or wire-interlaced springs) and the resulting cheeses or cones are then slipped on to perforated steel tubes suitably spaced to form a framework ready for lowering into a cylindrical container as shown at *A*. Arrangements are provided when the frame is within the dye liquor container and the top cover closed for dye liquor to be pumped continuously upwards through the perforated tubes and thence outwards through the cones or cheeses, thereby dyeing them. Periodically the direction of flow of dye liquor may be reversed to secure more even dyeing. At the end of the dyeing operation the spent dye liquor can be discharged to waste and the dyed yarn washed with water in the same machine. It is then possible to lift out the frame of dyed yarn and transfer it to a similar closed container so that hot air can be circulated through the yarn until it is dried.

If the above type of dyeing machine is suitably and totally enclosed it is possible to effect the dyeing of the cheeses and cones under high pressure at temperatures up to about 130° C. This high pressure high temperature method of dyeing is very suitable for the dyeing of synthetic fibre yarns such as nylon and Terylene, since for many dyes these fibres have only a small affinity when dyed at temperatures not exceeding 100° C.

By courtesy of The Longclose Engineering Co. Ltd

Dyeing assistants

Various assistants can be added to the dye liquor to make it more effective. For instance, an addition of a wetting agent can be very beneficial since this agent will have the effect of lowering the surface tension of the dye liquor so that the liquor penetrates the textile material more rapidly and more evenly. Such an assistant is especially beneficial when the textile material is not too well prepared for dyeing and tends to be water-repellent.

A dye dispersing or solubilising agent can also be usefully added to the dye liquor since it can break down the dye into smaller particles which more easily remain in suspension in the dye liquor and which become more easily absorbed by the textile material.

Metal sequestering agents

Most dyeing equipment is now made of stainless steel wherever this is possible, since this metal is completely inert to most dye liquors even if they are acid or alkaline. But the water used in preparation of the dye liquor may contain metal impurities, and these often are able to change the dyed shade so that it is slightly different in tone or duller. Because of this and where such trouble may be anticipated a so-called metal sequestering agent is added to the dye liquor, since it can solubilise and combine with the metal in a special way and render it inactive towards the dye although it remains present in its special chelated form in the dye liquor. Sequestering agents are much used when the water is likely to be contaminated with iron or copper.

Dye retarding agents

It is generally desired that the dye shall become absorbed slowly during the early stages of dyeing since it takes a certain amount of time, say 5 to 10 minutes, before all the textile material has come into contact and become saturated with the dye liquor. Thus the first entered portion of the textile material has an extra 5 to 10 minutes in which to absorb dye. So if the dye is of that kind which 'strikes' the textile material immediately it is often advisable to add a dye-restraining agent—such a product has the effect of hindering dye absorption.

Agents to assist dyebath exhaustion

While it may be useful to have present a dye restraining agent in the dyebath at the commencement, it is not desirable for this to be effective towards the end of dyeing when a large proportion of the dye has been absorbed by the textile material. So for assisting dye absorption at the end of the dyeing process there are a number of substances which can be added during that stage and which have the effect of forcing the dye on to the textile material, thus ensuring a good exhaustion of the dyebath. Thus in dyeing cotton with direct cotton dyes common salt can be used at a late stage of dyeing for this particular purpose. In the dyeing of wool with acid wool dyes the addition of sulphuric acid towards the end of the dyeing process will assist to exhaust on to the wool any dye remaining in the dyebath and not likely to become absorbed without such addition.

Softening agents

Dyeing, if carried out under some conditions governed by the substances present in the dye liquor or by the temperature of dyeing, can cause a harshening of the textile material. To prevent this it is possible to add selected types of softening agents which keep the textile fibres soft and supple. If the softening agent also behaves like the dye and becomes absorbed into the fibres then its beneficial effect is so much more desirably permanent.

Dye fixing agents

It is found that the shades produced by some dyes are liable to bleed so that the dye can migrate into adjacent textile goods which may be left lying in contact with the wet dyed material. Substances are available, usually known as dye-fixing auxiliaries, which can either be added to the dye liquor at the end of the dyeing operation and when the dye liquor is exhausted of dye or which can be applied to the dyed material in a fresh bath. These have the effect, probably through their combination with the dye in the dyed fibres, of reducing or eliminating any tendency for the colour to bleed out of the wet dyed goods.

Assisting dye absorption by synthetic fibres

It has been pointed out in describing the dyeing and other properties of the man-made hydrophobic fibres such as nylon and Terylene that these do not so readily absorb dyes as do the hydrophile natural fibres such as cotton and wool. This reluctance to absorb dyes is associated with a close packing of the molecules in

FIG. 51. Showing the dyeing of loose natural or man-made fibres. These fibres are evenly packed into a conical container having a perforated bottom; this is then lowered into a somewhat larger cylindrical dye liquor container in connection with a suitable liquor pump. After closure of the cover of this dye liquor container (it must be strongly bolted down if the dyeing is carried out at high temperatures up to 130° C and under high pressure, as may be necessary in dyeing man-made fibres) the dye liquor is forced upwards through the bottom of the fibre container and thence through the fibres, thus dyeing them; it then emerges from the top of the fibres into the outside liquor. Thus a continuous circulation of the dye liquor can be maintained until the required shade is obtained. Then can follow washing of the dyed fibres with water in the same machine, the lifting out of the fibre container and its unpacking.

By courtesy of The Longclose Engineering Co. Ltd

the fibres. So dyeing can be assisted by conducting the dyeing under conditions such that the fibre structure becomes loosened to a degree which will allow the dye molecules to penetrate the fibres more easily. This can be achieved in two different ways.

In the first, there is added to the dye liquor a substance which has the power of slightly swelling the fibres when employed at a suitable concentration in the dye liquor—some substances of this type can dissolve the synthetic fibres if applied at 100% concentration. Thus lactic acid is a useful fibre swelling agent in the dyeing of ordinary cellulose acetate fibres, while beta-naphthol can swell nylon fibres and make them more receptive towards dyes. In the second method, the conditions of dyeing are made more severe, so that they of themselves produce fibre swelling. For example, most synthetic fibres, and indeed many others, can be induced to absorb dyes more rapidly and to a greater degree by dyeing at temperatures exceeding 100° C. This method of dyeing nylon, Terylene, Dynel, Orlon, etc. is extensively used but it suffers from the disadvantage of requiring special closed dyeing machines capable of withstanding the pressure developed inside them. It is often found that although improved dye absorption can be obtained by using a fibre swelling agent or high temperature + high pressure dyeing conditions, the loosening of the fibre structure which takes place causes the fibres to contract in length at the same time and so may lead to an overall 5% or more area shrinkage in the goods being dyed, and this is a serious matter. The loosening of fibre structure can also be reflected in a loss of tensile strength in the fibres.

Optimum dyeing temperature

It is generally necessary to conduct a dyeing process at a temperature approaching 100° C, although since acetate fibres become delustred in boiling dye liquors it is usual to dye these at a temperature not exceeding 75° to 80° C. The high temperature is required to induce dye absorption to take place at a reasonably high rate and also to ensure that the dye is fixed within the fibres so as to be resistant to removal by washing. But nevertheless it would be extremely convenient if dyeing could be satisfactorily carried out in cold to warm dye liquors. If the fibres are swelled considerably then these conditions of dyeing can be used. For example, acetate fibre goods highly swollen with a strong aqueous ethyl alcohol can be dyed at low temperatures to give fast deep shades. Recently it has been shown that the addition of benzyl alcohol to the dye liquor employed to dye wool with acid wool dyes can allow satisfactory cold dyeing to take place.

Textile auxiliaries

It is thus evident that there are many substances (usually termed *textile auxiliaries*) which can be used to assist dyeing operations and particularly to induce the textile material to absorb dye more freely and uniformly and also to protect the fibres from adverse changes. Actually it may be said that at the present time the importance of the dyes is nearly matched by that of the auxiliaries which are used to assist dye application.

In using these dye assistants some consideration has to be given to the possibility that while they may aid one feature of the dyeing process, say dye absorption, they may be detrimental in another direction, say in causing the resulting shade to have reduced fastness. It is a fact that many very useful dyeing assistants cannot be used commercially because they do lower the fastness of the dyeings to light and to washing. Those assistants which become absorbed into the fibres at the same time as the dyes and which cannot be completely removed by after-washing are especially dangerous to employ.

Printing

PRINTING TECHNIQUES

The printing of coloured patterns on textile fabrics (yarns are seldom printed) involves the use of the same dyes as are employed in dyeing and must necessarily employ much the same conditions of dye fixation as are demanded by the different types of dyes used. Printing also uses much equipment which is employed in dyeing and related operations. But it is in the method of applying the dyes to the fabric that printing differs essentially from dyeing, for in printing the dyes according to a pattern upon fabric use is made of a roller printing machine or a screen printing apparatus, neither of which is to be found in an ordinary dyehouse. So attention will first be given to these two radically different printing devices.

ROLLER PRINTING AND THE ROLLER PRINTING MACHINE

Roller printing is the most convenient and satisfactory method for printing long 'runs' of a multi-coloured pattern on fabric, and the machine now in almost universal use was invented about 1783 by a Scotsman, James Bell. A typical fourteen-colour printing machine is shown in Fig. 52 and its essential constructional and

FIG. 52. A fourteen-colour roller printing machine. The fabric being printed is carried around the central large diameter pressure bowl *A* while the fourteen separate colour printing rollers *R* each impress upon it their particular coloured portion of the pattern. It is important before printing commences to ensure that the printing rollers are in register, that is they each impress their part of the pattern in the right places on the fabric and thus avoid an overlapping of the differently coloured parts. This 'register' is obtained by means of a special device provided for this purpose.

By courtesy of Mather & Platt Ltd

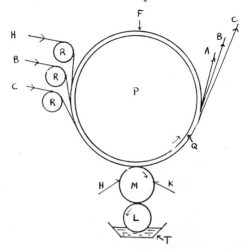

F I G . 53. Showing the essential features of a roller printing machine for printing coloured patterns on woven fabric. It is to be noted that the central pressure bowl *P* around which the fabric *C* being printed is carried is not positively driven but is caused to rotate by reason that the printing rollers (in this case only one, *M*, is shown) rotate (positively driven) and press against it. The process is described in more detail below.

operational features can most conveniently be described by reference to Fig. 53, which represents a roller printing machine for printing a one-colour pattern.

The machine is seen to comprise a central pressure cylinder *P* which is free to rotate on a horizontal axis and whose surface is covered with several layers of fabric *F* to give the cylinder surface a suitable and necessary degree of resilience. Passing around this pressure cylinder and pressing against its surface is a thick blanket *A* which is endless, a so-called 'back-grey' (unbleached calico) *B*, and the cotton fabric *C* which is being printed. These three fabrics move around together when printing is being carried out, being guided by rollers *R*.

Pressing against the pressure cylinder *P* is a much smaller printing roller *M* which is engraved with the pattern to be printed, and colour paste is conveyed to this roller by the colour furnishing roller *L* which is partly submerged in the trough *T* filled with colour paste. The printing roller *M* is positively driven and it causes the colour furnishing roller *L* to rotate also by frictional contact with it. Two razor-sharp so-called 'doctor blades' *H* and *K* press evenly against printing roller *M* and the function of one doctor blade *H* is to scrape off excess colour paste to leave only the engraved pattern filled with the paste while the function of the other doctor blade *K* is to scrape off from the printing roller bits of fibre or lint picked up by it from the fabric being printed. The pressure of rotating printing roller *M* (positively driven) against the central pressure cylinder *P* causes this latter to rotate and at the same time the printing roller transfers the colour paste from its engraved pattern to the fabric *C* being printed. It is, of course, important that there should be no slip between the printing roller and the printed fabric surfaces.

The function of the back-grey fabric *B* is to prevent colour paste from marking off on to the thick endless blanket *A* underneath it, since it is easier to remove the back-grey for washing and re-use than it is to remove and clean the endless blanket.

Multi-colour printing

The machine described above is capable of printing only one colour—the colour paste in the trough *T*. The use of several colours requires a printing roller together with a colour furnishing roller and colour paste trough for each separate colour to be printed. Thus there may be several of these printing roller units suitably arranged around the central pressure cylinder, each contributing to rotate this cylinder and each printing roller carrying the engraved parts of the pattern which are required to have the same colour. Thus an eight-colour pattern will require eight printing roller units while a fourteen-colour pattern will have fourteen printing roller units. Before printing commences it is necessary to check that all the printing rollers register so that they each contribute their part of the coloured pattern on the appropriate parts of the fabric as it passes steadily around the central pressure roller. Special devices are provided with each printing roller to allow this register to be accurately secured.

THE PRINTING OPERATION

When all adjustments have been made printing begins with all the printing rollers steadily rotating and continuously furnished with colour paste and pressing against the cotton fabric (cushioned by the back-grey and endless thick blanket underneath), which now

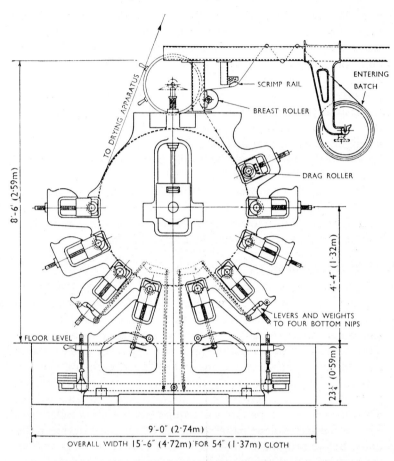

FIG. 54. Showing the arrangement of the printing rollers around the central pressure bowl of an eight-colour roller printing machine.

By courtesy of Mather & Platt Ltd

moves forward with the central pressure roller caused to rotate by the rotating printing rollers. As the fabric moves round with the central pressure roller it receives an impression of colour paste from each printing roller in turn, so that when it leaves the last printing roller to pass away from the printing machine it has received colour paste impressions which complete the printed pattern. So the printing continues at a steady rate with the attendant

Fig. 55. Showing a fabric being printed in a multi-colour roller printing machine (some of the printing rollers with their colour troughs and colour furnishing rollers have been withdrawn in order better to show the printing operation). The printing operator is shown adding printing paste to the colour trough so that it may be picked up by the colour furnishing roller rotating in it half submerged, and so transfer it to the upper printing roller (engraved with the pattern) to be impressed on the fabric which moves continuously around the large diameter centre pressure bowl.

By courtesy of The Cotton Board (Manchester)

operative constantly watching to see that the troughs are kept supplied with colour paste and that the portions of the pattern contributed by each printing roller register exactly to give a clear, well-defined coloured pattern free from smears and streaks.

Steaming after printing

Meanwhile the printed fabric is required to be run through a closed chamber where it is steamed in open width for about 5 to 10 minutes and sometimes, according to the dyes applied, for up to one hour. This steaming is necessary to fix the dye so that the coloured fabric will be fast to washing; it can also assist other reactions in the fabric necessary to dye fixation as will be shortly referred to in connection with reserve and discharge printing processes. Within the steaming chamber the fabric may pass over a number of rollers (an upper and a lower row) to utilise most economically the capacity of the chamber; alternatively the fabric can move forward through the chamber in the form of long vertical loops hanging from overhead horizontal rods, which move slowly forward to the point where the fabric leaves the chamber when they return to the fabric entry end to again pick up incoming fabric.

From the steaming chamber the fabric is then led through washing and soaping machines to remove all unwanted residual chemicals and loosely adhering dye so that the fabric can then be dried to be ready for finishing.

Preparing the fabric surface for printing

It should be mentioned that the cotton or other fabric printed should before printing have its surface prepared by a light brushing, followed by passage through a shearing machine to shear off protruding fibre ends close to the fabric surface. With the surface thus made uniformly smooth and free from motes and hairiness it becomes possible to print colour patterns with the maximum degree of clarity.

DISCHARGE AND RESIST PRINTING METHODS

It will be recognised that the above described method of printing only allows coloured patterns to be printed on white fabrics, that is, the production of a coloured pattern on a white ground. Yet it is desirable to be able to print a white or a coloured pattern on a

FIG. 56. A continuous festoon steamer as used for fixing the coloured pattern printed on cotton and other fabrics—without such steaming the printed colours may not be properly developed and may lack fastness to light and washing. The machine consists essentially of a large chamber capable of holding up to 1,000 yards of printed fabric suspended in festoon form with the folds well separated so as not to touch each other and cause colour marking-off. The suspension is from horizontal poles held at their ends on endless chains one at each side of the chamber. In operation the chains move steadily forward, carrying with them the poles and the fabric from one end of the chamber to the other. Automatic devices form the festoons over the poles at the entry end and at the other end they assist the passing of the fabric from the poles and out of the chamber. After the fabric has left the poles these continue their travel to the entry end of the chamber where they again come into use for suspending the fresh fabric in festoon form. While travelling through the chamber and carrying fabric the poles steadily rotate so that no part of the fabric remains for long resting on the pole—this might cause irregular development of the colours. Arrangements are provided to maintain the air suitably humid within the chamber and also at a suitable high temperature (usually at 100° C or slightly higher) according to the dyes present in the fabric. Such conditions are produced by the use of steam, and it is the aim of the designers of these steamers that they operate with the minimum consumption of steam. It is possible to run from one to four pieces of printed fabric through the steamer simultaneously if suitable precautions are taken to avoid marking-off of the colours from one fabric to another. With steam in the chamber it is important to avoid drops of condensed water falling on the fabric.

By courtesy of Messrs Mather & Platt Ltd

coloured ground. To achieve these results it is necessary to make use of so-called *discharge* and *resist* (or *reserve*) methods of printing which will now be described.

A *discharge* method of printing depends on the use of substances which under appropriate conditions (usually steaming) are able to destroy or *discharge* colour-dyed fabric to white. A *resist* printing process involves the use of substances which when present in a fabric *resist* absorption of the dyes applied.

Underlying principles

If it is required to produce a fabric having white spots or other pattern on a coloured ground (fabric) then either discharge or resist printing methods may be used. In *discharge* printing the fabric will be dyed all over to, say, a red shade and it will then be spot pattern printed with a paste containing a reducing or oxidising agent (the discharge agent) which is able to destroy the colour of the red dye. Following a steaming to assist the action of the discharge agent the fabric is washed to remove residual chemicals and the decomposition products of the red dye so that the spots will now be white. In *resist* printing the fabric will be spot pattern printed with a resist or reserve agent (this may be an alkali or acid or a reducing or oxidising agent or perhaps simply a metal salt, according to the nature of the red dye subsequently to be applied). Then the fabric is impregnated overall with a solution of the red dye and is then dried and steamed. Wherever the resist agent is present the absorption of the red dye is prevented so that after washing the steamed fabric there will be left the white spot pattern on a red ground like that obtained by the discharge method described above.

Coloured discharge and resist printing method

Some discharge agents are able to destroy some dyes but not others and the use of these agents makes possible colour discharge printing. For example, in obtaining the white spot pattern as described above by a discharge printing method it would be possible to add to the discharge printing paste a suitable amount of say a yellow dye resistant to the destructive action of the particular discharge agent present. Then on printing, steaming, and washing the fabric left would have a yellow spot pattern on a red ground—the result of the fact that the discharge agent employed had the power to destroy the red but not the yellow dye.

In much the same way it is possible to devise a colour resist printing process. For this the fabric would be printed with a resist paste containing a yellow dye whose absorption into the fabric would not be affected by the resist agent, while this same agent would resist absorption of the red dye.

By such methods it is possible to print white and multi-coloured patterns on coloured grounds making use of the appropriate dyes and resist or discharge agents and the conditions necessary to their chemical reactivity. It is seen that such patterns are in general produced by (1) printing a simple coloured pattern on a white fabric, (2) printing a white or a coloured pattern on a coloured fabric using a non-coloured or a coloured resist or discharge paste. Much skill is shown by the printer in the manner by which he obtains the coloured patterns, making use of the various types of dyes and resist and discharge agents at his disposal.

SCREEN PRINTING

It is found that a considerable proportion of the costs of roller machine printing arise from the high cost of preparing engraved copper printing rollers and the storage of these for future use, so that these costs can become almost prohibitive if the pattern is used for only a short run of fabric. To justify the cost of preparing the necessary printing rollers and the setting-up of the printing machine it requires that many thousands of yards of fabric be printed to the one pattern. Yet it is today more difficult than ever to secure such large orders for a single pattern. To overcome this difficulty recourse has during recent years been made to an alternative method of textile printing which is generally known as screen printing and which is a kind of improved stencil printing. In this case the stencils used consist of frames across which is stretched a fine mesh wire or silk material carrying the pattern. Such stencils are easier and cheaper to prepare than engraved copper printing rollers, it merely being necessary to fill up all holes in the mesh fabric of each screen except those which together form an area corresponding to all those parts of the pattern having the same colour. To achieve this, one method is to fill the whole of the mesh fabric with a special thick gum composition, covering with the selected part of the pattern, exposing to light, which has the effect of making the illuminated gum composition insoluble in water, and then

o

washing so that only the gum composition which was not illuminated under the superimposed pattern is washed out, to leave an open mesh through which colour paste can be forced as required.

Screen printing operations

For the screen printing operation it is usual to have long narrow tables on which the fabric to be printed is spread. An operative then lays a screen over the fabric at one end, brushes the colour paste through it, moves the screen to the next repeat of the pattern and again brushes colour paste through it, thus continuing along the full length of the fabric. Meanwhile another operative follows up with a second screen and at each repeat brushes the second colour paste through the screen to print the second coloured portion of the pattern. This method of printing is continued until all the coloured parts of the pattern have been stencil printed and the printing operation is complete. The fabric is then steamed within a small steaming chamber to fix the applied dyes, and is finally washed and dried.

Nowadays this method of screen printing has become at least partly mechanised, particularly in respect of those operations where the screens are moved over the fabric to suit the repeating of the pattern and where the colour paste is brushed through the screen.

It is generally acknowledged that screen printing can give as satisfactory multi-colour pattern fabric as can a roller printing machine. The choice of method of printing is thus mainly decided by economic factors, such as initial outlay in plant and the average length of fabric to be printed with each pattern.

COLOUR PRINTING PASTES

The composition and properties of the printing paste, whether it be used in roller or screen printing, can largely determine whether or not the printed fabric is satisfactory in respect of freedom from colour smears and streaks and clearness of pattern outline. An essential feature of the colour paste is its smooth consistency and its suitable viscosity, for on these properties mainly depends how satisfactorily it can fill up the engraved pattern on a printing roller or pass through the mesh of the printing screen, and also how it will be deposited on the fabric and allow transference to the fabric during steaming of the highest proportion of the dyes applied.

Preparation of printing pastes

Practically all colour printing pastes contain in addition to the dyes and resist or discharge agents a suitable thickening agent (say a gum, alginate, starch, dextrin, etc.) in proportions which will give the paste a desired viscosity. In addition, substances may be added to disperse the dyes more completely and so aid their transference to the fabric during the steaming stage, while other substances may be present to swell the fibres and make them more ready to accept and absorb the dyes applied to them from the printing pastes. There may also be present wetting agents, foam repressing substances, and substances which can sequester metal salt impurities which could dull or otherwise harm the colours of the pattern. Often, humectants or hygroscopic substances such as glycerine are added to prevent a drying out of the printed patterns on the fabric.

WOOL PRINTING

Wool fabrics are not so much or easily printed as cotton fabrics since wool absorbs dye only slowly. When wool is to be printed it is customary to chlorinate it to a suitable degree by treatment with a hypochlorite solution—this increases considerably the affinity of wool for dyes.

Questions for Chapter IV

1. State the essential reasons why fabrics and garments as they leave the loom or knitting machine have to be dyed and finished.
2. What impurities, natural and additional, can be expected to be present in woven and knitted cotton and wool materials?
3. Describe methods for bleaching based on the use of sodium hypochlorite and hydrogen peroxide. Which of these is unsuitable for wool and polyamide fibres?
4. What is 'kiering' and in what kind of apparatus is it carried out?
5. Describe a simple process for bleaching wool with hydrogen peroxide, stating how you would prepare the bleaching liquor. What would you do if you wished to use the liquor again for further bleaching?

6. How can solvent extraction aid the subsequent bleaching of cotton materials? What organic solvents would you use and why?

7. In bleaching cotton with hypochlorite bleach liquors it is possible to overbleach and impoverish the fibres. How would you detect and measure such overbleaching?

8. What is the purpose of singeing cotton and other fabrics? Describe the essential features of this operation.

9. If it is undesirable to kier mixture fabrics containing both cotton and viscose or acetate rayon, how would you remove from them starch impurities to make them suitable for subsequent dyeing?

10. What difficulties are encountered in bleaching synthetic fibre goods?

11. What is an optical bleaching agent (often termed a fluorescent whitening agent)? What advantages and disadvantages has it over a hypochlorite or hydrogen peroxide?

12. How were coal tar dyes first discovered and by whom? Why were they called coal tar dyes?

13. Who was Peter Griess and how did he make an important contribution to the manufacture of coal tar dyes?

14. Classify the various types of dyes now available in respect of their chemical nature and their applicability to different textile fibres.

15. Compare acid wool dyes with direct cotton dyes in respect of their applicability to cellulose and protein fibres. Describe a typical example of their application to textile materials.

16. What is a vat dye and how is it applied to cotton fabric? How have some vat dyes been converted into water-soluble forms and how are these applied?

17. Although basic dyes have no affinity for cotton they can be used for dyeing this fibre. How is this done?

18. Name those types of dyes by which really fast to light and washing colours can be obtained on cellulose fibre materials.

19. What are reactive dyes? Indicate their importance and describe how they can be applied to cotton materials to yield very fast-to-washing colours.

20. What are cationic (basic) dyes? How are they applied to acrylic fibres? What difference in fastness to light is found between the colours they give on cotton and on acrylic fibres?

21. Sulphur dyes are somewhat similar in properties to vat dyes. Show how this is so by reference to their application to cotton fabric and at the same time point out some differences.

22. State the nature and uses of disperse dyes.

23. What are insoluble azoic dyes? How are they applied to cotton materials and also to acetate rayon? Discuss the different methods of application generally used for these two types of fibre.

24. Describe the dyeing of cotton fabric with Aniline Black and discuss the fastness properties of the resulting dyed cotton. What other base or amine is now used largely instead of aniline and why?

25. Describe the dyeing of wool with chrome mordant dyes and refer to the three main methods used.

26. Describe the nature of pre-metallised dyes as now most widely used and indicate the way in which they differ from earlier types.

27. State the principles underlying the application of pigment dyes to cellulose fibre fabrics and indicate some important advantages of this method of colouring while pointing out possible defects.

28. Compare dyeing methods which depend on the use of a jigger or a winch-dyeing machine. Indicate how your choice of one or other of these methods would depend on the type of fabric being dyed.

29. Describe the general principles on which the dyeing of fabrics is based.

30. How can the absorption of dye by a textile material from a dye liquor be beneficially aided by the presence in the dye liquor of one or more dyeing assistants? Give examples.

31. In selecting a new dyeing assistant what essential tests would you apply to it to decide whether it would give satisfactory results?

32. State the essential differences between dyeing and printing techniques. Describe the principles of textile printing and also describe the essential parts of a multi-colour roller printing machine.

33. Describe how screen printing is carried out, indicating how it differs from the roller printing method referred to in the previous question. What principal advantage is obtained from screen printing?

34. Describe the essential difference between the use of discharge and resist printing processes for obtaining multi-coloured prints on coloured grounds.

35. What is comprised in a 'printing roller assembly' as used in a roller printing machine?

36. Why is it generally necessary for printed fabric to be steamed after printing with a coloured printing paste? Describe types of steaming apparatus used.

37. Why is it more difficult to print wool fabrics than those of cotton and viscose rayon? How is it possible to assist the absorption of dye by acetate fabrics in printing processes?

38. Describe how an engraved type of printing roller is made. What is a doctor blade and for what purpose is it employed in a printing machine?

39. Why are printing pastes thickened and what types of substance are used for this purpose? Name some thickening agents.

40. Give reasons for the greater difficulty encountered in printing fabrics made of synthetic fibres rather than cotton.

41. How would you prepare wool fabric for printing?

42. Indicate how fibre-swelling agents can assist dye absorption in dyeing and printing.

43. What are dye-carriers and how can they assist dyers of synthetic fibre materials? What special dyeing conditions can make dye-carriers less necessary?

CHAPTER V

Processing, continued—Finishing

In the various processes of bleaching, dyeing, and printing, textile materials become distorted so that they are stretched in length or width and are out of shape, their surface may be rough and their handle harsh instead of being smooth and soft, and in general they are in a state unacceptable and unattractive to those who will use or wear them. At the same time, it may also be required to give them special characteristics which they do not normally possess; for example, it may be required to give them added resistance to creasing or to shrinkage, or a high lustre, or perhaps water repellency to make them suitable for the manufacture of raincoats. All this treatment comes within the scope of textile finishing and this normally leaves the textile material in a state ready for packaging for despatch to its owner or user.

For the purpose of describing here the main operations involved in textile finishing, attention will first be given to processes which are essentially applied to all types of materials to bring them into an acceptable and presentable condition—these processes are concerned with fabric straightening, shrinking, or stretching to specified dimensions, and appearance. Then will follow an account of special finishing processes which have been developed in recent years to confer special characteristics on textile materials, mainly fabrics, which add to their attractiveness or usefulness.

Standard Finishing Operations

DRYING OF WET YARNS AND FABRICS

Bleached and dyed textile materials leaving the dyehouse have usually to be dried after first having removed from them excess of the water they contain. This removal of excess water is important from the viewpoint of making the drying operation more economical.

For water removal it is convenient to use mangles, hydro-extractors, and suction machines, and the choice is governed largely by the nature of the fabric—whether or not it will pass through the machine without risk of damage. Mangling is most rapid and efficient, while those machines in which the fabric is drawn over a slot in connection with an exhaust pump are slow and least efficient, though very useful for fabrics which could become damaged if other methods were used.

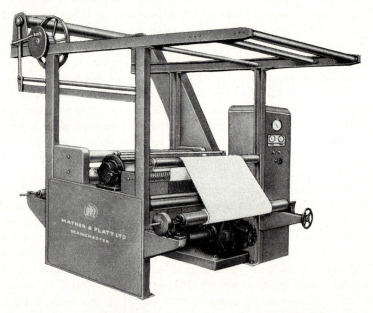

FIG. 57. A machine for removing excess of liquor from a wet fabric by suction instead of by mangling or hydroextraction. The fabric is drawn over a slotted tube connected to a vacuum pump. Under such conditions water is sucked out of the fabric to be expelled by the pump to waste. This method for removing excess liquor from a fabric is somewhat slower than is possible by the other methods mentioned above but is less damaging to fragile fabrics and does not introduce creases as is possible when using a hydroextractor.

By courtesy of Mather & Platt Ltd

Yarn drying

Yarns will be most probably in the form of skeins, and the modern method for drying these is to run them through a tunnel dryer through which hot air is circulated. In their passage through such a chamber or tunnel the skeins are freely suspended from horizontal rods whose ends are carried by endless chains which are continuously moving forward to the delivery end, when they return to pick up fresh skeins.

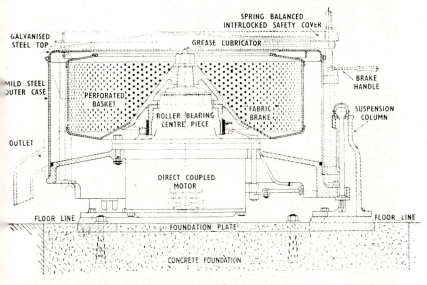

FIG. 58. Showing the construction of a typical hydroextractor. The inner perforated basket for holding the wet textile material is electrically driven from underneath. The liquor is thrown out from the fabric through the basket perforations (the basket is rotated at up to 1,000 revolutions per minute), is collected within the outer casing and then runs to waste via the outlet provided. The whole machine is suspended from three cast-iron columns located on a heavy cast-iron bed plate so as to eliminate vibration to the foundation which is liable to occur during running.

By courtesy of Thomas Broadbent & Sons Ltd

Fabric drying

Woven fabric is dried most easily by passage in open width over a number of rotating large diameter drums or cylinders closely spaced, with each drum internally heated by steam or hot oil—about twenty drums comprise a typical *drying cylinder* unit of this type. However, if it is desired at the time of drying to bring the fabric to specified length and width dimensions and to straighten the weft threads, then use is made of a *hot air stenter*.

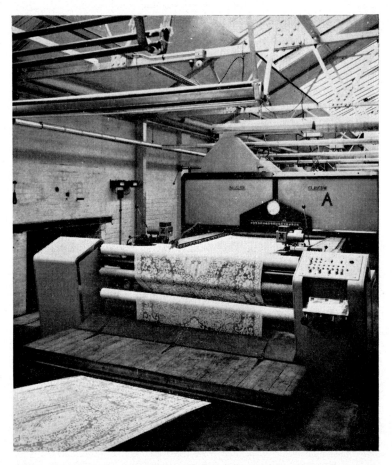

FIG. 59. A Dart drying and heat-setting stenter for woven and knitted fabrics with automatic devices whereby the fabric fed into the machine is centred relative to the combined pin-clip chains and also has any curl in its selvedges removed before these selvedges are gripped by the clips or impaled on the pins. The fabric can be fed into the machine at any controlled rate which may be faster than the forward rate of travel of the pin-clip chains so that in the drying the fabric is closed up lengthwise to a degree such that it will not shrink in washing.

As soon as the fabric is held by its selvedges by the pins or clips it is gradually brought out to the desired width as a result of the chains suitably diverging. Thereafter the chains run parallel to each other and through a chamber *A* in which hot air is directed on the fabric to dry it and set it at the desired width. Finally the fabric passes through a cooling section and is then led off from the stenter. Such a machine has press-button control throughout.

By courtesy of John Dalglish & Sons Ltd

This consists essentially of two endless chains which move forward continuously spaced apart at fabric width and which carry closely spaced pin plates or clips for gripping securely one or other of the fabric selvedges. Such a stenter machine is about 80 feet or more in length and the pin or clip chains over the greater part of their travel run through a heat-insulated chamber or housing within which is circulated hot air. Fabric is fed in horizontally in open width at one end where one selvedge is gripped or pinned securely by the clips or pins on one moving chain and likewise the other selvedge by the other moving pin clip chain. Various devices are provided to ensure that the fabric is advanced to be gripped by the chains at a rate which will ensure that it will be stretched lengthwise or closed up to dry to the specified length dimensions.

The fabric is thus carried forward to the delivery end through the hot air chamber. As it moves forward arrangements are provided so that the chains can be caused to diverge for a suitable distance to stretch the fabric to any desired width. With the chains now parallel to each other the fabric will continue to be carried forward and at the same time it will be dried so that at the delivery end it will be dry and have the specified length and width dimensions.

Drying of circular knitted fabrics

If the fabric is of the knitted tubular type it can be dried without being set to any particular dimensions by running it through a hot air drying machine, comprising a large closed chamber to contain the circulating hot air and also a continuously moving brattice on which the fabric in its tubular form, fed in at one end, is carried backwards and forwards at increasing higher levels through the chamber, to emerge at the far end completely dried. In another type of drying machine the fabric, while moving forward, has hot air blown into it—this hot air fully distends the tubular fabric into cylindrical form and in passing out of it through the interstices dries the fabric. At the remote end of the machine the dry fabric passes over a floating internal expanding device immediately in front of a two-bowl mangle or calender so that its width (controlled by the stretcher) is set and the fabric is at once wound on a small roller, thus having been in the one run dried and set to the specified dimensions.

Fig. 60. Machine for drying dyed knitted fabric *F* in tubular form. The wet fabric contained in the tub *A* is drawn upwards to pass through a chamber *B* and thence between a pair of small rollers to be finally 'plaited' (folded) down on a floor platform *C*. Hot air is blown into chamber *B* to pass inside the fabric and move downward within the fabric, thereby extending it as far as the tub *A* and passing out—this movement of hot air into and out of the fabric dries it free from creases.

By courtesy of Samuel Pegg & Son Ltd

Drying of flat knitted fabric

A considerable amount of flat knitted fabric (that is, not tubular but of open width similar to a woven fabric) is first converted temporarily into tubular form before dyeing by sewing together its selvedges. Fabric in this form is most convenient for dyeing since the selvedges cannot then roll in and thus dye unevenly. This may be dried in the tubular dryer as described above, or it can have the sewing threads drawn out of the sewn selvedges to restore it to its open width state and then be dried on a hot air stenter having special devices for uncurling the rolled-up selvedges as the fabric becomes impaled on the pin plates. The stenter will also have devices for centralising the fabric as it goes into the stenter and for overfeeding the fabric into the stenter to ensure that the resulting dry fabric which emerges at the far end is free from stretch and is closed up in length to enable it to satisfy the specified length and width dimensions.

Loose knitted garments and cotton and wool and rayon hose and half hose are usually dried on a brattice machine as described above while being carried forward lying on the continuously moving brattice and exposed to circulating hot air.

SOFTENING OF FABRICS

It may be thought necessary to introduce a softening agent into the textile material before drying, and in this case the material will be treated with an aqueous solution of the agent and then have to be mangled or hydroextracted to remove excess of the liquor.

Woven fabrics made of cotton or rayon often leave the drying machine somewhat firm in handle even if containing a softening agent. This firmness arises from fibre rigidity and can be removed to leave the fabric soft by running it over and under a number of small diameter rollers covered with large-headed brass studs which temporarily slightly deform the fabric all over as it passes over them. Sometimes passage between a pair of soft rubber rollers pressing upon each other is able to achieve the same softening.

DECATISING

In the finishing of wool fabrics and garments use is made of the highly plastic properties of this fibre as developed in conditions of high temperature and moisture. Thus fabric can be given a smooth soft lustrous handle by batching it on a perforated cylinder within a decatising machine and then blowing steam through it. The effect of the hot moist fabric layers pressing upon each other in the batch gives the desirable finish just mentioned. A similar finish can be obtained using a machine in which the fabric moves intermittently between hot flat plates under hydraulic pressure.

FIG. 61. A machine for decatising wool fabrics; this has more recently been found useful also for the finishing of cotton, rayon, and other fabrics. It allows the fabric to have steam blown through it while wound around a perforated hollow roller, and this gives a smooth, lustrous, soft-handling character to the fabric while stabilising it dimensionally.

By courtesy of James Bailey (Engineers) Ltd

HOT PRESSING AND SHAPING

Tubular knitted wool fabric which is later to be cut up and made into men's and ladies' vests is first suitably damped and is then drawn over flat wood or metal shapes and pressed in a hot press to set it into a smooth lustrous-surfaced fabric having a much improved handle and appearance. Men's wool socks can be similarly set to shape and given a soft lustrous appeal by pressing on shapes in a so-called two- or three-bed steam press.

Finishing of ladies' hose

Ladies' hose (stockings) are now dried and finished to shape and size by means of continuous finishing machines. These consist essentially of metal shapes attached vertically to a chain which continuously moves around a closed circuit comprising sections where the hose receive special treatments. Thus at the entry end an operative draws a stocking over each shape as it arrives at this point. The shape moving forward then passes through a section where the stocking is damped or wetted, lightly rolled on the shape to stretch it suitably in length down the shape. Thereafter the shape with its damp stocking drawn evenly over it passes through a drying chamber in which hot air circulates and leaves the stocking dry and hot. It is then led through a cooling and conditioning chamber just before it arrives near to where it started. The stocking, now set to shape and dry and cool, is stripped off the shape to be ready for pairing, examining, and packing while the shape moves forward to have another stocking drawn over it and repeat its travel circuit.

Fig. 62. Machine for finishing (setting to shape and hot pressing) men's socks. The operative on the right draws each sock over a vertical 'shape' so that with other similar 'shapes' attached to an endless continuously moving chain it moves round a closed circuit comprising a section where the shapes pass between pairs of vertical steam-heated plates to be pressed, and then through a cooling and conditioning chamber so that they return to the operative on the left. He takes the socks off the 'shapes' which then move to repeat their circuit with fresh socks drawn over them. The socks are slightly damp when drawn over the 'shapes' since moisture assists their setting to shape.

By courtesy of Samuel Pegg & Son Ltd

FIG. 63. Machine for pre- or post-boarding (setting to shape so as to resist shrinkage and distortion in washing) nylon stockings. The stockings are drawn over metal 'shapes' vertically closely spaced. These 'shapes' then automatically move to a central position when a cylindrical cover descends to enclose them. They are then exposed to a moist heat of about 250° F (121° C) for about three minutes. The cover then rises and the 'shapes' move to one side of the machine, where the stockings are removed while another batch of 'shapes' with stockings drawn on them move to the central position and are similarly heat treated. The effect of the moist high temperature treatment permanently fixes the shape given to the stockings by the metal 'shapes' on which they are drawn.

By courtesy of Samuel Pegg & Son Ltd

TREATMENT OF SURFACES

Brushing and raising—pile surfaces

Some fabrics are required to have a soft, hairy or so-called 'raised' or pile surface. This is achieved by running the fabric in open width through a raising machine, where it is brought in contact with rapidly rotating rollers covered with fine wire points (similar to those used in the carding machines earlier described) or with coarse carborundum. Thus a high pile or short pile can be formed on the fabric surface. Considerable care is required in controlling the passage of the fabric through such a machine, since any irregular or uneven presentation of the fabric to the rotating brushing rollers can easily and at once produce a thin place or hole in the fabric. Both woven and knitted fabrics are given this special finish—for example, wool blankets, woven cotton sheets, and knitted woollen gloves.

Shearing

By contrast the fabric may be required to have an exceedingly sheer surface with a minimum of protruding fibre ends. In this case the fabric will have to be run through a shearing machine which essentially contains one or more rotating cutting or shearing rollers somewhat similar to the grass-cutting roller of an ordinary lawn mower. Wool fabrics required to have a worsted finish are treated in this way.

Beetling of linen fabrics

Linen fabrics are frequently required to have a lustrous thready appearance and this can be produced by a so-called beetling machine. For this treatment several lengths of linen fabric are wound in open width on a strong roller of reasonably large diameter so as to build up evenly a few inches thickness of fabric layers. This roller is positioned horizontally in the machine so that over it is a row of closely spaced wooden fallers extending the full length of the roll of fabric and normally a few inches above the fabric roll. Arrangements are provided so that while the roll of fabric is slowly rotating each somewhat heavy wood faller is in turn lifted a few inches and then allowed to fall freely on the fabric below, the force of the blow being proportional to the weight of the faller and the distance through which it drops to

P

strike the fabric. All the fallers lift and drop in rapid succession and this treatment is continued until the fabric surface has acquired the texture and appearance desired. It is necessary half-way through the treatment to re-roll the linen fabric so that the inside end becomes the outside end and vice versa—the treatment of the fabric is thus made more uniform. There are two main types of beetling machine. In one, wooden fallers which drop by gravity are used, while in the other the fallers operate by spring pressure. In such a machine the fabric may be struck 300 to 400 blows per minute but the force is adjusted so as not to damage the fabric in any way.

Special Finishing Operations

As mentioned earlier a number of special finishes have in recent years been devised which usually call for special equipment and chemicals and are based on new techniques for modifying fibre properties. They have much scientific interest apart from their commercial value in enabling textile materials to be produced having especially useful or attractive features. It is now proposed to describe the principal features of the more important of these newer finishing treatments.

CREASE-RESIST FINISHES

Cotton, viscose rayon, linen, and most cellulose fibre fabrics become creased much more easily than do wool fabrics, and even if the latter do acquire creases they gradually lose them within a few hours if allowed to be relaxed. This crease-resistance of wool is a very valuable property and has naturally induced finishers to seek a method for making cellulose fibre fabrics equally crease-resistant. Success was first obtained about 1930 when Messrs Tootal Broadhurst Lee Co. Ltd of Manchester introduced their crease-resist finishing process based on forming a colourless synthetic resin (particularly that which results from combination of formaldehyde with urea in the presence of an acid catalyst and at a high temperature of about 130° to 160° C) within the fibres of the cellulose fibre fabric. Such a finish has not yet been found advantageous to apply to wool.

Experience with this process has led to its world-wide use and to appreciation of the important fact that the resin must ultimately be left within and not upon the fibres—outside resin merely confers stiffness and increased susceptibility to creasing. At the time it was found especially convenient and satisfactory to apply the process for making fabrics made of spun viscose rayon crease-resistant, since the 10 to 15% of urea–formaldehyde resin left in the rayon fabric also gave it a more substantial handle and appearance. The resin finish would have assisted the sale of spun rayon fabrics quite apart from the valuable crease-resistance simultaneously obtained.

Conditions for securing satisfactory crease-resistance

The combination of urea with formaldehyde in aqueous solution takes place progressively, with the resin molecules becoming larger and larger. In the early stages of combination the resin molecules are water-soluble, and if such a solution is applied to cotton or viscose rayon they are sufficiently small to pass into the interior of each fibre, where they may be further polymerised into very large complex water-insoluble molecules which then resist removal by simple washing. Thus to meet the requirement that the fully formed resin must be within and not upon the fibres the expedient must be adopted of allowing the urea–formaldehyde polymerisation to go as far as the first stage with formation of the relatively small water-soluble resin molecules; the textile material is then impregnated with such a solution and dried at a moderate temperature so as not to induce too much further polymerisation, and then the fabric is heated to about 150° C for a few minutes (the duration of the heating is governed by the temperature of heating) to promote full polymerisation of the resin within the fibres. Following a wash to remove any loosely adhering resin the fabric is dried and is then found to be satisfactorily crease-resistant if the amount of resin left within it is 10 to 15%. It is by such treatment that huge amounts of cotton and rayon fabric are today being made crease-resistant.

Crease-resistant linen

Since the introduction of the Tootal process much research has resulted in the discovery of new knowledge and several innovations. It was soon found that the related melamine–formaldehyde resin could be used instead of the original urea–formaldehyde resin.

FIG. 64. A three-bowl heavy-duty pneumatic padding mangle which is used for impregnating fabrics woven with dye and finishing liquors of various kinds (they may contain starches, resins, dyes, filling agents, etc.). It is much used for impregnating cotton and rayon fabrics with the resins employed to give such fabrics crease- and shrink-resistance and wash-and-wear characteristics. In such padding operations the fabric is led in open width through the lower trough containing the liquor and then between the lower and middle bowls of the mangle to pass again through the liquor and receive a final squeeze while passing between the middle and upper bowls of the mangle. It is important that by pneumatic devices the pressure upon the fabric can be kept uniform and thus ensure an even impregnation of the fabric with the liquor.

By courtesy of Mather & Platt Ltd

Then the process was found to be ineffective with linen materials until it was discovered that the resin-impregnated fabric must be mercerised under conditions which allow the fabric to shrink. At first cotton fabrics made crease-resistant as for viscose rayon fabrics suffered a considerable reduction in their resistance to wear (by abrasion) but this difficulty has been partly overcome by curing (polymerising) the resin in the fabric under more humid conditions.

Chlorine retention by crease-resistant fabrics

American experience with crease-resist fabrics soon showed that the whitening of such materials with hypochlorite in laundering resulted in a strong retention by the resin of active chlorine so that the fabric yellowed and when afterwards hot ironed or exposed to hot humid conditions it became much weakened. This undesirable chlorine retention led to much trouble and it was found to be peculiar to fabrics finished with nitrogen-containing resins (for example, those made from urea and melamine). Hence the introduction of new methods using non-nitrogeneous resins. This has solved the chlorine-retention problem but from the viewpoint of cheapness the urea– and melamine–formaldehyde resins are superior to most of the new ones.

Wear and strength losses caused by crease-resist finishing

Crease-resist finishing is now being carried out using epoxy and acetal resins and also with dimethylol ethylene urea and other resins, and advantages are being claimed for them, but it would seem that a fundamental defect of finishing cellulose fibre materials with all resins is that there is much risk of the material suffering a loss of wear value. The presence of the resin within the fibres makes them somewhat brittle if too much resin is used, and this brittleness is the cause of the fibres breaking down when exposed to abrasion. It also has the effect of making the resin-finished fabric tear more easily. So far, attempts to combat this loss of wear value and tear strength have taken the form of applying a lower proportion of resin and accepting a corresponding lowered crease-resistance, of including softening agents with the resin and thus reducing fibre embrittlement by giving fibre lubrication, and of similarly including selected polymeric substances, particularly copolymers of acrylonitrile and butadiene which are rubber-like.

Theory of crease-resistance

There has been some controversy concerning the manner in which the resin formed within the cellulose fibres gives increased resistance to creasing. It is agreed that to some extent the resilient resin simply fills space between the fibre molecules, but it is also considered likely that some of the resin forms part of numerous cross-linkages to hold the fibre molecules together laterally. Recently it has been found that most of the newer substances which give a high degree of crease-resistance also result in a high degree of cross-linking of the fibre molecules. It would seem that a cross-linking of the fibre molecules is essential to improving crease-resistance.

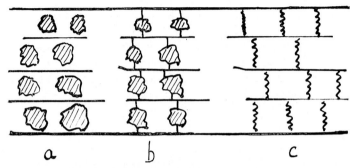

$$a \qquad b \qquad c$$

FIG. 65. Showing three ways in which the resin treatment of a cotton fibre can give it improved crease-resistance. At (*a*) the particles of resin are shown distributed between the fibre molecules but not attached to these, while at (*b*) the resin particles are shown similarly distributed but chemically united to the fibre molecules by short chemical chain molecules such as $-CH_2-$ or $-CH_2-CH_2-$. At (*c*) there are no resin particles but the fibre molecules are shown cross-linked by chemical chain molecules which may be short or long. At the present time it is believed that the most effective resin treatments for producing enhanced crease-resistance leave the fibres as shown at (*b*) or (*c*) but there is some doubt about the matter. Closely associated with this distribution of resin and its cross-linking effect is the loss of wear value and tear-strength which invariably accompanies crease-resist treatment.

WATER-REPELLENT FINISHES FOR CELLULOSE FIBRE GOODS

Early processes

An early and very satisfactory method for making say cotton fabric water-repellent, that is rainproof, consisted of treating it in succession with a solution of an aluminium salt and then with a soap solution so that an insoluble voluminous precipitate of aluminium-soap became deposited on the fibres. Later, compositions were devised combining the aluminium-soap with waxes, and these had the advantage that they could be applied in one operation followed by drying at a high temperature to insolubilise the water-repellent ingredients. By such methods the fabric could be left not only water-repellent but also permeable to air—an important feature when the fabric was for making-up into raincoats.

Recent developments

The water repellency thus obtained was not fast to repeated washing and dry cleaning, but later it was found that this desirable fastness could be obtained by applying to the fabric a special type of substance consisting of a hydrocarbon or similar strongly hydrophobic atomic grouping and a water-solubilising component such as pyridine in loose combination. Such a substance, typified by Velan (I.C.I.), could be applied to the textile material from its aqueous solution or dispersion so that on subjecting the material to a high temperature, say 150° C, for a few minutes the substance split into its original components whereby the hydrophobic component became fixed in the fibres while the other component could be washed out. Several water-repellent agents of this type have become available and they confer a high degree of water repellency which is usually fast to washing and dry cleaning. As yet the treatment is expensive.

Velan PF has the following chemical structure:

Hydrophile pyridine residue ⟶

Hydrophobic hydrocarbon residue ⟵

$$Cl \quad CH_2OCH_2(CH_2)_{16}CH_3$$

Stearyl methyl ether of pyridinium chloride

and when heated in cotton fabric the hydrophobic $-CH_2.O.CH_2$ $(CH_2)_{16}CH_3$ hydrocarbon portion liberated becomes fixed strongly within the fibres. This fixation is so fast to external influences that it is thought possible for it to become chemically combined with the cellulose fibres thus:

$$Cell-O-CH_2.O.CH_2(CH_2)_{16}CH_3$$

Such chemical combination would afford an explanation of the permanence of the water-repellent finish obtained. It is to be noted that Velan PF is applicable to both vegetable and animal (cotton and wool) materials and a high degree of softness accompanies the water repellency.

Silicone water-repellent finishing

More recently considerable improvements in giving textile materials a water-repellent finish have come from the use of silicones which are strongly hydrophobic polymerised organo-silicon compounds having linear molecules and which can be caused to adhere (and possibly chemically combine) with cellulose fibres. At the present time the most satisfactory results are being obtained by application to the textile material of a mixture of two related types of silicones whose linear molecules are represented by

$$\left[\,-\!\!-\!\!\text{O}-\underset{\underset{\displaystyle H}{|}}{\overset{\overset{\displaystyle CH_3}{|}}{Si}}-\text{O}-\underset{\underset{\displaystyle H}{|}}{\overset{\overset{\displaystyle CH_3}{|}}{Si}}-\,\right]_n$$

and

$$\left[\,-\!\!-\!\!\text{O}-\underset{\underset{\displaystyle CH_3}{|}}{\overset{\overset{\displaystyle CH_3}{|}}{Si}}-\text{O}-\underset{\underset{\displaystyle CH_3}{|}}{\overset{\overset{\displaystyle CH_3}{|}}{Si}}-\,\right]_n$$

In the form in which these silicones are applied the value of n is relatively small so that the linear molecules are of moderate length. Application is made of either an organic solvent solution or an aqueous dispersion of the silicone mixture, and after evaporating off the organic solvent or the water, the textile material is heated at about $150°$ C for a few minutes when, it is believed, the small amount of moisture in the fibres causes the silicones to polymerise further (the value of n increases considerably) and become strongly fixed in the fibre surfaces, thus making these strongly water-repellent.

Beneficial use of catalysts

Important recent improvements have shown that the presence of a butyl titanate, $Ti(OC_4H_9)_4$, or similar zirconium compound so strongly catalyses the further polymerisation of the silicon mixture in the fibre surfaces that the finishing treatment can be conducted at much lower temperatures, in some instances at room temperature if sufficient time is allowed, and thus avoid any harmful effect on the fibre strength. It requires only about 3% of the silicone deposited on the textile material to give a satisfactory water repellency. Such a finish has been found very suitable for the water-repellent finishing of synthetic fibre materials.

FIG. 66. Showing how textile materials can be made completely water-repellent by treatment with silicones. Water thrown over nylon tulle material which has been silicone treated is seen to become scattered as droplets which remain as such and do not spread and penetrate as they would similar but untreated tulle. On shaking the tulle all the droplets fall off leaving it completely unwetted. It is an important point that water repellency obtained by means of silicones retains its permeability to air so that raincoats and other garments which have been silicone treated are comfortable to wear—this advantage is not possessed by textile materials which have been rubberised.

By courtesy of Midland Silicones Ltd

Self water-repellent fabrics

It may here be mentioned that water repellency in a fabric can be obtained without the use of any waterproofing agent if the fabric is woven in a special manner. The well-known Ventile fabrics are of this type.

If one considers an ordinary cotton woven fabric it will be seen that the passage of water through it takes place in the interstices formed by the interlacing of the weft and warp threads—the more open the texture of the fabric the more easily can water pass through. So a step in the direction of making a fabric self water-repellent is to weave it with the threads very closely interlaced. There is, of course, a limit to this and even with the most closely woven fabric the interstices are sufficiently large to allow water to pass through. But there is a further factor to be considered. When a cotton fibre is wetted it tends to thicken to the extent of 20 to 30% and it is capable of exerting considerable force to achieve this lateral swelling in much the same way as wood swells under wet conditions. So in the case of the closely woven fabric which is wetted the fibres soon thicken and at the same time close up the interstices until there comes a point at which these are too small to allow water to pass through. Thus with a suitable woven texture a fabric can be self water-repellent. Even fire hoses can be made on this principle. This type of fabric, water-repellent and impervious to wind, is now used considerably for the making of outdoor sports jackets and other garments.

SHRINK-RESIST FINISHES FOR CELLULOSE FIBRE FABRICS

Causes of shrinkage in cellulose fibre fabrics during washing

Relaxation shrinkage. Most types of textile materials tend to shrink during repeated washing for the reason that in making them acceptable for wear or use they become somewhat stretched. It is a fundamental fact that any textile fibre which is stretched to a moderate degree tends to return more or less completely to its unstretched length as soon as the stretching force is removed. But if the fibre is damp or wet when stretched and it is dried while held taut then it becomes set in its stretched state and maintains this state until it is wetted, when it at once returns to its unstretched state. Most textile materials are thus temporarily set during ordinary finishing operations to a larger shape or to dimensions which are larger than those natural to them and so quite rapidly they return to their natural form as soon as they are washed. This is generally termed relaxation shrinkage and it can be quite objectionable in an article or garment which cannot again be damped and stretched and temporarily set by hot ironing or other similar treatment. It would be much better if the textile material was finished originally free from stretch so that it will retain its shape and size during both wear and washing. In recent years textile finishers made much progress in finishing fabrics and garments so that these have no latent tendency to shrink even in conditions such as washing which will allow shrinkage to take place.

Shrinkage because of fibre's wet swelling. In producing shrink-resistant cotton and regenerated cellulose fibre (for example, viscose rayon) fabrics it is important to recognise that washing shrinkage arises primarily as a result of relaxation of the fibres from a temporarily set stretched state but that it can also arise from the thickening of fibre which always results from its absorption or imbibition of water during immersion in water. Consideration will be given to the latter point first.

Fabric changes arising from wetting

When a fabric is wetted and the cellulose fibres imbibe say at least 50% of their own weight of water they swell laterally about 30%. In this swelling the threads have to become thicker to accommodate the swollen fibres of which they are made, and since in the thread these fibres are twisted together the thread shrinks somewhat in length to accommodate this thickening. The result of these fibre and thread changes is that the fabric shrinks while the weft and warp threads, because of their interlacing with each other, become more crimped or wrinkled. These changes occur even if the fibres and threads in the original fabric are completely free from stretch and are of their natural length. If the wet fabric is now dried in a slack condition so that it is free to change its structure, then the fibres will lose their water content and will revert to their original thickness and the threads will also tend to return to their original thickness and length. But the fabric has a structure of sufficient rigidity to resist to some degree these reversionary movements of the fibres and threads and so the fabric will fail to return absolutely to its original shape and size. The shrinkage thus produced is due to the fibre thickening as a result of wetting and to the fabric rigidity hindering a return of the fibres and threads to their original positions and form in the drying stage. It is not in any way connected with the shrinking of stretched fibres because it is assumed in this particular case that they are completely relaxed and unstretched. This kind of washing shrinkage will take place mainly during the first wash but it will continue steadily to a small degree during succeeding washes. It is a kind of shrinkage produced in most kinds of fabrics.

Fabric shrinkage on washing

Thus, considering more particularly cotton and rayon fabrics, the washing shrinkage during the first wash will be equal to the sum of the relaxation (from stretching) and the 'increase of thread crimp' shrinkages, and in most cases the former will be much greater than the latter. Progressive washing shrinkage will be due entirely to the 'increase of thread crimp' shrinkage and the extent of this will diminish rapidly with repeated washing. However, since viscose rayon fibres imbibe much more water than do cotton fibres this latter type of shrinkage can be more pronounced with rayon fabrics.

Prevention of fabric shrinkage

From the above it is evident that the production of shrink-resistant cotton and rayon fabrics can be achieved by one or both of two distinctly different methods. In the first, the threads of the fabric are closed up with consequent reduction of the size of the interstices to a degree such that on washing the fabric shows a tendency neither to shrink nor to extend. A shrink-resist finishing of this kind will thus involve purely mechanical treatment of the fabric. In the second method, the fabric will be treated chemically or otherwise so that the fibres are made less hydrophile and so that by having a lowered power to imbibe water they thicken less when wetted than they would in their original state.

Mechanical shrink-resist finishing methods

Experience has shown that for cotton materials very satisfactory shrink-resist finishing can be achieved by a mechanical closing up of the threads alone, but while this can be achieved with rayon fabrics of certain types there are others which have so 'lively' a structure that they must be processed by both methods to obtain a satisfactory resistance to washing shrinkage. The most satisfactory mechanical shrink-resist finishes are very similar and are known as Rigmel and Sanforized finishes; the chemical shrink-resist finishes are best obtained by treatments involving the use of resins or formaldehyde (or an equivalent of this substance such as glyoxal).

The Rigmel (British) and Sanforize (American) shrink-resist finishes are both based on the peculiar behaviour of a thick flexible blanket or rubber belt while it passes around a guiding roller and then leaves this to travel flat. Referring to Fig. 67 where is shown a blanket (of exaggerated thickness) passing around a roller R, let attention be given to a short length *PQ* as it leaves the flat to pass around the roller and then leaves this to become flat again. It is to be noted that while the blanket is around the roller its outer surface becomes stretched while its inner surface remains unchanged. Thus the distance *PQ* at (*a*) and (*c*) is less than at (*b*) and this difference will be greater as the blanket is thicker and the curvature of the roller is greater.

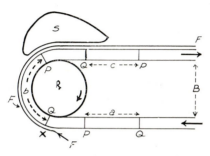

FIG. 67. Showing how a thick blanket running over a roller of comparatively small diameter can be used to close up a fabric lengthwise. The underlying principle is largely employed in modern 'compressive shrinkage' finishing machines as used for the production of fully shrunk fabrics which do not shrink in washing.

If a length of fabric is brought in contact with the blanket on the roller at (*X*) and is held closely to it while travelling forward, then the fabric will have to contract in length by the time it reaches position (*c*) and it will suffer this contraction by crinkling along its length. But if a hot metal plate or shoe suitably presses downward on the slightly damp fabric as it gradually changes from its curved to its flat position, these crinkles will be pressed into the fabric as fast as they form and the fabric at (*c*) will be permanently flat and smooth with its weft and warp threads closed up on each other. The fabric will have become shorter and slightly thicker in texture to accommodate this shortening. The amount of shortening will approximate to the difference between distances *PQ* at (*a*) or (*c*) and at (*b*).

Rigmel and Sanforize finishing machines

The Rigmel and Sanforize machines operate on the above principle. In the Sanforize machine the fabric, in open width, is led into the machine so as to pass over a small diameter roller covered with a thick blanket and on leaving this it is immediately stabilised in its length contracted form by a hot pressing device (a Palmer finishing machine). This comprises a large steam-heated cylinder which steadily rotates, and at one part comes adjacent to the shrinkage roller just mentioned to allow this endless blanket and the fabric to continue their path of travel around the cylinder, until the fabric in its finished shrunk state is led away for further processing while the blanket continues on its path to pass again round the shrinkage roller. As the fabric passes with the blanket around the shrinkage roller it is pressed thereto by heated shoes which extend across the width of the fabric and roller, thus serving to consolidate the shrinkage of the fabric as it commences its travel around the large Palmer cylinder and while being pressed thereto by the endless blanket moving with it.

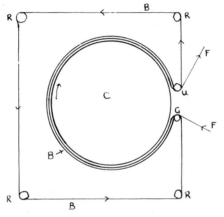

FIG. 68. Showing the essential features of a Palmer finishing machine for setting fabric with a smooth soft lustrous finish. The machine consists of a large diameter hollow sheet-metal drum which rotates on a horizontal axis and it is internally heated by steam under pressure. An endless wool blanket passes around the drum and around guiding rollers *G* and *R* forming a closed circuit. The fabric *F* which is to be finished enters around lower guiding roller *G* and is pressed in close contact to the surface of the drum by the blanket, so that all three move forward together without any slippage between them until the fabric and blanket leave the drum at upper guiding roller *U*. The entering fabric is first suitably damped since this moisture assists the finishing treatment.

In the Rigmel machine, which is considerably smaller, an endless rubber belt about 1 inch thick is used to effect fabric shrinkage as it passes around a roller; a small Palmer finishing machine is used but it plays no essential part in the lengthwise shrinking of the fabric other than fixing this shrinkage.

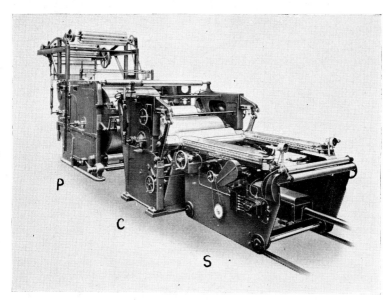

FIG. 69. A gearless rubber-belt compressive shrinking machine for the production of woven fabrics carrying the 'Sanforized' (Registered Trade Mark) shrunk finish. It allows a fabric to be closed up in length to a point at which when washed it suffers no dimensional change, that is, it neither shrinks nor extends. The machine comprises three parts—the short clip stenter *S* which serves to straighten and bring to a uniform width the incoming fabric, so that this can pass into the compressive shrinkage unit *C* and there be suitably shortened and finally pass through the Palmer finishing unit *P*, where it is dried and set with a surface finish by passing around a large diameter cylinder (internally steam-heated) while being pressed against the surface of this by a thick woollen blanket—all three of the surfaces of the cylinder, fabric, and blanket move forward together without slip at the same rates.

By courtesy of Mather & Platt Ltd

Recently the inventors of the Sanforizing machine have been able to use a 2-inch thick rubber belt in a modified machine and so enable fabrics to be shrunk up to 20% in length.

Machine for shrinking synthetic fibre fabrics

Another fabric shrinking machine now being developed by the B.D.A. Ltd of Bradford is for the shrinking of fabrics of nylon,

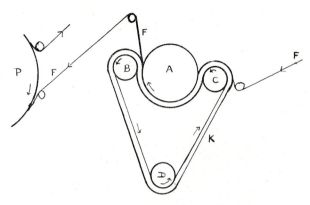

FIG. 70. Showing essential features of a compressive fabric shrinking machine which uses an endless thick rubber belt and which is used for closing up woven fabric in length so that in washing it does not shrink more than 1%. As the fabric F enters the machine between the thick rubber belt K and the surface of the internally steam-heated polished steel cylinder A it comes in contact with the rubber in a stretched compressed state. The rubber recovers to its normal non-stretched state while moving around cylinder A, thus shrinking the fabric in length so that the fabric leaves cylinder A suitably shrunk and has no tendency to shrink in length when washed. This shrunk non-shrinkable finish is then set by passing it (with drying) around the hot cylinder of a Palmer machine P.

Terylene, and other fibres amenable to heat-setting—the shrinkage produced can be heat-set in the one run through the machine whose essential features are described below.

This new type of machine, which is capable of shrinking a synthetic fibre fabric up to 30% in length and simultaneously heat-setting it to its new dimensions, is shown, as regards its essential features, in Fig. 71. It is seen to consist of three rotating rollers suitably spaced and with a smooth polished metal block fitted between the two roller nips as shown. Rollers A and C are covered with soft rubber while roller B is covered with hard rubber. Roller speeds are such that the fabric is drawn faster into the first nip than it is pushed out at the second nip. Under these conditions the fabric shortens and thickens within the space between the three rollers and the metal block, which is heated so that it becomes consolidated (without puckering or wrinkling) and emerges from the second nip a smooth surfaced but shortened fabric.

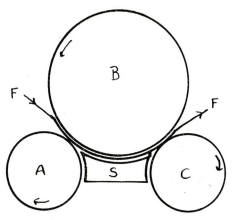

FIG. 71. Showing the principle on which another type of compressive shrinkage machine operates. The fabric F is run between rubber-covered rollers A and B, and B and C, with rollers A and B running at the same peripheral speed while roller C runs at a controlled lower speed. Although all three rollers are rubber-covered, the rubber covering of A and C is softer than that of B. S is a smooth steel shoe which may be heated and it presses against the fabric. Under these conditions there is a tendency for the fabric to enter the nip between B and A faster than it can leave the nip between B and C and thus it becomes closed up in length.

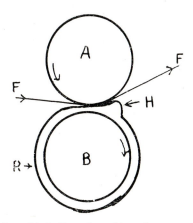

FIG. 72. Showing how fabric F can be subjected to compressive shrinkage (a closing-up in length) by passage between a hard-surfaced roller A and a soft rubber-covered roller B. Where the two rollers make contact under pressure the rubber stretches but on leaving the area of contact it contracts with formation of a small hump (exaggerated in the drawing) which exerts a back-pressure. Thus fabric passing between the two rollers tends to leave the 'nip' of the rollers more slowly than it enters and so becomes closed-up in length. The degree of this closing-up can be adjusted as desired by variation of the conditions of rubber compression.

Q

Testing for washing shrinkage

In bringing cellulose fibre fabrics into a shrink-resistant state by means of compressive shrinkage machines of the types described above it is usual first to wash a sample of the fabric under conditions which will produce all the shrinkage likely to be produced during its useful life and then measure this shrinkage and use the result to determine how much the fabric shall be closed up in length in passing through the machine. It is to be noted that it is only the length shrinkage that is here considered—width shrinkage will have been taken care of when the fabric was dried and stentered, for it is in such a machine that the width can be brought to any desired value.

Use of resins to give shrink-resistance

Present developments, even for cotton fabrics, are in the direction of impregnating the fabric with a resin (somewhat less than is commonly employed for securing crease-resistance), drying, and then passing it through a compressive shrinkage machine. The shrunk fabric is then cured (thus completing full polymerisation of the resin within the fibres) in the usual manner by leading it through a chamber so as to expose it to a temperature of about 150° C for about 6 minutes. The resin thus fixed in the fabric definitely stabilises or makes more permanent the new dimensions obtained mechanically.

Chemical shrink-resist finishes for cellulose fibre fabrics

Some types of viscose rayon fabrics still shrink in washing after having been given a compressive shrinkage treatment as described above. Such fabrics have therefore to be made shrink-resistant by a chemical (including resin) treatment. Large amounts of cotton fabric are also made shrink-resistant by the same kind of treatment.

In crease-resist finishing cotton and rayon fabrics using say a urea–formaldehyde resin it is usual to notice that the resin treatment also makes the fabric less liable to shrink in washing, and so a resin treatment is now largely employed for shrink-resist finishing cotton and rayon fabrics—such treatment can be combined with a mechanical compressive shrinkage treatment.

The resin is usually applied (but only about one-half of the usual quantity for securing crease-resistance, say not more than 7% of the weight of fabric being processed) to the cotton or viscose rayon fabric in much the same manner as for a crease-resist finish. The usual types of resin can also be employed and if the defect of chlorine retention must be avoided then nitrogenous resins should not be used.

Cross-linking shrink-resist treatments

But instead of resins there is an alternative of using formaldehyde or the dialdehyde glyoxal. For this, the cotton or rayon fabric is impregnated with an aqueous liquor containing the aldehyde and an acidic catalyst such as tartaric or lactic acid, then dried at a moderate temperature, and finally cured at about $150°$ C for 3 to 4 minutes. Thereafter the fabric is washed and dried. It is believed that the effect of the formaldehyde is to produce a cross-linking of adjacent cellulose fibre molecules thus:

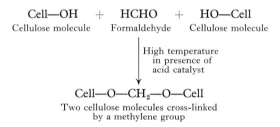

Cell—OH   +   HCHO   +   HO—Cell
Cellulose molecule   Formaldehyde   Cellulose molecule

High temperature
in presence of
acid catalyst

Cell—O—CH$_2$—O—Cell
Two cellulose molecules cross-linked
by a methylene group

This cross-linking of cellulose molecules lowers the power of the fibres to imbibe water and thus to swell when wet—changes which favour resistance of cotton and rayon fabrics to shrinkage during washing.

It is unfortunate that the acid conditions which exist during the curing stage can cause a weakening of the fibres, so that the greatest care must be taken by control of the curing conditions to keep this weakening within reasonable limits.

An American process

In one American process for shrink-resist finishing cotton and rayon fabrics a resin is used which results from the reaction of starch and acetone under alkaline conditions—the resulting fabric does not retain chlorine. The use of glyoxal, CHO.CHO, instead of formaldehyde is the basis of the Sanforset shrink-resist process, which is used for rayon fabrics having a pronounced tendency to shrink in washing. Both of these treatments can be used in conjunction with the ordinary compressive shrinkage processes (Rigmel and Sanforize).

Unshrinkable wool

Felting the cause of wool fibre shrinkage. If wool fabric were by a compressive shrinkage or other mechanical method brought into a non-stretched state with its constituent fibres and threads also in a normal unstretched state, this same wool fabric would progressively shrink during repeated washing until the fabric had thickened and shrunk so much that the fibres could not close up further. This continued shrinkage is the result of the unique felting power of wool as previously described. The shrinkage which occurs with wool materials in washing is thus much different from that of cellulose fibre goods and it is not possible by subjecting wool to compressive shrinkage to bring it into a stage which could be designated unshrinkable. To make wool materials really unshrinkable in washing it is necessary to bring them into a relaxed state by suitably closing up the threads and also to take away their felting properties.

The liability of wool materials to felt during washing must not be regarded entirely as a defect since it is used to a considerable extent in the finishing of wool materials when it is desired to make them more dense and soft. Wool fabrics as they leave the loom or knitting machine often have a thready appearance accompanied by a firm handle, and in addition they may appear too open. These defects can be corrected by subjecting the fabric to a so-called milling treatment, which is equivalent to washing under conditions such that the fabric is squeezed or compressed to a controlled degree while in contact with the washing liquor (this is usually a warm soap solution but occasionally it is an acid solution, since both acids and alkalis promote felting). In such treatment the wool fabric gradually shrinks by a closing-up of the fibres, which is facilitated by a loosening of the threads which the mechanical treatment induces.

Woven wool fabrics are usually milled in so-called milling machines, but knitted fabrics are milled in ordinary scouring machines or in so-called 'dolly' machines in which the fabric is mechanically pounded in a soap liquor. Sometimes considerable shrinkage of the fabric is required, but in the case of many fabrics, particularly those of the knitted type, only a moderate degree of felting is necessary.

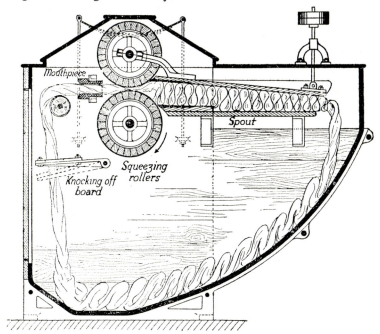

Fig. 73. Showing the construction of the wool fabric milling machine in respect of its essential features. The fabric in rope form is continuously circulated within the machine in a clockwise direction by the action of the rotating squeezing rollers. The fabric itself is thoroughly wetted with a soap liquor. Under these conditions the fabric tends to accumulate in the tapered spout, thus becoming subject to compression, which in its turn causes the fabric to close up by a felting of the wool fibres and so gradually become denser and shorter and narrower. Whenever the fabric accumulates to an excessive degree in the spout the knocking-off board acts to open the spout against pressure and so allows the fabric to pass out more freely. This operation of milling is continued until the fabric has acquired the desired finish as regards density, shrinkage, and softness of handle.

By courtesy of The Textile Institute

As previously explained, the felting power of wool fibres is due to the epithelial scale covering of each fibre such that it is always rougher in the tip-to-root than in the opposite direction. This special roughness determines that when a mass of wool fibres is repeatedly squeezed and relaxed in a warm soap (or other fibre lubricant) liquor they steadily close up on each other until a solid fibrous mass is obtained with the fibres firmly interlocked. This same phenomenon is observed in the washing of a wool yarn or fabric although it is not until the structure is loosened to allow fibre movement that felting takes place at a rapid rate.

Anti-felting treatments

The most satisfactory method for reducing the felting power of wool is that of acting on the surface of each fibre so as to gelatinise the scales, and thereafter leave them changed so that the fibre roughness is about the same in either direction or the scales are so smoothed that the wool fibres are fairly smooth. Since the scales protect the interior of the wool fibre from damage by external influences it is evident that any process for reducing the felting power of wool can at the same time carry the risk of so damaging the scales that the fibre interior (cortex) becomes exposed with consequent fibre weakening.

Special treatments

It is generally agreed that aqueous liquors containing chlorine itself or a hypochlorite are most effective in so changing the epithelial scales as to leave the treated wool substantially non-felting. But by such simple treatment it is not possible to avoid penetration of the wool fibre by the non-felting agent and damage to the cortex at the same time as the epithelial scales are being modified as desired. For this reason, recourse has been made to treatments of the wool with dry chlorine gas or with solutions of such substances as sulphuryl chloride or caustic soda in anhydrous organic solvents, since it has been found that by such special treatment the attack on the wool is mainly confined to the epithelial scale layer. One method of ensuring that the attack is confined to the epithelial scale layer is to use in an organic solvent (or otherwise ensure substantial absence of water) a substance whose molecules are too large to pass through the scale layer into the interior of the wool fibre. The requirement that water should be absent is because the fibre would absorb this and swell to allow the penetration of larger molecules than with dry fibres.

Wet chlorination processes

It has been found that after wool fibres have been treated with an anti-felting agent under acid conditions a further gelatinisation of the epithelial scale layer can be produced (and such gelatinisation contributes to a further reduction of felting power) by an alkaline treatment.

Much unshrinkable wool is being produced by a treatment of the wool with an alkaline or acidified solution of sodium hypochlorite (there should be present about 3 to 5% of active chlorine calculated on the weight of wool) followed by washing and an anti-chlor treatment with a solution of sodium bisulphite to remove the last traces of residual chlorine. But perhaps a larger amount is being treated by a so-called Dylan process in which the wool material is treated with a cold aqueous liquor containing potassium permanganate and sodium hypochlorite. Under these conditions the epithelial scales are chlorinated and oxidised (brown manganese oxide is deposited in the wool fibres at the same time) and this treatment is continued until almost complete unshrinkability is obtained without material depreciation of the wool, which is then washed and treated with an acidified solution of hydrogen peroxide to dissolve the manganese oxide and so leave the wool white and non-felting. This process also leaves the wool soft.

A recently devised process for reducing the felting properties of wool without damaging the fibres consists of steeping the wool material in a dilute aqueous solution of potassium permanganate nearly saturated with common salt at about 25° C for one to two hours, then rinsing, treating with a 5% solution of sodium bisulphite to remove the brown deposit of manganese dioxide on the fibres, washing, and drying. The presence of the common salt is essential since it aids the action of the potassium permanganate yet protects the wool fibres from chemical damage.

Treatment of wool with an acidified solution of sodium hypochlorite gives complete unshrinkability coupled with an excellent whiteness, but the treatment is difficult to control so that it is uniform and does not damage the wool. Consequently it is not much favoured.

It is usual to find that unshrinkable wool produced by the methods indicated above has an increased affinity for dyes.

Use of resin treatment to give unshrinkable non-felting wool

Unshrinkable wool can also be produced by treating it with a synthetic resin so as to obscure the special roughness of each fibre which gives the wool felting power. Only selected resins have proved efficient for this purpose and that most recommended is a methyl etherified melamine–formaldehyde resin—a urea–form-aldehyde resin is not nearly so effective. Although it has been established that the resin applied to the wool does suitably reduce the unequal roughness of the wool fibres as between the tip-to-root and root-to-tip directions, it is believed that a certain amount of resin spot-cements the wool fibres together and thus hinders the free fibre movement which is essential to the felting of wool. On the whole, wool made unshrinkable by a resin treatment tends to be yellower and firmer in handle than untreated wool and this is a disadvantage. Generally it is preferred by wool finishers to make wool non-felting and therefore unshrinkable in washing by a treatment with hypochlorite.

Changes in the wool fibre internal structure

Although a smoothing of the epithelial scale layer of each wool fibre is essential to reducing the felting power of wool, it seems to be accepted that this smoothing ultimately results from the action of the applied anti-felting agent breaking the disulphide (or cystine) bonds which hold the long wool keratin molecules together later-ally within the wool fibres. There is ample experimental evidence to show that such agents as chlorine, hypochlorite, caustic soda, and sulphuryl chloride can easily react with wool to break these important bonds.

The treatment of wool to make it non-felting usually has the simultaneous effect of making the wool more soluble in caustic soda solution. The adverse effect of such treatment can thus be measured by the increase of alkali-solubility of the wool and a test of this kind has been standardised and is much used.

Wool fibre whose epithelial scale layer has been excessively attacked in an anti-felting treatment (this can be revealed by its increased alkali-solubility and its increased affinity for dyes) is much less durable than untreated wool. If a hypochlorite treat-ment has been used in this way it will be found that the wool becomes somewhat slimy when immersed in a dilute solution of sodium carbonate or caustic soda.

LUSTRE FINISHING PROCESSES

It has previously been indicated that the lustre of silk can be improved by de-gumming in a boiling soap liquor the double-filament raw silk, that the lustre of man-made fibres, such as viscose and acetate rayons and the synthetic fibres, can be reduced by any desired degree by adding white opaque titanium dioxide pigment to the fibre-spinning solution or melt, that ordinary acetate rayon materials can by boiling in a soap liquor have their lustre much reduced, and that the lustre of cotton can be permanently increased by mercerisation with a strong caustic soda solution under conditions wherein the cotton yarn or fabric is stretched out to its original dimensions before removal of the caustic soda liquor by washing, acidification, and final washing. Yet there is another method for modifying the lustre of a fabric and this is by mechanical treatment alone, although under certain circumstances such treatment can be assisted by a resin treatment.

Fabric surface smoothing

One of the most convenient methods for conferring increased lustre on a fabric is to press its surface, say by contact with a hot smooth metal plate, and thus smooth out surface irregularities. If the fabric is damp and the plate is hot, then the fibres under the combined influence of the moisture and pressure acquire a degree of plasticity which results in the flattening of the fabric surface being more complete and also more permanent. A fabric appears to be more lustrous when its surface is smooth with all the threads lying in one plane than when its surface is wavy and broken by the interlacing warp and weft yarns.

Lustring machines

Although some of the machines for lustring fabrics are of the plate type, for instance the two- and three-bed steam presses used for hosiery goods and the hot hydraulic presses used for compressing wool fabrics, it is generally preferred to use, wherever possible, a type of machine in which the hot metal surface is in the form of a roller running in contact with a non-metal roller so that fabric can be led through such a machine at a steady rate. The metal lustring roller will be hollow so that it can be internally heated by burning gas or by electrical means and even by circulating hot oil. It is not satisfactory to run a fabric between two metal rollers or bowls under pressure since there is great risk of damaging the fabric—it is always better to have a resilient non-metal bowl running against the metal bowl.

Thus most types of fabric can be given increased lustre by simply running them between a highly polished metal bowl and a resilient non-metal (compressed paper or cotton) bowl with the metal bowl internally heated and with the fabric initially damp to promote permanence of the fabric flattening. Under these relatively simple conditions of lustring the fabric runs through the nip of the two bowls at the same rate as they rotate and there is no slip between the fabric and the metal bowl surface.

Friction lustring machines

If a higher degree of lustre is required, it is necessary to both flatten and polish the fabric surface and this is achieved by arranging that the surface speeds of the two bowls are not equal. Under these conditions there is slip between the fabric and the polished metal bowl to produce a kind of hot ironing under pressure. Quite a high degree of lustre can thus be imparted to the fabric.

Calender machines

The machines used in this manner for lustring fabrics are usually termed calenders. The pressure maintained on the bowls has to be high and it may be produced by means of weights and levers or hydraulically. In some calenders there are several bowls, metal bowls alternating with non-metal bowls one above the other, so that in the one run through the fabric can be nipped not once but two or three times by passing successively between pairs of bowls. When the bowls are geared to run at different speeds the calender is usually termed a 'friction calender'. The maximum lustre to be obtained by calendering is when the fabric is wet and is run through the machine having heated rollers several times so that it is dried in the process. But although it has a very high lustre it is generally unacceptable because the fabric is so flattened as to resemble paper in both handle and appearance. This makes it convenient to note here that while calendering can be a most useful means to give a lustre increase to fabrics it must be controlled so that the fabric is not too much flattened or smoothed so as to lose its fabric appearance, that is, it must still appear to be made by the interlacing of warp and weft yarns.

FIG. 74. Showing cotton fabric (after being stentered to bring it to the desired width and length) being given an increased lustre with an accompanying modification (softening) of its handle by passage through a calender finishing machine which comprises two or more rollers (bowls) under high pressure.

The rollers may be of polished steel or compressed cotton or wool paper (on a steel shaft) and the type of 'finish' produced can be modified as desired by variation in the manner of running the fabric through the machine and also of the combination of different kinds of bowls used. It is usual for the fabric to be suitably damped before such calendering treatment since it then responds better to the pressure of the bowls upon it. It can be arranged that one bowl rotates faster than another so that the fabric surface becomes friction-polished with production of a much higher lustre.

By courtesy of The Cotton Board (Manchester)

Calendering of knitted fabrics

Knitted fabrics are calendered just like woven fabrics but need less pressure and greater care. Generally it is most convenient to calender knitted fabrics in tubular form since this allows their better control in the operation. The most satisfactory method of handling such fabric is to lead it into the nip of the calender bowls by passing it over an internal floating stretcher which fixes the width and straightens the fabric at the same time.

Where only a moderate increase of lustre is desired and it is wished to leave the fabric with a soft full texture, the expedient of covering the bowls of the calender with a few layers of fabric is adopted—the greater resilience thus obtained is very beneficial and it certainly prevents the production of a paper-like appearance in the calendered fabric.

Use of resins

In recent years advantage has been taken of the experience obtained in applying synthetic resins to textile materials and now some very useful calendered finishes can be produced by first impregnating the fabric (say a cotton fabric) with a resin (as in crease-resist finishing), drying at a moderate temperature so as not to promote further polymerisation of the resin within the fabric, then hot calendering, and finally (without stretching the fabric or otherwise disturbing the flattening of the fabric surface produced by the calendering) curing the fabric at say 150° C for a few minutes. In this way the lustrous smooth finish obtained is reasonably fast to several washes. If the resin is not present then one wash is usually sufficient to destroy an ordinary calender-produced lustre, for in the wetting the fibres swell, also the yarns, and so the fabric surface again acquires its original roughness. It is, indeed, one of the disadvantages of calender finishes that they are so easily destroyed by wetting or washing.

It is possible in calendering resin-impregnated fabrics to effect the curing at the time of calendering, since the metal bowl of the machine can be heated sufficiently to achieve this. But it is often not advantageous to combine the two operations, and the method of curing the calendered fabric separately has much to commend it. The very useful wash-fast lustrous chintz curtain materials now widely available (e.g. those sold under the trade name of Everglaze) are produced by friction calendering a resin-containing fabric.

Schreiner calendering

There is yet another method for producing highly lustrous cotton and rayon fabrics which uses a special type of calender known as a Schreiner calender. In this machine the polished metal bowl has numerous parallel lines engraved in its surface and they run askew across the bowl—there are about 300 lines per linear inch. In operating this Schreiner calender all slip between the fabric and the rotating engraved metal bowl must definitely be excluded since it is the object of the process to impress the lines clearly and evenly upon the surface of the fabric. Any slip would result in a blurred impression. The angle of the parallel lines to the horizontal axis of the metal bowl is such that the lines impressed on the fabric run approximately parallel to the twist in those (warp or weft) threads which are most prominent in the fabric surface. Schreiner calendering is usually carried out with the metal bowl heated to a high temperature and with the fabric suitably damp; the pressure of the bowl on the fabric is very high and is obtained hydraulically or pneumatically.

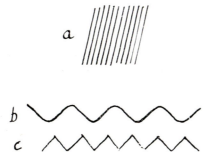

FIG. 75. Showing (*a*) very closely spaced parallel Schreiner lines impressed on fabric by use of a Schreiner calendering machine—about 300 or more such lines are impressed per linear inch. The lines may be impressed (*b*) undulating or (*c*) sharply delineated with acute angles.

The lustre increase produced is due to the flattening and smoothing of the fabric surface as in ordinary calendering, but there is a further lustre increase which arises from the impressed parallel lines—these regularise the reflection of the incident light so that when viewed from suitable directions much more light is reflected than would be without the lines. This method of lustring a fabric is much employed for finishing fabrics which are to be used as lining fabrics. It is unfortunate that the highly lustrous and attractive appearance obtainable by Schreinering is not fast to wetting, but the fastness can be much improved by the use of resins as previously described for the production of washable glazed chintz fabrics.

FIG. 76. A Schreiner calender for producing an exceptionally high lustre on cotton fabrics, but now much less used than formerly owing to the availability of high-lustre man-made fibre fabrics. It comprises an upper hollow special steel bowl highly polished, whose surface is engraved with very fine closely spaced parallel lines; it is internally heated by gas or otherwise to a high temperature. The lower bowl is of compressed cotton or woollen paper and is thus resilient. Hydraulic means are used to produce a very high pressure between the two bowls. Because of the high temperature used the bearings of the bowls have to be water-cooled. In operation cotton fabric is run between the two bowls so as to receive an impression of the lines and because these are parallel and so closely spaced, and also because they are suitably askew to the horizontal axis of the steel bowl and when impressed on the fabric run roughly parallel to the angle of twist of the fibres in warp or weft threads (whichever are predominant in the fabric surface), the surface of the fabric becomes very attractively lustrous but there is no evidence of the impressed lines. Because this finish is produced mechanically it is not fast to washing.

A modified form of Schreiner calender has recently been found useful for treating nylon knitted fabrics to give them increased opacity.

By courtesy of Mather & Platt Ltd

Schreiner calendering of nylon fabrics

It may be noted here that recently the useful discovery has been made that a light Schreiner calendering can very effectively and desirably make more opaque the gossamer sheer and transparent knitted nylon nightwear fabrics which have recently become available. The passage of this fabric through a Schreiner calender with the temperature of the metal bowl and the pressure upon it suitably reduced just flattens the thermoplastic nylon threads so as to fill out the interstices in the fabric yet without (because of the imprinted parallel lines) impairing the fabric lustre.

EMBOSSED FINISHES

It has above been described how in a Schreiner calender there is employed a hot highly polished metal bowl engraved with numerous parallel lines which allows fabrics to be impressed with these lines and so confer an increase of lustre. Obviously this bowl can be replaced by one having not engraved lines but an engraved pattern, say spots or a floral pattern, and thus allow the production in a similar manner of embossed fabrics.

The embossing of fabrics has long been carried out, but in recent years with the production of synthetic fibre fabrics more amenable to hot embossing than fabrics of cotton and rayon, this method of finishing has acquired increased popularity. But by the use of synthetic resins say of the urea– and melamine–formaldehyde type employed in crease-resist finishing, superior embossed finishes can now be obtained on cotton and other cellulose fibre materials. If a resin is used then the embossed finish is much faster to washing, so that now it is possible to produce wash-fast embossed cotton and rayon fabrics suitable for making up into blouses, dresses, etc., which can give much improved service because they can be washed many times without appreciable loss of their original appearance.

FLAMEPROOF FINISHES

The flameproofing of textile materials has in recent years aroused considerable attention arising out of various reports on the large number of fatalities caused by fires in the home and places of amusement, directly attributable in the first instance to the catching fire of some garment or other form of textile material. Children have suffered particularly and legislation has been passed or promised which has for its object the encouragement of finishing textiles so that they will resist catching fire and in the event of burning that they will not leave behind a char residue which will continue to afterglow.

Defects of earlier treatments

Actually many treatments are known by which textile materials, particularly those made of cellulose fibres, can be made flameproof and in any event leave a char which does not afterglow, but they all suffer from some disadvantage, which may be high cost but more generally the defect that they adversely affect the handle, colour, durability, or appearance. Simple drying into a fabric of a solution of say borax or ammonium phosphate can much reduce any tendency it may have to catch fire, but so much of the flameproofing substance is required that the attractiveness of the fabric might be quite spoiled. Further, these particular agents and several others like them can be readily washed out of the fabric and this is a particularly unsatisfactory feature.

Action of a flameproofing agent

When a cotton or similar textile material burns it forms volatile gaseous and tarry compounds which are inflammable and take part in the flaming, and also a char residue consisting mostly of carbon together with any mineral substances present in the fabric. If a flameproofing agent has been previously incorporated in the fabric, then on burning a much lower proportion of the inflammable gaseous and tarry products is formed, but there is a correspondingly larger amount of char left. By reducing the gaseous and tarry products the flameproofing agent hinders or prevents the burning with a flame, but by causing the formation of a larger amount of char it makes it more important that the afterglowing of this char should also be hindered or entirely prevented, since such glowing can in certain circumstances be as dangerous as a burning flame.

Modern flameproofing finishes

Without reviewing all the numerous flameproofing processes which have in past years been proposed and mostly ultimately abandoned it will be sufficient here to deal with three recent processes which are effective and in commercial use although to but a limited extent—they are the Proban treatment (Albright & Wilson Ltd associated with the B.D.A. Ltd) which uses tetrakis-hydroxymethyl-phosphonium chloride, the Lifeguard process (Peter Spence Ltd) based on a combination of titanium and antimony oxy compounds, and the Antiflamm method (Associated Lead Manufacturers Ltd associated with Horrockses Spinners & Manufacturers Ltd) which uses a mixture of antimony oxide and a polyvinyl chloride. It is general experience that if hydrochloric acid is liberated in the burning of a cellulose fibre material then this at once acts as a flame retardant—it is noticeable that this acid can be liberated in materials flameproofed with two of the above methods.

The Antiflamm finish

In the Antiflamm process the fabric or other textile material is impregnated with an aqueous emulsion essentially containing antimony oxide, polyvinyl chloride, and a chlorinated paraffin wax, together with a plasticiser to soften and make more flexible the film of polyvinyl chloride left in the fabric, and is then dried. There follows a curing or heat treatment at 120° to 140° C for 2 to 4 minutes. Quite a large amount of the solid ingredients of the flameproofing emulsion must be deposited in the fabric to give complete protection against fire, say 20 to 30%, but it is claimed that this add-on usefully increases the strength and, of course, the weight of the fabric. The flameproof effect is claimed to be sufficiently fast to washing and dry cleaning to out-last the expected life of the textile material.

The Proban finish

The Proban flameproofing process is essentially based on the use of tetrakis-hydroxymethylphosphonium chloride, which is often designated more simply as THPC and is formed by reaction between phosphine and formaldehyde in hydrochloric acid solution as indicated below:

$$PH_3 \quad + \quad 4HCHO \quad + \quad HCl$$

Phosphine   Formaldehyde

$$\downarrow$$

$$(CH_2OH)_4PCl$$

Tetrakis-hydroxy methyl phosphonium chloride

R

By applying this substance together with a urea and a melamine-formaldehyde condensation product which by further heating resinifies it is possible to flameproof cotton with excellent resistance to repeated washing.

Future progress

Numerous flameproofing treatments are at the present time being developed. Many of them are based on complex organo-phosphorus compounds which are today expensive. It would appear that one important direction of progress lies in the use of phosphorus compounds which can chemically combine with the fibres to which they are applied or which are capable of being converted in the fibres by high temperature conditions (curing) into highly insoluble resins—in either case the flame-proofing will thus be resistant to removal in washing and dry cleaning treatments.

ANTI-STATIC FINISHES

All textile fibres tend to accumulate a high charge of electro-static electricity when rubbed if they are sufficiently dry at the time. If they are damp or wet any charge that might be developed is conducted away to earth as fast as it is made, since a damp fibre can be a sufficiently good conductor of electricity in this state. Normally the natural fibres under the usual conditions in which they are used in manufacturing yarns and fabrics do not accumulate electrostatic to a degree which can be a nuisance, but the fibres which are more hydrophobic, as for example di- and tri-acetate fibres, and the synthetic fibres nylon, Terylene, Orlon, Courtelle, etc., can do so. The electric charge makes the fibres or threads or fabrics repel or cling to each other according to the nature of the charge and this makes their control during mechanical manipulation (yarn winding, fabric weaving and knitting, etc.) more difficult.

If the air in the neighbourhood of the machine handling yarns or fabrics liable to accumulate electrostatic is ionised, then this air will act as a conductor and render harmless any charge developed. This expedient is employed in some textile works to avoid electro-static troubles. But it is often much more useful and satisfactory to impregnate or size the textile fibre, yarn, or fabric with a composition which is hydrophile or mildly hygroscopic and is thus able to confer electrical conducting properties to the textile material. Such compositions will contain hydrophile or even hygroscopic substances such as glycerol, glucose, polyethylene glycols, and sulphated fatty alcohols, together with oils and waxes which additionally lubricate the fibres.

FIG. 77. Showing how the accumulation of static electricity on a thread *Y* which is passing between fixed guides *A* and *B* can cause the individual fibres of which the thread is composed to repel each other and so cause 'ballooning' sufficient to make the manipulation of the thread difficult. Such ballooning is characteristic of synthetic fibre threads since these have a low electrical conduction. A cure for such difficulty is to size the thread with a composition which makes it electrically conducting and promotes dissipation to earth of static electricity immediately it is formed. Alternatively the surrounding air can be made electrically conducting by raising its moisture content and/or ionising it by suitable devices which are now available.

ROTPROOFING FINISHES

While most of the synthetic fibres and to a considerable degree also di- and tri-cellulose acetate fibres are highly resistant to attack under damp conditions by various types of micro-organisms, cotton, linen, and other cellulose fibres are liable to deteriorate rapidly under such conditions. It is thus very useful to be able to treat materials made of these non-resistant fibres so as to acquire a satisfactory degree of immunity to attack.

Use of copper compounds

Rotproofing can very conveniently be achieved by impregnating the textile material with an ordinary copper salt such as copper sulphate, but it is found much better to use copper naphthenate (as in Cupranil), copper oleate, and copper stearate, but preferably the former, since less of the copper naphthenate than of the other compounds is required to give satisfactory protection. This copper naphthenate is much used for the protection of sandbags such as are used in guarding against flooding by rivers, etc. Often this particular copper compound is used together with 2,2'-methylene-bis (4-chloro-phenol). A basic copper acetate can be an effective rotproofing agent.

Other treatments

Recently it has been discovered that by acetylation and cyanoethylation to a limited degree cotton can be given increased resistance to attack by micro-organisms such as flourish in damp earth, but these treatments are as yet somewhat expensive.

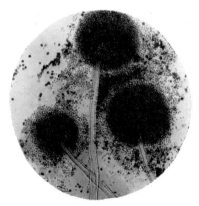

FIG. 78. Showing a type of mildew growth which attacks cotton and cellulose fibres—*Aspergillus niger* in a process of producing spores by which fresh mildew growth can be spread.

By courtesy of The Cotton, Silk and Man-made Fibres Research Association

The resistance of wool materials to attack by fungicides and bacteria can be much improved by impregnating them with sodium silico-fluoride, sodium fluoride, and Shirlan (the anilide of salicylic acid).

Shirlan is also much used for protecting cotton against mildew attack. A number of complex organo-mercury compounds are also effective for this purpose. It has been claimed that Santobrite (Monsanto Chemicals Ltd), consisting of sodium pentachlorophenate, is more effective than Shirlan and that it does not discolour white goods.

FIG. 79. A type of mildew growth capable of living on and attacking cellulose fibre materials—*Fusarium* species.

By courtesy of The Cotton, Silk and Man-made Fibres Research Association

THE MOTHPROOFING OF WOOL

Cellulose fibres and all the synthetic fibres (including cellulose acetate fibres) are not attacked by moth, but wool is a fibre which is especially liable to damage from moth. The damage is done not by the moth but by the small larvae which hatch out from eggs laid in the wool material by the moth. It has been recorded that a moth lays eggs daily to the extent of about 150, and it is when these hatch, say within ten days, that wool damage commences, for the freshly hatched larvae or grubs feed greedily before they form themselves into a cocoon from which moths emerge later to start the life cycle again. It would seem that the fact that wool fibres contain about 3% of combined sulphur makes them palatable and nourishing to the larvae, since these do not attack silk fibres, which have a somewhat similar protein composition to that of wool but contain no combined sulphur.

FIG. 80. Showing a grub of the clothes moth which greedily feeds on wool fibres and is thus the cause of much damage to wool materials. During the storage of wool clothes and other wool materials any eggs which may have been laid in them by clothes moth hatch out into numerous grubs which then live by feeding on the wool. Hence the protection against moth attack which can be given to wool materials by previously treating them with a substance such as Mitin (Geigy), which has the effect of poisoning the grubs as soon as they eat the wool. A treatment of wool such as this is the only sure protection against moth attack—the hungry freshly hatched grubs are not deterred by the smell of camphor balls, cigar ends, printers' ink, etc., which are sometimes used. The moth grub shown is many times enlarged; actual length is about half an inch.

By courtesy of The Geigy Company Ltd, Manchester

Mothproofing treatments

In order to protect wool goods against this so-called moth attack it is necessary to impregnate the wool with a substance which will either deter the larvae from eating the wool and thus cause them to die from starvation or which will poison the larvae when eaten. It is extremely unlikely that moth will be seriously prevented from laying eggs in wool materials in which have been placed any of the many substances recommended from time to time, even cigar ends. Reliance has more to be placed in the destruction of the larvae before they can eat much of the wool. But it is true that if the wool material is considerably disturbed, hatching out of the eggs can be hindered and that brushing and shaking of the wool may dust off a fair proportion of the eggs.

Many substances poisonous or abhorrent to moth larvae have been suggested from time to time, and among these may be mentioned the Eulans (I.G.) which it is believed owe much of their efficacy to a content of potassium bifluoride. The Eulans include also many complex organic substances of the type of chloro-benzene derivatives. One such compound is $2:2'$-dihydroxy-$3:5:3':5'$-tetrachlorotriphenylmethane-$2''$-sulphonic acid, and its formula is given below:

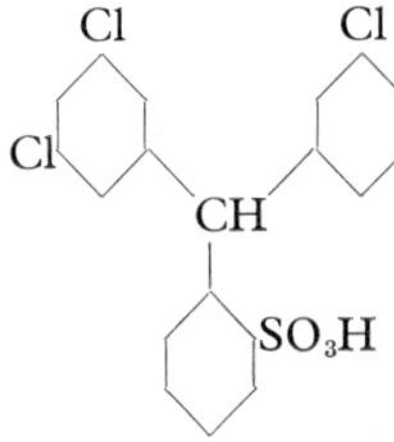

Eulan New

More recently Mitin FF (Geigy Co.) has proved a very satisfactory mothproofing agent, since it is retained by wool even after various kinds of wet processing, so that it may actually be applied during a dyeing operation. It has the formula:

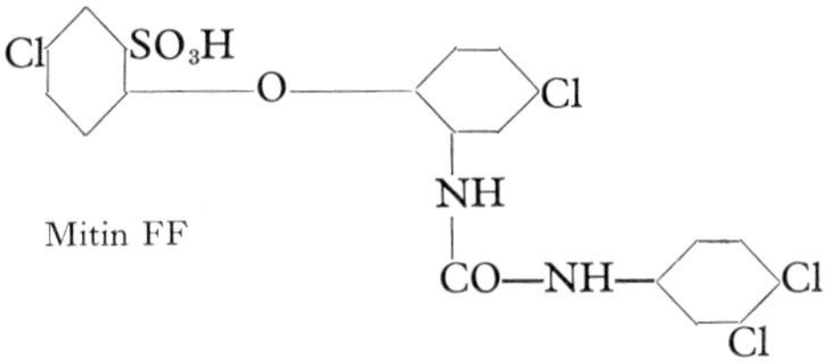

Mitin FF

It can be definitely stated that if users of wool materials are prepared to pay the extra cost involved they can now have them adequately proofed against moth attack.

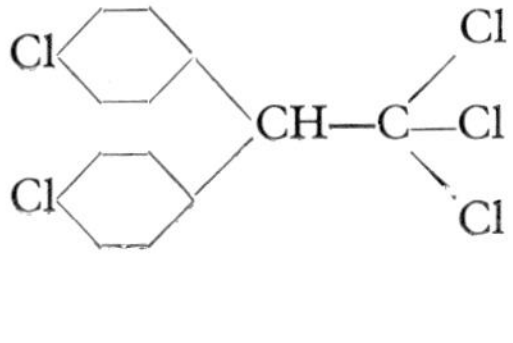

Proprietary preparations such as Irgatex (Geigy Co. Ltd), which contain the well-known insecticide DDT or para-para-dichloro-diphenyl-trichloroethane of formula can be used to protect wool against moth attack, and indeed DDT is a very powerful stomach and contact poison for all kinds of insect pests which can attack textile fibres.

Dieldrin is one of the most used wool mothproofing agents. It is a complex highly chlorinated naphthalene compound which also finds extensive use in tropical countries for destroying mosquitoes and thus preventing malaria. Wool readily absorbs this substance from an aqueous emulsion of it, and if the treated wool then contains not less than 0·05% of dieldrin it will completely resist attack by moth and carpet beetles even after repeated washing and dry cleaning.

ANTI-SLIP FINISHING

The older natural fibres have a much rougher surface than the newer man-made fibres, and the same differences are found in the yarns made from these fibres. In the manufacture of a woven fabric consideration has to be given to the closeness of packing of the warp and weft yarns, for if they are spaced too far apart the fabric will readily show frays where its surface has been rubbed or pulled. In resisting such fraying the roughness of the yarns plays a part, and it can happen that although the yarn packing may by itself allow fraying, the fact that the yarns are rough will just give that little extra resistance to their sliding over each other (this occurs in the development of a fray) which is required to make the fabric sufficiently resistant to fraying.

Use of synthetic resins

In many instances the fabric manufacturer reduces the close packing of the yarns with the idea of cheapening the fabric and he will do this as near as possible to the limit where fraying becomes a definite risk. Now when the very smooth new synthetic fibres are used it is found that there is a greater tendency to produce fabrics which are liable to fray—the increased smoothness of nylon, Terylene, etc. yarns makes it necessary to have a closer packing of these yarns in woven fabrics. This adds considerably to their cost and yet perhaps apart from cost it is still desirable to make a fabric of loose texture. Thus has arisen the necessity for being able to finish synthetic fibre fabrics liable to fray so that the yarns of which they are made grip each other better and have an increased cohesion. This can now be done by impregnating the fabric with a composition containing a synthetic polymer or similar substance which becomes insoluble on drying at a high temperature and gives the surface of each fibre an increased roughness sufficient to make the fabric resist fraying. It is desirable, of course, that the polymer adheres tenaciously to the fibres.

WASH-AND-WEAR (DRIP-DRY) FINISHING

With the introduction of nylon wearing apparel such as shirts, pants, vests, etc., it soon became evident that these had a special natural property of great value to travellers and others. Such garments could be washed and then hung up overnight to dry with a simultaneous shedding of the creases left in them from the washing, so that the garments could be worn the next day without requiring ironing or pressing to restore to them their original appearance. The rapid drying and crease-shedding properties so characteristic of nylon materials are shared also by garments made with the newer synthetic fibres such as Terylene, Orlon, etc. To a large degree these properties arise from the strong hydrophobic character of such fibres whereby they absorb so little water when wetted.

It is easy to understand how the demand has arisen for a treatment which can be applied to cellulose fibre materials so that they can compete with synthetic fibre garments and fabrics. So today very large amounts of cotton and viscose rayon materials are finished with what is now known as 'wash-and-wear' and 'drip-dry' and 'easy-care' and 'minimum-iron' finishes.

Use of resin treatments

All of these new finishes are based on the use of resins such as are employed for the crease-resist finishing of cotton and viscose rayon fabrics, but particular attention has to be paid that the application of such resins is made under conditions which will not only give resistance to creasing when the fabric is in a dry state but also that any creases introduced into it during washing and the removal (by mangling or spinning) of excess moisture will shed themselves during the drying. Success in this direction is obtained by applying the resins under conditions such that a considerable degree of molecular cross-linking occurs in the fibres. Investigations have shown that wet creases are largely introduced into cotton and viscose rayon articles in the spin dryer which is now commonly used in association with the home washing machine.

Requirements of a wash-and-wear finish

Since it is known that the fabrics and garments which would normally be finished in this special way will be frequently washed or laundered it is desirable that the resin applied shall become fixed in the fibres so strongly that it is able to resist removal as a result of repeated washing, and it is also desirable that the resin shall be of a type which does not retain chlorine if the washing is supplemented by a whitening treatment with a liquor containing active chlorine in the form of hypochlorite. Thus it is evident that it is not sufficient for carrying out a wash-and-wear finish to apply exactly the same resin treatment as might be used for a fabric not liable to be so frequently washed; it is necessary to be more particular about the nature and amount of resin used.

Wet crease-resistance

Recently it has been found that a superior wash-and-wear finish on cotton and viscose rayon goods can be obtained if these are first treated with a solution of caustic soda to swell the fibres and then this is removed by thorough washing and drying without stretching or creasing. For cotton goods it is satisfactory to use a caustic soda solution of mercerising strength, but for viscose rayon fabrics it is necessary to use a much weaker liquor, say about 5 to 6%, since at medium concentrations, say 10 to 12%, the fibre swelling is so great that some dissolution of the cellulose fibre occurs and the fibres are left thinner and harsher as a result of the treatment. By this alkaline swelling the cellulose fibre material is given increased power to shed creases in the wet state, that is, after a wash.

The finishing treatment applied to produce a wash-and-wear finish also gives the fabric or garment added dimensional stability so that it resists shrinkage and change of shape. So far, these specially finished cotton and rayon materials are not so satisfactory as synthetic fibre articles, but improvement is steadily being made.

It should be noted that a further requirement of fabrics and garments claimed to have wash-and-wear characteristics is that pleats should be left in their original state. Since this also concerns methods for permanently pleating textile materials this aspect of wash-and-wear finishing will be considered together with permanent pleating.

Wash-and-wear wool fabrics

Although wash-and-wear finishing has so far been discussed in relation to cellulose fibre goods, attention has recently been given to the finishing of wool materials so as to confer on them similar characteristics. It is obvious that a treatment to reduce the felting properties of the wool will form a part of the wash-and-wear finishing of wool, since this will be required to give the wool dimensional stability. A treatment to make wool less hydrophile will be required. However, this problem is only as yet being tackled— perhaps a greater associated problem will be that of leaving the wool with its original desirable properties of softness, warmth of handle, and high resiliency.

PERMANENT PLEATING OF FABRICS AND GARMENTS

In taking into use a new or cleaned fabric it is always pleasing to see that it is nicely smoothed and folded. It is much the same with new clothes, but in this case it is often required that during wear the creases or pleats should persist and not gradually become blurred and later fall out altogether. So much importance is attached to creases and pleats that the periodic pressing of clothes is now commonplace—often it accompanies a dry cleaning.

Pleating and fibre properties

In the past, wool materials have been found to respond to pressing. If such pressing is applied at an elevated temperature and with the wool material slightly damp, the resulting creases have a fair degree of permanency. However, they tend gradually to fall out, especially in a damp atmosphere, and of course they disappear completely if the material is actually washed. It was consequently hailed as a great advantage that synthetic fibre fabrics and garments such as those made of Orlon, Courtelle, Acrilan, nylon, etc. could be creased or pleated at a high temperature and thereafter retain these creases and pleats during prolonged wear and even through washing. Today much use is made of the fact that hydrophobic synthetic fibre materials can be creased and pleated permanently so as not to require the periodic pressing necessary with materials made of the older hydrophile fibres.

Synthetic fibre fabrics

Synthetic fibre fabrics allow themselves to be permanently creased because they are thermoplastic and capable of being heat-set. When a synthetic fibre is heated near to its softening point, which is somewhat short of its melting point, its molecular packing becomes loosened and the fibre allows itself readily to be deformed, say by folding. Moreover the fibre molecules at the high temperature (this temperature will vary with the type of fibre since they soften at temperatures varying from 60° C for Vinyon to 160° C for Courtelle and above 220°C for nylon and Terylene) then readily move relatively to each other to accommodate the fold. If the fibre in this folded state be then cooled it retains the fold and will thereafter always do so even if repeatedly washed, provided that in any such treatment the fibre is not exposed to a temperature higher than or closely approaching that at which it was set in the folded state. The same considerations apply to yarns and fabrics made of synthetic fibres. For the production of a permanent crease or pleat the fabric has simply to be suitably folded and then subjected to pressure at a temperature near to but short of the melting point. It is general experience that in the case of a fabric consisting of a mixture of a synthetic fibre and a natural fibre, this can be permanently pleated by the above method if there is not less than about 80% of the synthetic fibre present in the fibre mixture.

Heat-setting of synthetic fibre goods before wet-processing

While heat-setting is now of great value in connection with maintaining an attractive appearance in clothes and fabrics, it has a special use in assisting the wet processing (scouring, dyeing, and finishing) of synthetic fibre goods. If, for instance, ladies' nylon stockings were, straight from the knitting machine, to be entered into a dye liquor and dyed for the usual period of $\frac{1}{2}$ to 1 hour, it would be found on taking them out of the dyeing machine that the hose would be much distorted and shrunken and full of creases which could not be removed; they would in fact be ruined. To prevent this, the dyer first draws each stocking over a metal shape and this with many others is then placed in a closed chamber where it is heated with steam for 2 or 3 minutes at a high temperature. When the hose are then taken off the shapes and dyed as described above they do not distort or crease but persistently retain the shape to which they were heat-set.

It has been found that this heat-setting is very useful and in many cases necessary for the protection of synthetic fibre materials of all kinds just before they are wet processed under conditions where they are free to shrink, become distorted and creased—a heat-set fabric or garment always tends to retain its shape and size provided it is not exposed to a temperature closely approaching that at which it was heat-set. There is perhaps one point which should be noted—repeated distortion of a heat-set material at a temperature somewhat below the heat-setting temperature can gradually counteract the effect of the heat-setting, since by such distortion movement of the fibres and even the molecules within them can be facilitated. Thus it is always advisable to handle the heat-set goods with reasonable care.

Permanent pleating of wool fabrics

Present-day use of synthetic fibre clothes has drawn attention to the fact that creases and pleats cannot be set so permanently in cotton and wool materials, and so recently investigations have commenced to discover methods for permanently creasing these latter materials. So far not much success has been obtained in the case of cotton, since to modify the form of a cotton fibre permanently it is necessary to subject it to a chemical treatment of some kind and this is not convenient in dealing with clothes and garments. But more definite progress has been made with wool materials.

It has earlier been pointed out that in a wool fibre the long keratin molecules of which wool is built up are held together laterally by numerous cross-linkages or bonds consisting of a chain of carbon atoms stretching from one molecule to another. When a wool fibre is deformed these bonds stretch or deform to accommodate the deformation of the fibre, but on release from the deforming force they bring the fibre back to its normal state. The disulphide bonds previously mentioned are important in this matter, and experience with wool creasing indicates that if these bonds are broken by some suitable chemical treatment at the time that a wool fibre is folded, the fibre molecules can the more readily adjust themselves to the folding by taking up fresh positions relatively to each other. Further, if at the same time fresh bonds can be formed simultaneously with or immediately after these changes, then the fibre accepts its folded state as normal and thereafter persistently tends to retain it. It is by taking advantage of these facts that recently two methods have become available to enable permanent creases and pleats to be formed in wool materials, but it has to be admitted that the permanence of such creases and pleats is less than that obtainable with a synthetic fibre material.

Wool pleating treatments

One method of permanent pleating is known as the Si-Ro-Set process. It was discovered in Australia and involves spraying or otherwise suitably applying to the wool fabric adjacent to where the crease is required a solution of ammonium thioglycollate (a reducing agent which when heated with wool has the power to break the disulphide bonds) and then hot pressing for a few minutes. Under these conditions the disulphide bonds of the fibres within the crease area are broken and new ones are formed which tend to keep the wool fibres in their new deformed state. Creases so produced are reasonably resistant to washing and dry cleaning.

In applying such a treatment to wool consideration has to be given to the possibility of the ammonium thioglycollate changing the colour of the dyes present.

The second method for permanently creasing wool arises from the results of research over many years on wool by Professor J. B. Speakman of Leeds University. Speakman found that when wool is treated with a solution of sodium bisulphite (a reducing agent) the disulphide bonds become broken. Further, the wool can then be washed free from the reducing agent and dried (under mild conditions) without causing an appreciable proportion of these broken bonds to re-unite or the formation of new bonds. Thus the wool fabric can now be hot pressed in a folded state under conditions which favour the formation of new bonds so that the creases or pleats imparted to it have a useful degree of permanency.

In this latter method of producing permanent creases and pleats in wool fabric it is believed that the changes in the bonds cross-linking adjacent wool fibres can be represented thus:

(1)   Wool molecule—CH_2—S—S—CH_2—Wool molecule
                 (disulphide bond)

$$\downarrow \text{Reduction with sodium bisulphite } NaHSO_3$$

Wool molecule—CH_2—SH + HO_3—S—CH_2—Wool molecule

(2) Wool molecule—CH_2—S—SO_3H + NH_2—R—Wool molecule

Wool molecule—CH_2—S—NH—R—Wool molecule

(new cross-link between
adjacent wool molecules)

Recently it has been found that ammonium thioglycollate and sodium bisulphite may be with advantage replaced by mono-ethanolamine bisulphite. For producing permanent creases a 30 to 40% aqueous solution of this substance should be sprayed either all over the fabric or only around the intended crease areas and the fabric or garment then be Hoffman pressed. The creased parts will be left with marked resistance to unwanted creases while the creases will be left reasonably fast to washing but certainly fast to dry cleaning.

PREVENTION OF PILLING IN FABRICS

With the wider use of the smooth-surfaced synthetic fibres for the production of soft handling knitwear garments such as sweaters, cardigans, etc. the defect of *pilling* has become more noticeable. The corresponding wool garments are also often found to *pill* and in many instances just as badly as the synthetic fibre garments. Finishers of such materials have thus become faced with the problem of finding a method for eliminating or at least reducing this fault.

Pilling reveals itself by the formation of numerous well-scattered small *pills* or tufts of entangled fibre ends loosely attached to the surface of the fabric. Closer examination shows each pill to be attached to the fabric surface by a relatively few fibres anchored at one end in the pill and at the other end in the fabric. The pill can be detached by pulling it away from the fabric. It is noticeable that with some fabrics the pills are strongly attached whilst in others the attachment is weak. Pilling seriously spoils the appearance of a garment or fabric.

Formation of pills on fabric surface

The formation of a pill is primarily due to a rubbing of the fabric surface to cause a number of fibre ends to protrude and then become entangled—it would appear that this working-out of the fabric surface by the fibre ends is because the fibres are smooth and thus not well anchored in the fabric. Obviously this fibre movement is more likely to occur in fabrics having a soft loose texture while it is much restricted (so that pills do not form) in fabrics made from hard twisted yarns. As the fabric is used some pills rub off while new ones are formed, so that the number of pills on the fabric at any particular time represents the balance between those being formed and those being rubbed off.

Preventive treatments

The problem of how to reduce the tendency of fabrics and garments to pill has been solved to some degree but not completely by so finishing the textile material that it has as sheer a surface as possible with no protruding fibre ends. This can be achieved by well singeing the fabric at as late a stage in dyeing and finishing as possible and by sizing the fabric with a composition which sticks the fibres together in the fabric (a difficulty here is to do this without giving the fabric undesirable stiffness), thus hindering their movement. The manufacturer can also help by avoiding the production of textile materials which are so loosely constructed that the movement of fibre ends out of the fabric surface is extremely easy. The synthetic fibre manufacturer can assist by producing fibres having a higher degree of roughness so that in yarn and fabric they grip each other more strongly.

However, it has been found that pilling can be reduced by a somewhat novel method with some types of fabric. This method requires that the surface of the fabric be brushed to give a pile which is then sheared to a uniform height. The fabric is then subjected to a treatment which causes the protruding fibre ends to shrink so strongly as to bury themselves firmly in the fabric surface. So far this method has achieved most success with nylon and Orlon materials.

Influence of fibre properties

It is to be noted that some of the new synthetic fibres being introduced carry the claim that in the form of fabric they have special resistance to pilling. Examples are Dacron Type 64, and Orlon Type 42. Fibres having a round cross-section are more liable to give fabrics which pill than are fibres of irregular shape such as those which are ribbon-like.

The tensile strength of the fibres can play a part in pill formation, since if this is high the pills will not readily become detached and vice versa. A fabric made of weak fibres prone to pilling might thus appear satisfactory since the pills would be brushed off shortly after formation and thus not accumulate to a point at which they appear numerous.

Apparatus is available to test the susceptibility of a fabric to pilling. It usually is of a type which allows a piece of the fabric to be rubbed or tumbled with itself or a standard abrasive surface so that after a definite period the number of pills formed per unit area can be counted.

Questions for Chapter V

1. Describe the use and construction and performance of a modern hot air stenter. Why are pin plates often used instead of clips for holding the fabric selvedges?

2. Knitted fabric is more easily distorted than woven fabric; indicate the additional arrangements which have to be provided with a hot air stenter to deal with knitted fabrics.

3. How can circular knitted fabrics be most conveniently dried and brought to a desired width?

4. Describe a brattice machine for drying loose knitted articles.

5. Describe how a 2- or 3-bed steam press can be used for the hot pressing of wool fabric or men's socks and so set them to desired dimensions or shape.

6. Linen fabrics are frequently beetled to give them a lustrous thready appearance. Describe two types of beetling machine for this purpose.

7. Give the essential constructional details of machines for raising a pile or hairy surface on fabrics.

8. Describe a machine which is used for shearing-off protruding fibre ends from a fabric so as to give it a sheer appearance or for bringing a pile surface to a desired thickness.

9. Describe a machine by which ladies' hose of nylon, rayon, or other fibre can be completely finished and set to shape during their passage through it at a steady rate.

10. Describe the basic principles which underlie crease-resist finishing processes as applied to cotton and rayon fabrics. Indicate the necessary precautions which should be taken to obtain a satisfactory result.

11. It is generally found that in changing one property of a fabric it

s

is impossible to avoid changing its other properties—often adversely. Discuss this with particular reference to the crease-resist finishing of cellulose fibre fabrics.

12. How would you measure the increase of crease-resistance obtained?

13. What special additional stage of processing must be introduced into an ordinary crease-resist treatment to make it satisfactory for linen fabrics?

14. What types of fabric (mention the type of fibre of which they are made) are not amenable to crease-resist finishing using resins?

15. Discuss how far crease-resistance is obtained by simple deposition of a resin within a fibre and how far by cross-linking of the fibre molecules.

16. Describe how you would remove a urea– or melamine–formaldehyde resin completely from cotton fabric.

17. What do you understand by the term 'chlorine retention' as applied to resin-finished fabrics? How can this property be considered a grave defect? Describe various types of resin or 'reactants' used in crease-resist finishing and indicate how far they effect molecular cross-linking and whether or not they confer 'chlorine retentive' properties on the fabric.

18. What do you understand by a wash-and-wear or minimum-iron or drip-dry finish and how can it most easily be obtained on cotton and viscose rayon fabrics?

19. Discuss the weakening and reduction of abrasion resistance which can result from resin-finishing cellulose fibre materials.

20. What are methylol compounds and what is their significance in crease-resist finishing?

21. Discuss the importance of the curing stage in the resin-finishing of fabrics. What is the effect of having a suitable small proportion of steam present?

22. Although ordinary crease-resist finishing is used to produce wash-and-wear characteristics in cotton and rayon fabrics it has been found desirable to apply an alkaline swelling pre-treatment to ensure *wet* crease-resistance. Discuss this.

23. At what stage in the home washing of clothes is there most risk of introducing creases which do not disappear in the final drying? Discuss this with regard to home-washing apparatus now in use.

24. Describe how early processes for making fabrics water-repellent or showerproof have been developed and improved.

25. Discuss modern water-repellent finishing methods based on the use of organic silicon compounds and on special organic compounds which allow a hydrophobic substance to be left combined with the fabric so finished.

26. Describe methods and apparatus for measuring the water repellency of fabrics.

27. Discuss wet fibre swelling in relation to the water repellency of a fabric and indicate how water-repellent sportswear can be produced without an application of a water-repellent agent.

28. Describe how a mixture of methylhydrogen– and dimethyl-silicones can be used to make cotton fabric water-repellent.

29. What do you understand by Ventile fabric? How is it made?

30. Compare the ways in which shrinkage occurs in cotton and in wool fabrics during washing.

31. Describe how washing shrinkage of a cotton or rayon fabric can be reduced practically to zero by the application of compressive shrinkage. Describe the essential features of Rigmel and Sanforizing machines as used for this purpose.

32. Why is it more difficult to obtain by compressive shrinkage methods zero washing shrinkage in viscose rayon than in cotton fabrics?

33. Discuss the effect of a resin finish in giving cellulose fibre fabrics reduced liability to shrink during washing.

34. Discuss the relationship between wet fibre swelling and the shrinkage which can take place in washing a cotton fabric.

35. Describe the various processes now available for making wool fabric less liable to felt and shrink during washing. Indicate their advantages and disadvantages.

36. Discuss the current theory that the main reason why wool materials shrink in washing is because each fibre is covered with numerous small overlapping scales and that these give the fibre a roughness which is greater in the tip-to-root than in the root-to-tip direction.

37. Describe the Dylan process for making wool unshrinkable.

38. How can resins be used to make wool unshrinkable? Explain their power to do this.

39. Describe treatments of wool materials which are beneficial yet depend on a shrinkage of the wool as made possible by the wool having the power to felt.

40. How can cotton fabric be given a high lustre by a mechanical treatment?

41. Describe how the handle and lustre of a fabric may be modified by passing through a calendering machine. Discuss the importance in this treatment of having suitable conditions of temperature, humidity, and pressure.

42. What is a Schreiner calender and also a friction lustring calender? How do the effects they produce on cotton fabric differ and for what reason?

43. Describe how resins can be used to produce washable glazed chintz cotton fabrics.

44. How are cotton and other fabrics embossed? Describe the machine used for this purpose. An ordinary embossed finish can be easily washed out; how can it be made wash-fast?

45. Describe the various flameproofing treatments now available and as generally applied to cotton and rayon materials. What do you understand by the term flameproof?

46. Explain the significance in connection with flameproofing treatments of the 'volatile products' and 'residual char' formed by the burning of textile material. What significance has 'afterglow'?

47. Draw up two lists of all the textile fibres, classifying into two groups those fibres which readily ignite and those which are difficult to burn.

48. Name some simple substances which can be dried into fabrics, thus making them difficult to ignite or burn.

49. Indicate the importance of various phosphorus-containing compounds which have been found useful for giving a wash-fast flameproof finish to textile materials.

50. What is the Proban process for flameproofing textile materials?

51. Discuss how electrostatic electricity can be formed in the mechanical handling of textile fibres and its objectionable character. Discuss how this 'static' is mainly associated with hydrophobic fibres although it can also be associated with hydrophile fibres if these are handled in a very dry condition.

52. What three methods are commonly used in the textile industry to combat the objectionable effects of 'static'? Describe the principles on which anti-static agents are compounded.

53. How is the electrical conductance of a fibre concerned with its tendency or otherwise to accumulate charges of electricity when handled so as to be subject to rubbing or friction?

54. Describe the susceptibility of hydrophile and hydrophobic fibres to attack by micro-organisms and also describe protective treatments which can be given.

55. Describe how wool materials are attacked and damaged by moth. Are any other kinds of fibre similarly attacked by moth? Describe any treatment by which wool can be made mothproof.

56. The smoothness of the fibre surface can affect the properties and usefulness of the fibre—discuss this fact. How does the structure of a fabric influence its liability to fray and how can this fault be prevented or corrected?

57. Discuss the wash-and-wear and drip-dry characteristics of synthetic fibre materials and describe processes which are now being used to give similar properties to cotton and rayon materials.

58. Discuss the influence of the wet swelling properties of a fibre in relation to its wash-and-wear characteristics in the form of fabric.

59. Indicate some special modifications of wool which will be necessary (by the use of finishing treatments) to give it wash-and-wear characteristics.

60. Explain the formation of a crease in a fabric and indicate the circumstances under which it could be fast to washing. Describe two recently devised processes for the permanent pleating of wool fabrics.

61. Describe so-called heat-setting treatments for synthetic fibre materials so that they acquire increased dimensional stability. What improvements in the usefulness of triacetate fabrics can be obtained by a heat-treatment for a short period at up to 250° C?

62. Why are ladies' nylon stockings heat-set to shape under dry or moist high temperature conditions before being wet processed, for instance by scouring and dyeing?

63. What do you understand by the term pilling? Mention types of fabric particularly liable to this defect. How can the tendency for a fabric to pill be measured?

64. Describe methods which have been recommended to overcome or reduce pilling in a wool or synthetic fibre material.

65. How does the strength of a fibre affect the formation of pills under ordinary conditions of wear?

CHAPTER VI

The Washing and Laundering of Fabrics and Garments

All textile materials have the power to collect dust and dirt (now-adays often referred to as *soil*) arising from their use for decorative purposes or as articles of clothing. Those materials made with smooth fibres soil less easily than those made with rough fibres, for obvious reasons. Actually today much research is being carried out to improve the soiling-resistance of textile fibres and one method is that of applying to them a suspension of extremely fine particles of an inert substance in order to fill up the irregularities of each fibre surface so that soil cannot be so readily collected in them. Another method would be that of making textile fibres uni-formly smooth, but such smooth fibres would create other prob-lems, mainly concerned with fabric and garment manufacture. It has therefore to be accepted that textile materials will always periodically have to be cleaned.

Choice of a cleaning treatment

The cleaning of a textile material can be accomplished by one or other of two main methods—*washing* with aqueous detergent liquors or *dry-cleaning* with organic solvents substantially free from water. The choice of method will depend not only on the type of textile material but also on the nature of the soil present in it. If the fabric or garment is one which in water will lose its finish (for example, lustre, handle, or embossed pattern) or will shrink (either by relaxation from a stretched state or, in the case of wool, by felt-ing) then it should not be washed in an *aqueous* detergent liquor but be cleaned with a dry cleaning method. On the other hand, if the textile material is not harmed by contact with water it should be washed with an aqueous detergent liquor since this is usually the cheaper and more efficient method. However, it must be re-membered that greasy soil (but not soil containing protein and mineral matter) is most easily removed by an organic solvent and that all soil other than that containing much fat, wax, or oil is best removed by aqueous detergent liquors.

Synthetic detergents

Dry cleaning at home is not practicable, but ordinary washing is much practised. It is thus fortunate that although organic solvents are very effective for the removal of greasy soil, the housewife now has available to her many new detergents and washing products which can make an ordinary aqueous detergent liquor nearly as effective as a dry cleaning solvent in removing greasy impurities from most types of textile material. These modern detergents are described later.

HOME LAUNDERING

Nature of soil

Turning now more particularly to the washing of fabrics and garments in ordinary aqueous detergent liquors at home, it is useful to consider the composition of the soil to be found in the goods and how they can be removed. The soil will normally include mineral matters, greasy substances, proteins, and dried perspiration. Some of these will be water-soluble and the others insoluble. Protein impurities are likely to be soluble in cold or warm water but to be made insoluble by contact with boiling water—they are likely to be made water-soluble by treatment with alkali, hot or cold. In general, most types of impurity will be more soluble in hot than cold water, and hot to boiling water has the advantage that it can more readily penetrate fabric and yarn to reach the individual fibres. From these facts it is evident that often a useful degree of cleaning can be obtained by simply rinsing the soiled textile material in cold to warm water—boiling water is to be avoided since it might make protein impurities insoluble before they are dissolved in the rinsing water.

Emulsification of soil in the detergent liquor

While such simple rinsing treatment is useful it cannot take the place of the main washing process in which detergents are used. In this process the prime object is to apply a detergent liquor which will emulsify the greasy impurities and thus facilitate their passing out of the textile material into the main bulk of the detergent liquor together with the other impurities (bound to the fibres by the greasy impurities), which are either water-soluble or which by the grease emulsification become detached from the fibres. After a suitable period of contact of the textile material with the detergent liquor most of the impurities should thus have passed into this liquor, either in an emulsified or soluble or suspended form, and if this liquor could instantly and completely be removed the textile material would be left clean. Unfortunately this instantaneous complete removal of the detergent liquor cannot be achieved—it has to be removed in successive stages of mangling (or by hydro-extraction using a 'spinner' or centrifuge) and rinsing with fresh lots of water, and this makes complete removal of the impurities more difficult to attain.

Re-deposition of soil

So long as the textile material is in contact with the detergent liquor a two-way action takes place. At the same time that soil is passing out of the fabric into the main bulk of detergent liquor some of this soil is passing from this liquor into the fabric and there being re-deposited on the fibres. Cleaning takes place when the rate of soil removal exceeds the rate of soil re-deposition, and this is governed partly by the character of the detergent liquor, the amount of liquor, its movement relative to the fabric, and its temperature and soil-suspending power. Obviously it is better to use a large volume of detergent liquor, but only if it is economically satisfactory to use the larger amounts of detergent and other products in it required to maintain its satisfactory emulsifying and soil suspending power.

CONDITIONS FOR EFFICIENT WASHING

Useful facts concerning the nature and use of a detergent liquor for washing clothes are given below.

1. *Movement of liquor*

Washing is most effective when there is a free flow of detergent liquor *through* the textile material. However such materials are washed it is necessary that they move relatively to each other and the detergent liquor. In some home washing machines the goods are directly propelled within the liquor while in others the liquor is propelled to move between the goods. Both of these methods are satisfactory only if they ensure that the liquor passes *through* and not *over* the surface of the textile materials. A fabric (woven or knitted) contains innumerable interstices and when the moving liquor meets it in a washing machine this liquor will partly be deflected to pass over the fabric surface and will partly pass through the interstices—much will depend on the force of the moving liquor and also on the compact nature of the fabric. But if it is somewhat difficult for the moving liquor to pass through the fabric interstices it will be even more difficult for it to pass through the yarns and between the individual fibres of which they are made, although it is this penetration of the yarns which is required. Fibre swelling has the effect of making it more difficult for the detergent liquor to penetrate and pass through yarn as distinct from fabric.

Need for thread penetration by the detergent liquor. It is obvious that any soil actually within the yarns of which the textile material is made is much more difficult to remove than is soil simply deposited on the surface of the fabric. Assistance in securing the desired liquor penetration can be obtained by adding substances to the detergent liquor which lower the surface tension of the washing liquor (ordinary soap does this and most of the recently introduced proprietary washing powders and detergents contain substances having this special property), for with reduced surface tension the liquor has increased wetting and penetrating powers. Also, a boiling liquor has excellent power to enter even tight yarns, since its surging action can physically cause a separation of the individual fibres.

2. *Content of emulsifying and detergent products*

Pure water alone makes a very poor washing liquor since it has a high surface tension and thus finds it difficult to penetrate textile materials, while it has no emulsifying action on greasy impurities and but little power to decompose and solubilise protein and similar substances. Its washing power is almost confined to its ability to dissolve out soluble impurities in the textile material. Hence the universal addition to the washing liquor of soaps and other products.

Use of soap. Soap is an extremely useful washing assistant since it serves several purposes simultaneously. It much lowers the surface tension of water, thus assisting to increase its wetting and penetrating powers. It has the power to emulsify greasy sub-ances. A further important property is that if used in sufficient concentration it gives 'body' to the detergent liquor so that it can keep in suspension finely divided water-insoluble impurities which have been washed out of the textile material. The grease-emulsifying and soil-suspending power of a soap liquor can hinder considerably the re-deposition upon the textile material of impurities which have been removed from it in the washing process.

Some soap-containing proprietary washing powders also contain mild alkalis and silicates and phosphates which are termed 'builders', since they boost the detergent action of the soap and prevent the development of any acidity in the washing process which could cause a decomposition of the soap with consequent loss of detergent power. They may also contain carboxymethyl cellulose (CMC) which is a white water-soluble product having strong soil-suspending power.

Nowadays ordinary soap is often largely replaced by the so-called synthetic detergents which are not adversely affected by hard water. These valuable products will be described later in dealing with hard and soft water.

Use of ammonia. The presence of ammonia in a detergent liquor containing soap is often advantageous. Firstly it is a weak alkali and as such does not cause damage to any type of textile material including wool. Secondly it can convert part of the usual sodium soap into an ammonium soap which is more liquid and thus better able to penetrate the textile material and effect improved cleaning. Sodium carbonate or sodium bicarbonate can be used instead of ammonia, but not if wool is present. At temperatures above 40° C sodium bicarbonate changes into sodium carbonate and this latter alkali can be harmful to wool, especially in hot washing liquors.

3. *Temperature*

Provided that the impurities in the textile material are not of a type which are made water-insoluble by boiling water and provided that the material does not contain loose dyes, it much assists the detergent power of a washing liquor to maintain it at or near to boiling temperature. At about 100° C maximum decomposition with accompanying water-solubilisation of impurities can occur and, of course, a surging boiling liquor is much better able to pene-trate thoroughly the textile material and remove impurities occluded in the yarns themselves. Unfortunately, in home washing it is sometimes difficult to employ boiling liquors and many types of home washing machines are not adapted to their use. However, with wool materials it is not advisable to employ a boiling detergent liquor since this can accelerate felting shrinkage and can cause the discoloration of white wool materials. Actually in dyeing and finishing works wool goods are frequently boiled for one or two hours without harm, but the boiling liquor is acidic to a degree not to be tolerated in home washing—it is the boiling in a neutral or alkaline liquor which damages and discolours wool. In boiling water protein impurities become insoluble.

THE WHITENING OF WASHED TEXTILE MATERIALS

Following a washing treatment some white textile materials are left off-white to a degree which indicates that they should be lightly bleached to a purer white. This bleaching should not be undertaken at home unless it is definitely required, since it is comparatively easy to overbleach and do damage to the textile material.

Cotton and wool materials can be whitened by steeping for a few hours, say overnight, in a warm (about 40° C) two-volume solution of hydrogen peroxide to which has been added quite a small proportion of ammonia and sodium silicate. The ammonia should bring the bleaching liquor to pH 9 to 10, while the sodium silicate stabilises the liquor so that no bubbles of oxygen gas should be liberated from it. After the desired degree of whitening has been obtained it is merely necessary to wash thoroughly.

Hypochlorite whitening treatment

Cotton and other cellulose fibre (but not wool or nylon) materials can alternatively be whitened by a similar steeping in a cold liquor containing sodium hypochlorite (the liquor should contain 0·5 to 1·0 grams per litre of active chlorine). After the necessary whitening the goods should be thoroughly washed in water and then in a hot soap solution which acts as an anti-chlor.

When bleaching by either of the above methods it is useful first to test the fastness of any coloured threads which may be present in the textile material. The further information previously given on bleaching should also be studied.

It may also be here recalled that many of the synthetic detergent

powders contain an optical bleaching agent of the type previously
described, so that it may be possible by their use to secure the
degree of whitening required and so avoid the use of hydrogen
peroxide or hypochlorite. Some of the proprietary detergent
powders contain a peroxide or perborate which is capable of acting
similarly to hydrogen peroxide.

THE WASHING OF COLOURED GOODS

In washing coloured textile materials there is always the risk of
loss of colour, either by destruction of the dye or by its bleeding
into the detergent liquor (in this case there is the further risk of
staining adjacent materials). There is only one really satisfactory
method of deciding whether such colour loss is likely to be in-
curred—to conduct a small preliminary test. However, it is generally true that vat, sulphur, reactive, and insoluble azoic dyes on
cellulose fibre materials are fast enough to withstand ordinary
washing, while chrome mordant and pre-metallised dyes on wool
have similar useful fastness properties. In washing coloured wool
goods it is advisable to avoid the use of alkaline liquors since the
alkalinity favours removal of dye—by contrast the presence of
some acid in the liquor assists dye fastness.

Direct cotton dyes on cellulose fibre goods are liable to bleed if
left lying while saturated with a hot alkaline soap liquor. Such
materials should always be rinsed in cold water immediately after
washing and then not allowed to lie in a heap while wet, for the
pressure of the heap can assist a marking-off of colour.

SHRINKAGE OF FABRICS AND GARMENTS IN WASHING

Cotton, linen, and other cellulose fibre articles which are in a
stretched state will certainly shrink to their true size and shape as
soon as wetted. Continued washing will cause only a moderate
degree of shrinkage, if any. On the other hand, following the relaxation shrinkage to which wool materials are subject in the same way
as cotton goods, there can follow shrinkage due to progressive felting in which the wool fibres close up on each other because each
fibre is covered with an epithelial scale layer as previously described. This felting shrinkage can continue up to the point that
the fabric cannot physically become more dense with the fibres so
strongly entangled that they cannot be separated from each other.

Felting shrinkage of wool goods

The shrinkage of wool materials is greater as the fibres have more freedom of movement, and it arises from the fact that when a mass of fibres is squeezed they become interlocked, aided by the protruding edges of the scales, so that they can never return completely to their former open state—the mass of fibres becomes more compact with each squeeze. The presence of a warm soapy or similar aqueous liquor is necessary to felting since it swells the fibres and lubricates them as part of the felting process. Thus in the washing of wool materials it is important always to remember that repeated squeezing, either by hand or mangling, is the most important cause of felting with the shrinkage that it entails. Wool materials should always be worked in the detergent liquor as lightly as possible with avoidance of all unnecessary squeezing. It is sometimes suggested that felting shrinkage can be avoided by the use of soft water and better quality soaps, but it can here be definitely stated there is much doubt about this, and in any case the protection against felting which might be so obtained is very very small as compared with that securable by avoiding squeezing and working of wool material.

From what has been stated above it will be evident that loosely constructed wool materials are much more subject to felting shrinkage than those tightly constructed with hard twisted yarns. Before tightly constructed wool materials can felt appreciably their structure has to be loosened sufficiently in the washing process to allow the fibre movement which occurs in felting.

THE WASHING OF RESIN-FINISHED FABRICS

Many fabrics and garments are today finished with a synthetic resin to give them resistance to creasing and shrinkage, and other desirable characteristics which are generally considered to be fast to washing. These characteristics depend on the presence in the textile material of a water-insoluble resin and a certain degree of cross-linking of the cellulose molecules of which the cotton, viscose rayon, linen, etc. fibres are built up. If this resin is removed and the cross-linked structure broken down in washing then the valuable characteristics are lost.

The resins employed are of a type which do resist being washed out of cellulose fibre materials if the washing is carried out with care. But if the washing conditions are too drastic then the resin will gradually be removed and the cross-links broken. It is thus advised always to wash such materials carefully with avoidance of much rubbing and of boiling detergent liquors.

Hypochlorite whitening requires care

The whitening of resin-finished cotton or similar materials with hypochlorite preparations is also to be avoided because the material (according to the type of resin present) can greedily absorb and retain the active chlorine thus applied and thus cause yellowing and (in hot ironing) a serious lowering of strength. A whitening with hydrogen peroxide instead of hypochlorite is preferable.

Wash-and-wear and drip-dry cotton and rayon materials are usually resin-finished and the washing and whitening precautions noted above should be taken with these materials.

HARD AND SOFT WATER

The success of washing textile materials is largely dependent on the kind of water employed. If it is hard and no special detergents are available so that ordinary soap has to be used, then it may be practically impossible to wash fabrics and garments so that they really become clean. In hard water soap forms a voluminous precipitate which easily collects the soil removed from the textile material being washed, and this precipitate re-deposits on the goods and cannot be completely removed however much they are subsequently rinsed. Unfortunately hard water is the only kind of water to be obtained in many parts of Britain—areas such as those around Glasgow and Manchester are exceptionally fortunate in having a household water supply of almost zero hardness.

Mineral content of hard water

Hard water arises from rain sinking through the earth and dissolving certain mineral salts, especially those of calcium and magnesium, and more particularly the carbonate, bicarbonates, chlorides, and sulphates of calcium and magnesium. All of these salts added to a solution of soap cause the precipitation of this in the form of a voluminous scum.

Temporary and permanent hardness

The hardness of water can, of course, be determined by the

amount of soap which it will precipitate under standardised conditions, and perhaps this method of measurement is of most practical importance to those in charge of washing and laundering processes. Hardness is usually expressed in terms of the number of parts of calcium carbonate per 100,000 parts of water.

When hard water is boiled any calcium and magnesium bicarbonate (both soluble) are converted by loss of carbon dioxide into the corresponding carbonates (both insoluble). Thus if the hardness of the water is determined before and after such boiling there will be a significant difference in the values obtained if there is much calcium or magnesium bicarbonate originally present. The difference will be due to the separation of the carbonates of calcium and magnesium which are formed thus:

$$Ca(HCO_3)_2 \xrightarrow{\text{Heating}} CaCO_3 + H_2O + CO_2$$

Calcium bicarbonate	Calcium carbonate	Carbon dioxide
(soluble)	(insoluble)	(gas)

The hardness of water due to calcium and magnesium bicarbonates present in the water is termed *temporary hardness*, while that residual hardness after boiling to convert the bicarbonates into carbonates and the filtering off of these calcium and magnesium carbonates is termed *permanent hardness*—both are usually expressed as the number of equivalent parts of calcium carbonate ($CaCO_3$) per 100,000 parts of water. The *total hardness* is the sum of the *temporary* and *permanent* hardness values.

Both temporary and permanent hardness are effective in causing the precipitation of a soap scum.

Water softening

It is possible to wash reasonably satisfactorily with hard water even when this is very hard, say 40 degrees of hardness, by avoiding the use of ordinary soap and employing in its stead synthetic detergents not adversely affected by hard water. But this would be expensive. From this viewpoint it is profitable to soften hard water before use and this can be achieved by use of a zeolite softening apparatus. However, there is a method of softening termed the lime-soda process which is, on the large scale, often found suitable for reducing the hardness of very hard water so that it is more suitable for further softening by the zeolite method.

The lime-soda softening method consists of adding to the hard water having both temporary and permanent hardness a mixture of lime and soda ash (sodium carbonate) whereby the following reactions take place:

Reaction of lime—Removal of temporary hardness due to presence of calcium and magnesium bicarbonates.

1. $Ca(HCO_3)_2 + Ca(OH)_2 = 2CaCO_3 + 2H_2O$
2. $Mg(HCO_3)_2 + Ca(OH)_2 = Mg(OH)_2 + 2CaCO_3 + 2H_2O$
3. $CO_2 + Ca(OH)_2 = CaCO_3 + H_2O$

It is to be noted that the lime converts the calcium and magnesium bicarbonates into insoluble calcium carbonate and magnesium hydroxide respectively, which can be settled and filtered off. Also any free dissolved carbon dioxide gas in the hard water is removed by its conversion into calcium carbonate.

Reaction of soda ash—Removal of permanent hardness due to presence of calcium and magnesium chlorides and sulphates.

4.
$$\begin{matrix} CaCl_3 \\ + \\ CaSO_4 \end{matrix} + 2Na_2CO_3 = \begin{matrix} CaCO_3 + 2NaCl \\ + \qquad + \\ CaCO_3 \quad Na_2SO_4 \end{matrix}$$

5.
$$\begin{matrix} MgCl_2 \\ + \\ MgSO_4 \end{matrix} + \begin{matrix} 2Na_2CO_3 \\ + \\ 2Ca(OH)_2 \end{matrix} = \begin{matrix} 2Mg(OH)_2 \\ + \\ 2CaCO_3 \end{matrix} + \begin{matrix} 2NaCl \\ + \quad or \\ Na_2SO_4 \end{matrix}$$

It is here again to be noted that the calcium is removed as calcium carbonate and the magnesium as magnesium hydroxide.

As a result of lime-soda softening most of the temporary and permanent hardness can be removed and corresponding amounts of sodium chloride and sodium sulphate are left dissolved in the water. Since the above reactions do not go to completion under the conditions customarily existing, the water is left with some residual hardness, say equivalent 3 to 5 parts of $CaCO_3$ per 100,000 parts of water. But the nearly softened water can then be passed through a zeolite softening process and brought to practically zero hardness.

The *zeolite softening process* depends on the use of natural or artificial zeolites in a granular state; these are sodium aluminium silicates. When hard water is passed over the granules there is a rapid exchange of the sodium of the zeolite for the calcium and magnesium in the hard water and this continues up to a point when substantially all the exchangeable sodium has passed into the water (it is present there as sodium chloride and sulphate) and the zeolite may be considered to be saturated with an equivalent amount of calcium and magnesium. The water will have been softened proportionally to this removal from it of calcium and magnesium thus:

$$\text{Na Zeolite} + \begin{matrix} \text{CaCl}_2 \text{ (or SO}_4) \\ \text{MgCl}_2 \text{ (or SO}_4) \end{matrix} = \begin{matrix} \text{Ca} \\ \text{Mg} \end{matrix}\Big\} \text{Zeolite} + \begin{matrix} \text{NaCl} \\ \text{or} \\ \text{Na}_2\text{SO}_4 \end{matrix}$$

Regeneration of zeolite

At this stage the zeolite granules can be restored to their original state by passing over them a strong solution of common salt (sodium chloride) when the calcium and magnesium become displaced by sodium thus:

$$\begin{matrix} \text{Ca} \\ \text{Mg} \end{matrix}\Big\} \text{Zeolite} + \text{NaCl} = \text{Na Zeolite} + \begin{matrix} \text{CaCl}_2 \\ \text{MgCl}_2 \end{matrix}$$

The common salt solution leaving the zeolite and now containing calcium and magnesium in the form of soluble chlorides is run to waste, as also is the water which is afterwards used to wash the regenerated zeolite free from retained common salt solution. After such treatment the zeolite now again consists of its original sodium aluminium silicate and is ready for the softening of a further amount of hard water. These processes of softening and regenerating can be repeated for a very large number of times, and the zeolite thus affords a very convenient method of water softening, especially if the water is only of moderate hardness. By such softening it is possible to reduce the hardness of water equivalent to about one part of $CaCO_3$ per 100,000 parts of water—a state in which the water is extremely suitable for washing textile materials even if ordinary soap is used.

Use of sequestering agents for hard water

The value of certain sequestering agents in dyeing has already been mentioned, and it should now be noted that some of these can be very useful, since when they are added to hard water, which may also be contaminated with iron, the adverse effects in the washing of textile materials are largely counteracted. Important sequestering agents which when added to hard water in

T

suitable proportions sequester the calcium and magnesium so as to allow the use of soap without formation of objectionable soap scum, include sodium pyrophosphate, $Na_4P_2O_7$, and especially hexametaphosphate $(NaPO_3)_6$. The latter substance is also very useful for sequestering iron impurities in the water.

More recently sequestering agents based on ethylene diamine tetra-acetate having the formula

$$HOOC.CH_2 \diagdown \qquad\qquad \diagup CH_2COOH$$
$$N-CH_2.CH_2-N$$
$$HOOC.CH_2 \diagup \qquad\qquad \diagdown CH_2COOH$$

have become available, and they are even more effective than the phosphates mentioned above according to the temperature and other conditions of washing. By use of these sequestering agents it is possible to avoid the softening of the washing water, but they are relatively expensive.

SOAPS AND SYNTHETIC DETERGENTS

Many natural fats as obtained from animal and vegetable sources (for example, lard and coconut oil) consist of glycerides of fatty acids. These glycerides can be decomposed by acid or alkaline saponification into their components, glycerine and fatty acids. The fatty acids are similar in composition in conforming to the general formula, R—$COOH$, in which R stands for a hydrocarbon radical consisting of a long linear chain of carbon atoms to which are also attached hydrogen atoms. Well-known fatty acids which enter into the formation of soaps and which are obtained from the glycerides mentioned above include palmitic, stearic, and oleic acids having the following formulae:

$C_{17}H_{33}COOH$	$C_{15}H_{31}COOH$	$C_{17}H_{35}COOH$
Oleic acid	Palmitic acid	Stearic acid

$(C_{15}H_{31}COOH$
$= CH_3CH_2CH_2CH_2CH_2CH_2CH_2CH_2CH_2CH_2CH_2CH_2CH_2CH_2CH_2COOH)$

A characteristic of these fatty acids is that they readily form water-soluble ammonium, sodium, and potassium soaps having (for stearic acid soaps) the formulae:

$C_{17}H_{35}COONH_4$	$C_{17}H_{35}COONa$	$C_{17}H_{35}COOK$
Ammonium stearate soap	Sodium stearate soap	Potassium stearate soap

and these have detergent properties. The sodium soaps are usually hard, whereas the ammonium and potassium soaps are soft. The sodium soaps are cheaper to make and are more used than the others. The hardness of the soap can also be influenced by the fatty acid from which it is made. For instance, oleic acid (a so-called unsaturated acid because it contains two fewer hydrogen atoms than the maximum with which the carbon atoms can combine) usually gives softer soaps than do palmitic and stearic acids.

Insoluble metal soaps

The corresponding calcium, magnesium, iron, aluminium, and other metal soaps are water-insoluble, and this explains how it is that when, say, a sodium soap solution is added to a solution of one of these metal salts, say calcium chloride, the insoluble calcium soap is formed and precipitated thus:

$$2C_{17}H_{35}COONa + CaCl_2 = (C_{17}H_{35}COO)_2Ca + 2NaCl$$

Sodium stearate soap	Calcium chloride	Insoluble calcium soap	Sodium chloride

It is thus not satisfactory to use ordinary soap in hard water for the washing of textile materials, and its defect of forming an insoluble soap scum by reaction with calcium or magnesium salts in the hard water appears to come from the reactivity of its carboxyl group (COOH) in combining with the calcium or magnesium. If, therefore, it is desired to make a soap not subject to precipitation in hard water yet containing the hydrocarbon radical ($C_{17}H_{33}$ or $C_{15}H_{31}$ or $C_{17}H_{35}$), then it seems desirable to replace the carboxyl group by some other similar water-solubilising group but differing from the carboxyl group in giving a water-soluble compound with a metal such as calcium, magnesium, iron, etc. It has been found that the sulphato group, $O.SO_3H$, fulfils this need as shown below:

$$C_{18}H_{37}O.SO_3Na + CaCl_2 = (C_{18}H_{37}O.SO_3)_2Ca + 2NaCl$$

Soluble		Soluble	

Such new soap substitutes are formed by first converting the fatty acid into the corresponding fatty alcohol by reduction and then sulphonating this with concentrated sulphuric acid, thus:

$$C_{17}H_{35}COOH$$
Stearic acid

Reduction

$$C_{18}H_{37}OH$$
Stearyl alcohol

Sulphonation

$$C_{18}H_{37}O.SO_3H$$
Stearyl sulphate
(detergent substitute for sodium stearate soap)

For some years the sodium salts of the sulphates of fatty alcohols instead of fatty acids proved most useful soap substitutes in so far as they could be used without precipitation in hard water; they are still in use today. But it has in recent years been found better to replace the fatty alcohol component of the detergent by an aromatic component based on benzene or naphthalene since this avoids the use of raw materials having a food value. Thus two very popular synthetic detergents in use today are dodecyl benzene sulphonate having the formula

$$C_{12}H_{25}$$

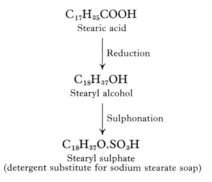

$$SO_3Na$$

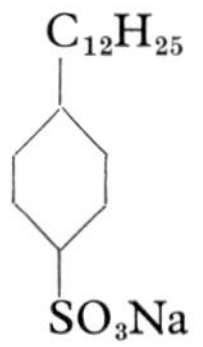

and dibutyl naphthalene sulphonate having the formula

$$C_4H_9$$
$$C_4H_9$$ —$$SO_3Na$$

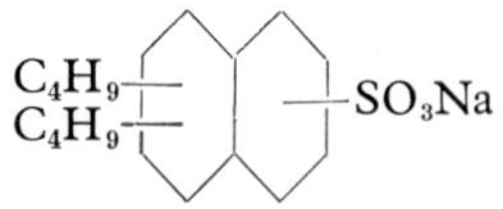

It is now seen that by considering the chemical structure of ordinary soap (the sodium or other water-soluble salt of a high molecular weight fatty acid such as stearic acid) in relation to its defect of forming insoluble calcium, magnesium, and other metal soaps so that ordinary soap is not a satisfactory detergent for use with hard water, and then replacing the carboxyl group (COOH)

of the ordinary soap by a sulphato ($O.SO_3H$) or sulpho (SO_3H) group, this defect has been overcome so that new soap substitutes having soap's detergent properties, and also the additional valuable property of being substantially unaffected by the metal salts in hard water, have become available to make the washing of textile materials so much simpler and more efficient.

Surface active agents

During the past thirty years much research has been carried out with a view not only to discovering soap substitutes but also to gaining new knowledge about all the various factors which affect the wet processing of textile goods. It has previously been indicated that in such processing it is desirable to have available substances which can be added to the aqueous processing liquor which can exert specific functions, e.g. to promote wetting of the material, emulsify grease impurities washed out of it, counteract any adverse influence which metal salts may have on the efficiency of the wet processing, and give softness of handle to the textile material being processed. Now several hundred different substances of this kind are available and many of them are in use.

Composite nature of modern detergents

From the viewpoint of washing textile materials it is most important that the soap or other substance employed should have high detergent properties and that it should also preferably have excellent wetting, grease-emulsifying, and penetrating powers. As might be expected it is not generally possible to have all these desired properties to their maximum power in one substance and so in general it is better to employ in any washing liquor a mixture of such substances, each able to contribute its own particular assistance to the washing process. This is the practice today in offering to the public proprietary so-called synthetic detergents—they are compounded of ingredients of the kind noted above so that washing can be carried out efficiently in water whether it be hard or soft and whether the materials being washed are soiled with greasy impurities or not. In addition, many of these detergents contain a proportion of an optical bleaching or fluorescent whitening agent of the type previously described.

Most of the substances of this kind are included in a group termed '*surface active agents*' or more briefly '*surfactants*'. These terms indicate that the substances have special influence in the boundary zone which can exist in a washing process between the fibre surface and the applied detergent liquor. It is, for instance, especially important that most of these substances can lower the surface tension of water and so promote a more rapid spreading of the detergent liquor over the surface of the fibres, with an accompanying more complete penetration of the fibre substance than can be obtained with water not containing them.

Classification and nature of surfactants

Surface active agents or surfactants can be usefully classified into three main groups—*anion-active*, *non-ionic*, and *cation-active* —but in general their special value in the washing and other wet processing of textile materials derives from the fact that their molecules contain a hydrophobic hydrocarbon residue (aliphatic or aromatic) consisting of several carbon atoms joined together to form an open chain or a closed ring (see previous formulae). Detergent, wetting, grease-emulsifying, softening, and other properties are due to this long hydrocarbon residue. However, such a hydrocarbon residue is insoluble in water and to be used in the wet processing of textile materials it must be brought into a water-soluble form. This can be attained by attaching to the hydrocarbon residue a water-solubilising group which may be chosen from quite a number including carboxyl (COOH), sulpha to (O.SO$_3$H), sulpho or sulphonic (SO$_3$H), hydroxyl (OH), amide (CONH$_2$), etc. It is thus seen that the usual surface active agent is a substance which is soluble in water or can be dispersed in water so as to be easily applicable to textile materials from aqueous liquors, and that it contains a hydrophobic component which is generally a hydrocarbon residue united to a hydrophile component which will be one or other of the water-solubilising groups mentioned above. This special structure of a surface active agent is made clearer by the following formulae:

Hydrophobic (anion) component	*Hydrophile (cation)* or *water-solubilising* component
$-$ve	$+$ve
CH$_3$.CH$_2$········CH$_2$.CH$_2$—————O.SO$_3$H	
(An aliphatic or open chain of carbon atoms)	A sulphato group

A sulphated fatty alcohol

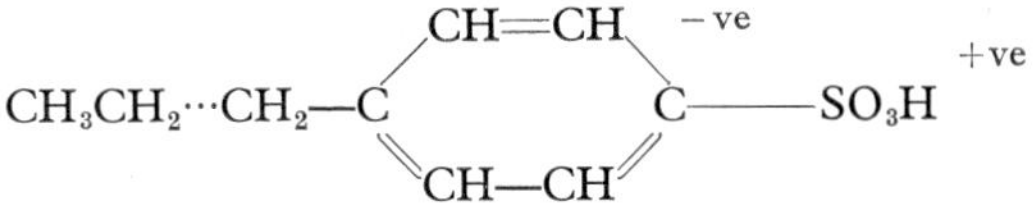

$$CH_3CH_2\cdots CH_2\!\!-\!\!C\!\!\begin{array}{c} CH\!\!=\!\!CH \\[2pt] \\[2pt] CH\!\!-\!\!CH \end{array}\!\!\overset{-\text{ve}}{\underset{+\text{ve}}{C}}\!\!-\!\!SO_3H$$

[An aromatic (ring) chain of carbon   A sulphonic
atoms having an attached aliphatic   group
or open chain of carbon atoms]

A sulphonated alkylbenzene

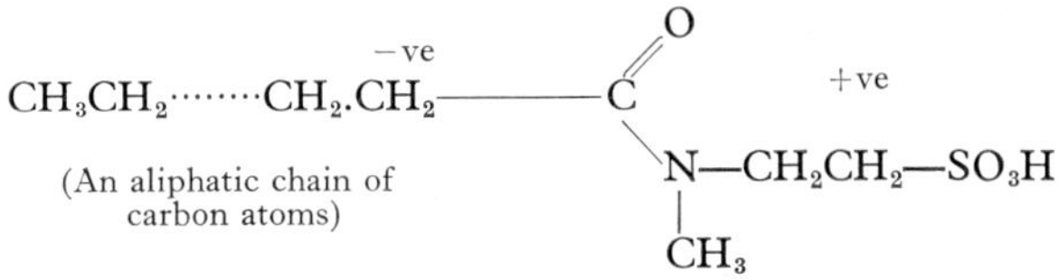

$$CH_3CH_2\cdots\cdots CH_2.CH_2\overset{-\text{ve}}{-\!\!-\!\!-}C\!\!\begin{array}{c} O \\ \\ N\!\!-\!\!CH_2CH_2\!\!-\!\!SO_3H \\ | \\ CH_3 \end{array}$$

(An aliphatic chain of   +ve
carbon atoms)

A sulphonated amide
group

A sulphonated amide

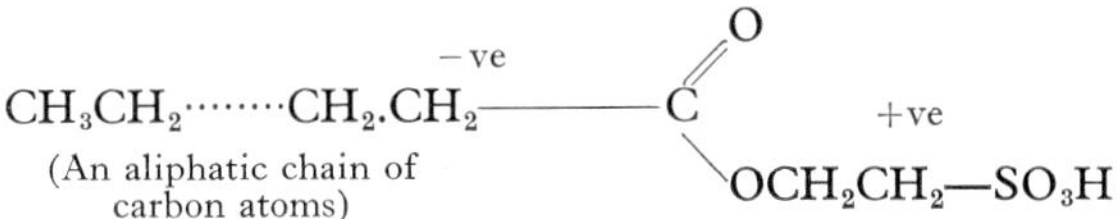

$$CH_3CH_2\cdots\cdots CH_2.CH_2\overset{-\text{ve}}{-\!\!-\!\!-}C\!\!\begin{array}{c} O \\ \\ OCH_2CH_2\!\!-\!\!SO_3H \end{array}$$

(An aliphatic chain of   +ve
carbon atoms)

A sulphonated ester
group

A sulphonated ester

All the above surface active types are *anion-active*, that is, the effective hydrophobic component is present in the anion when the substance is dissolved in water and ionises into anions and cations.

The *non-ionic* surface active agents do not ionise when dissolved in water and thus do not contain sulphonic acid groups since these would give the agent ionising power. The water-solubility of this type of agent is thus mainly obtained by the presence of one or more hydroxyl (OH) groups. The effective component of a non-ionic agent is thus the whole molecule, and it is effective since it contains hydrophobic aliphatic or aromatic chains of carbon atoms in combination with mildly hydrophile groups (OH). Typical non-ionic surface active agents are shown below:

$$CH_3(CH_2)_7CH\!\!=\!\!CH(CH_2)_7COOCH_2CH_2(CH_2CH_2O)_nCH_2CH_2OH$$

Polyethylene glycol oleate
(a fatty acid ester product)

$$CH_3(CH_2)_7CH\!\!=\!\!CH(CH_2)_8O\!\!-\!\!(CH_2CH_2O)_nCH_2CH_2OH$$

Oleyl polyglycol ether
(a fatty alcohol ester product)

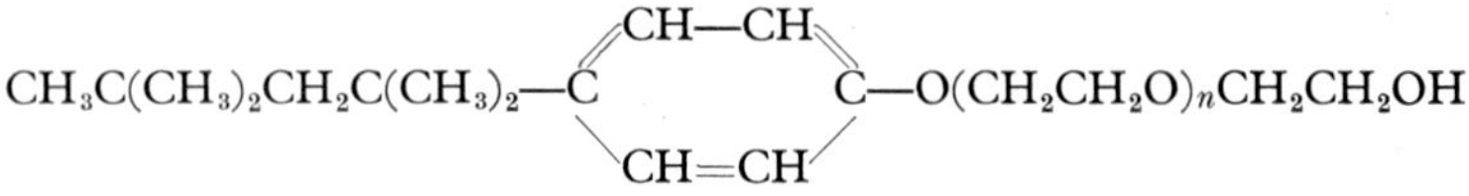

$$CH_3C(CH_3)_2CH_2C(CH_3)_2 - C \begin{matrix} CH-CH \\ \\ CH=CH \end{matrix} C - O(CH_2CH_2O)_nCH_2CH_2OH$$

Dipropyl-benzene polyglycol ether
(an aliphatic-aromatic polyglycol ether)

The *cationic* surface active agents are not important as detergents but rather as substances which can confer softness, increased fastness of a coloured material to light, washing, and gasfading, etc., increased smoothness and draping qualities, resistance to fibre soiling, etc. Most of them are salts of amines and in ionising when dissolved in water the effective complex amine component constitutes the cation. Typical cation-active agents are shown below, but they can have a very varied and complex chemical structure.

Hydrophobic (cation) component	*Hydrophile (anion) or water-solubilising component*

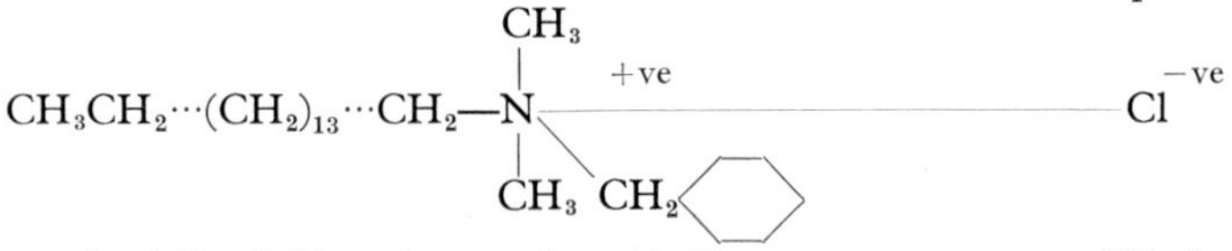

$$CH_3CH_2 \cdots (CH_2)_{13} \cdots CH_2 - N \begin{matrix} CH_3 \\ | \\ | \\ CH_3 \end{matrix} \overset{+ve}{\underset{CH_2}{\diagdown}} \qquad \overset{-ve}{Cl}$$

Cetyl dimethyl benzyl ammonium chloride   Chlorine
(a softening agent containing aliphatic and
alkylaryl components linked to a nitrogen
atom)

$$\diagup N \overset{+ve}{\underset{C_{16}H_{33}}{|}} \qquad \overset{-ve}{Br}$$

Cetyl pyridinium bromide   Bromine
(a dye-fixing agent containing an aliphatic
hydrocarbon linked to the nitrogen atom of
a pyridine residue)

The above description of typical *anion-active, cation-active* and *non-ionic* surface active agents which can be utilised in the washing and other wet processing of textile materials should indicate that in general the molecules of these agents are long. It should further indicate that whereas the whole of the molecule plays an important part in the textile treatment in the case of a non-ionic agent, it is only the *anion* or the *cation* of an anion-active or cation-active agent respectively which is thus effective. A distinction between *anions* and *cations* is that the former are negatively electrically charged while the latter are positively electrically charged. The relationship between such anion-active, non-ionic, and cation-active surface active agents can be perhaps shown more clearly in the following way, where the effective components of the agent's long molecules and the water-solubilising or ineffective component are also distinguished.

Component effective towards textile material	*Ineffective but useful as water-solubilising group*

Anion-active

$-$ve ———————————————— ◯ $+$ve
Anion   Cation

Non-ionic

————————————————◯
Whole molecule electrically neutral

Cation-active

$+$ve ———————————————— ◯ $-$ve
Cation

ANTI-FOAMING AGENTS

In the washing of textile materials foaming of the liquor can generally be considered to be a reliable indication that the detergent liquor has good wetting power and that it will be able to penetrate satisfactorily in and between the fibres of the textile material. But sometimes excessive foaming can be something of a nuisance since it may lead to loss of detergent liquor by its overflow from the washing machine. For this reason various substances have now been made available (these include *n*-octyl alcohol, emulsified turpentine, and certain organic silicon compounds) which can be added to washing liquors to keep the foaming within reasonable limits. The existence of only a moderate amount of foam must not therefore be regarded as a sign that the detergent employed has not satisfactory penetrating and wetting power.

On the other hand, it is highly desirable that the rinsing water used for washing out residual detergent and impurities from textile materials following the washing operation should have the utmost possible wetting and penetrating power, and that this power should not be adversely affected by hard water. It is thus always advantageous to add to such rinsing liquors a good wetting agent and, if necessary, tolerate the foaming with loss of rinsing liquor by overflow.

Questions for Chapter VI

1. State the main features about a soiled textile material which have to be considered in deciding how to clean it—by ordinary washing or dry cleaning.

2. Enumerate the more important types of soiling. Describe the way in which soap or other detergents can assist the removal of soil.

3. Point out the ingredients and their function which may be present in a satisfactory and balanced washing powder or similar composition.

4. What is the importance of having a soil-suspending agent present in a detergent liquor?

5. Indicate the usefulness of using a *boiling* detergent liquor, but point out circumstances which would not allow its use.

6. What special care has to be taken in the washing of wool materials? Give reasons for your answer.

7. In dealing with synthetic fibre materials, point out conditions of washing which would be unsuitable for some of the fibres now in use.

8. Describe the bleaching agents which can be used to whiten off-white materials, and their limitations. Why is it advisable to anti-chlor after the use of a hypochlorite bleaching agent?

9. Explain why there is a risk in whitening resin-finished materials (for example, crease-resist and wash-and-wear cotton and rayon goods) with a hypochlorite liquor. What risk-free alternatives could you use for whitening these?

10. Describe difficulties encountered in the washing of coloured materials. What types of dyes present would help you to avoid such difficulties?

11. What do you understand by 'colour bleeding'? What dyes are especially liable to this and how would you endeavour to avoid it?

12. The avoidance of fabric shrinkage in washing is important. What steps would you take to avoid it? Point out any types of textile material which would require special attention from this viewpoint.

13. What do you understand by the terms *hard* and *soft* water? Explain how water becomes hard, and differentiate between the two types of hardness generally recognised.

14. How is the hardness of water generally expressed? What maximum degree of hardness could be tolerated for washing textiles without using special detergents?

15. List five towns in Britain where the water is very soft and another five where it is very hard. Give reasons for these differences.

16. Explain the formation of a soap scum in hard water. How would you endeavour to prevent soap scum formation either by softening the water or by the use of soap substitutes unaffected by hard water?

17. Describe the nature of an ordinary soap and then describe the progress made in recent years to overcome the defects of soap by reference to modern synthetic detergents.

18. Describe the use of zeolite products for softening water, and the construction of a home softening apparatus based on the use of such products.

19. What is a metal-sequestering agent and how can it be useful in the washing of textile materials?

20. What are the nature and usefulness of the following: sodium palmitate, potassium stearate, dodecyl benzene sulphonate, and stearyl sulphate?

21. What do you understand by a 'surfactant' or 'surface active agent'? Describe the basis of their classification into three main types and indicate their chemical differences.

22. Name two substances which have anti-foaming properties and say why these can be useful in the laundering of textile goods.

CHAPTER VII

Stains on Textile Materials and their Removal. Dry Cleaning

Stains on textile materials arise from various causes and they occur not only in the home but also in works where textile materials are processed, including dyeing and finishing. Usually the first consideration in seeing a stain on some fabric or garment is the treatment which will remove it, but this is not always an easy matter. In dealing with a stain it is generally advisable to ascertain so far as is possible its nature and also to decide of what type of fibre the material is made, since these factors always play a part in determining the treatment to be applied. Whether or not the material is white or coloured is also a decisive factor—it is generally so much more difficult to treat a stain on coloured material without at the same time affecting this colour.

Since the two main features of stain removal are the nature of the stain and the substances which are able to remove them, the following notes from this viewpoint are given.

STAIN REMOVERS

Substances able to remove stains comprise acids, alkalis, reducing and oxidising agents, organic solvents, and stain softening and dispersing agents. With the aid of these it is generally possible to remove a stain satisfactorily in a textile works, but unfortunately some of these useful stain-removing substances are not available in the home.

Acids and alkalis

Acids are useful for removing metal stains and it is iron rust stains that are most frequently encountered. The acids available are *mineral* and *organic* and of these the former are stronger and potentially liable to damage the textile material if used at too high a concentration or too hot, but damage may be avoided by shortening the period of application and by at once washing out residual acid, preferably with an addition of ammonia or sodium carbonate to neutralise it. Hydrochloric and sulphuric acids are the mineral acids most readily available; they should be used not stronger than as a 10% aqueous solution but preferably weaker.

The organic acids such as acetic, formic, oxalic, tartaric, and citric acids are weaker than the mineral acids so that more latitude is possible with their use. However, they can damage textile material during storage if left in the fabric after treatment of the stain, so that a thorough washing after stain removal is advised, preferably with the addition of one or other of the alkalis mentioned above. Acetic acid is much weaker than the other acids.

It is to be noted that cellulose fibres such as cotton and viscose rayon are easily liable to damage from acid treatment; wool is less sensitive. On no account should any acid be dried into cotton or rayon goods since even a very low acid concentration can produce weakening of the fibres.

If a coloured material is being treated this may change in shade, but often the original colour will return when the acid is washed out or neutralised.

Alkalis are useful to assist the action of a detergent such as soap. Useful alkalis are ammonia, sodium carbonate, and borax. They are not harmful to cotton and other cellulose fibre goods but can weaken protein fibres such as wool, especially if used hot and concentrated or allowed to remain in the textile material after the stain removal. An aqueous solution of soap containing ammonia is very useful if applied with rubbing to both cellulose and protein fibres, since the wool is not harmed by ammonia—it is the weakest of the alkalis but yet is very effective in cleaning textile goods.

Alkalis are liable to cause the colour of wool goods to 'run' while acids will prevent this. So after treating coloured wool with an alkaline stain remover it is advisable to neutralise with acetic acid and wash well as soon as possible—the acid will prevent further running of the colour and will restore the original shade if this has changed in the treatment. Most colours on cotton are unaffected by alkaline treatment unless it is hot and prolonged—if any change does occur the fabric should be rinsed finally with cold weak acetic acid and then with water.

Alkalis can assist the removal of fat and wax stains, especially if assisted with soap. Emulsification of the fat and wax takes place so that their removal is facilitated. But it will generally be found better to remove such stains by the use of an organic solvent.

Reducing and oxidising agents

Reducing agents are most useful for treating colour stains on white goods, since the colouring matter, especially if it be a cotton or wool dye, and often if it is a fruit stain, can be destroyed by reduction. It is often found that the action of the reducing agent can be much assisted by employing it as a hot rather than a cold solution, and that sometimes it is useful to assist its action by adding an acid or an alkali. It is generally advisable to wash the treated stain immediately afterwards, to remove not only the reducing agent but also the products of reduction of the stain; otherwise these may oxidise in air and again become fixed as before.

Useful reducing agents

Reducing agents include sodium metabisulphite, sodium bisulphite, sodium hydrosulphite, sodium formaldehyde sulphoxylate (this acts similarly to sodium hydrosulphite but is more stable and thus only becomes effective in a hot treatment of the stain), and stannous chloride. Of these sodium or potassium metabisulphite and sodium bisulphite will be most readily available for use in the home.

Iron rust stains which can be difficult to remove can often be reduced from their *ferric* (brown) to their ferrous (nearly colourless) form and thus become more readily removed from textile material by an acid treatment, say with warm oxalic or hydrochloric acid treatment. If this subsequent acid treatment is not applied the brown stain will soon reappear as a result of aerial oxidation of the *ferrous* to the *ferric* state of the iron remaining in the fabric.

Oxidising agents can be generally useful for treating most types of stains excepting those due to metal salts and to fats, oils, and waxes. By oxidation it is possible for dirt, dyes, and organic staining substances to undergo decomposition to form colourless water-soluble products which can be washed out with water preferably containing also soap and ammonia.

Useful oxidising agents

The two most convenient oxidising agents are hydrogen peroxide and a solution of sodium hypochlorite. Of these a solution of hydrogen peroxide is to be preferred if it is effective, since it leaves in the textile material no harmful residue, especially if the treated stain is finally rinsed with water. Hydrogen peroxide can be applied to all types of textile fibres without fear of damage, but hypochlorite is liable to damage all fibres if applied for too long at a high concentration, and if not finally thoroughly washed out of the treated stain—preferably with water containing a small proportion of a reducing agent such as sodium metabisulphite to destroy residual hypochlorite.

In dealing with stained coloured goods it is generally much safer to use hydrogen peroxide instead of sodium hypochlorite, since the latter is the more liable to destroy dyes. However, sodium hypochlorite is especially good for dealing with fruit stains. The action of the hypochlorite can be assisted by adding a few drops of acetic acid to the stain already in contact with the hypochlorite.

Organic solvents

A large number of these are available, especially in a textile works, and they include important ones such as carbon tetrachloride and trichloroethylene (both non-inflammable), petroleum ether and ethyl ether, benzene, acetone, petrol, and methylated spirits (all inflammable and to be kept away from a flame). These organic solvents are very effective for the removal of grease, oil, fat, and waxes by a sponging treatment. No one organic solvent is able to dissolve all such stains and so it is often better to use a mixture of solvents—a number of proprietary mixtures are available and their ingredients are compounded to dissolve quite a large number of different waxes, fats, oils, and greases and even tar.

In using an organic solvent it is often possible, by sponging the stain with liberal amounts of the solvent, to remove the staining substances completely. But often the stain appears to be removed by being spread over a larger area of the surrounding fabric. Thus it may be considered advisable finally to remove the spread stain by application of an aqueous solution of soap and ammonia or of a synthetic detergent (some of these detergents have an especially high power to emulsify fats and waxes, etc.). It is often necessary to complete the removal of a tar stain by such after-treatment with a soap solution, in the application of which rubbing can much assist.

Oil and grease stains not easily removable

In the case of grease, fat, wax, and oil stains which prove difficult to remove by simple sponging with an organic solvent or mixture of such solvents, recourse can be made to a method of softening the stain so that it can then be removed otherwise. This useful method consists of adding a few drops of a saponifiable oil (that is one which by heating with an alkali can be converted into a water-soluble soap) such as olive or castor oil to the stain, and if this is hot so much the better. This oil will mix with the staining grease, oil, wax, etc. Then on washing the stain with a hot aqueous liquor containing sodium carbonate and some synthetic detergent or soap, the alkali will partly saponify the added oil and thereby break up the stain and emulsify the fat, wax, etc. to facilitate its removal by washing with rubbing.

It should be noted that the solvent action towards a fat, wax, grease, etc. of an organic solvent can be very much more powerful at an elevated temperature. So if the boiling point of the organic solvent is not too low the solvent will be much more effective if used when hot.

Action of organic solvents on synthetic fibres

In using organic solvents for stain removal it is important first to consider whether or not the textile fibre under treatment will be adversely affected—some of the man-made fibres such as acetate, polyamide, polyester, acrylic fibres may dissolve or soften in certain organic solvents, especially if they are applied when hot. For example, ordinary acetate fibres dissolve readily in acetone even in the cold. A preliminary test is advised when in doubt.

Many of the modern synthetic detergents contain surfactants which in concentrated solution have so strong an emulsifying action on greases and waxes that they can be almost as good as an organic solvent in removing grease, oil, and wax stains from textile materials, especially if they are applied hot.

DRY CLEANING

Dry cleaning has today become a very popular method for dealing with clothes and certain types of decorative fabrics which have become soiled and possibly distorted, since in many instances it allows cleaning to be effectively carried out yet avoiding a loss of original finish and without appreciable shrinkage. These advantages come from the use of organic solvents, which may contain also a small proportion of emulsified water and a solvent-soluble soap, instead of aqueous detergent liquors.

It is a fact that many of the dyes and the finishing substances and assistants used to give textile materials their desired colour, handle, lustre, draping qualities, etc. are much more freely soluble in water than in the organic solvents used by the dry cleaner, so that whereas they would be removed in ordinary washing they remain unchanged following a dry cleaning treatment. But there is another factor which assists dry cleaning to leave a textile material substantially with its original appearance and free from shrinkage. It is concerned with wet fibre swelling.

No shrinkage in organic solvents

In dealing with the various textile fibres it was noted that those which were hydrophile (cotton, wool, silk, linen, etc.) became much thicker when wetted, and that with a fabric this fibre swelling led to area shrinkage. It is almost impossible to wash a fabric in an aqueous liquor without involving fibre thickening and some consequent fabric shrinkage accompanied by distortion of shape. But in dry cleaning these changes do not occur, since hydrophile fibres do not swell when immersed in an organic solvent which itself is strongly hydrophobic. It is in this respect that dry cleaning has a great advantage over washing with aqueous detergent liquors.

As at present being carried out dry cleaning involves the extraction of dirt, and grease, oil, fat, and wax stains from all kinds of textile materials by treatment with a hot organic solvent such as benzine, trichloroethylene, tetrachloroethane, and carbon tetrachloride. Thereafter the textile goods are freed from excess of solvent by hydroextraction and are then freed from residual solvent by a hot air treatment, and are finally hot pressed to their original size and shape. As far as possible no organic solvent is wasted since used solvent can be collected from all stages of processing and then be purified for re-use by distillation.

In recent years the increasing use of synthetic fibres has caused some concern to dry cleaners, since they have to check that the particular organic solvents they use do not soften or dissolve these fibres. For this reason it can much help them if goods sent for dry cleaning are marked to show what type of synthetic fibre is present.

U

Questions for Chapter VII

1. Discuss the general principles involved in the examination of stains and their removal.

2. Enumerate the types of chemicals which can be used for stain removal and give the names of particular ones of each type.

3. In the removal of a stain from cellulose materials requiring the use of an acid, why is it better to use an organic rather than a mineral acid? Give the names of useful mineral and organic acids.

4. Why should alkaline treatment of wool be avoided? What is the alkali which is least harmful to wool?

5. What types of chemicals would you use to remove fruit stains?

6. Discuss the uses of oxidants for stain removal such as hydrogen peroxide and sodium hypochlorite, having regard to cotton and wool fabrics.

7. Discuss the removal of oil, fat, and greasy stains by sponging with an organic solvent. What mixture of such solvents would you prefer to use?

8. State the precautions you would use in treating synthetic fibre materials with organic solvents.

9. Describe the fundamental difference between washing with an aqueous detergent and the dry cleaning of textile materials.

10. Name the organic solvents normally used for dry cleaning and state how a dry cleaning liquor is often modified so as to remove soil which is water-soluble and insoluble in organic solvents. Why is dry cleaning used when the textile material is liable to shrink in water?

Index

We have an interesting list of practical, general and educational books, written by experts, carefully edited and in most cases illustrated. Please send a postcard for our catalogue.

ALLMAN

MILLS & BOON LIMITED

50 Grafton Way, Fitzroy Square, London W.1

Euston 2571

(and see overleaf)

INTERMEDIATE DOMESTIC SCIENCE
by W. Munn Rankin and E. M. Hildreth

Two comprehensive books suitable for students at Ordinary and Advanced levels, containing numerous practical scientific tests that can be carried out in the laboratory or housecraft centre.

Part I—FOODS AND NUTRITION

Deals with the underlying principles of nutrition, the primary foodstuffs and the industrial aspects of preparing them for the consumer. The book has been developed on a broad basis of elementary chemistry and physiology, with an especial emphasis on experimental exercises with food materials in great variety.

412 pages; illustrations in line and half-tone; 6th (revised) impression;
17s 6d
(A)

Part II—TEXTILES IN THE HOME

Briefly outlines the important facts about fibres and fabrics, natural, regenerated and synthetic; dyes and dyeing; laundry materials and processes; stains and their removal. There are numerous practical and easily arranged experiments.

130 pages; 16 illustrations in line and half-tone; 3rd (revised) edition;
9s 6d
(A)

HOW TO DESIGN
YOUR OWN DRESS PATTERNS
by Adele P. Margolis

The use of this book to anyone studying dress designing as a career, or for examinations, is obvious. It is most useful, too, to the home dressmaker who uses commercial patterns but needs to alter them (not as simple as it might seem). Teachers will like the way the author prescribes exercise after exercise until each new principle is thoroughly mastered—and yet she never becomes dull or plodding. Students will find that they have insensibly improved their eye for style, line and fashion. The admirable diagrams will not date.

9½ × 6 ins.; 286 pages; 337 line diagrams; 3rd printing; 35s net
(M & B)

PATTERN WISE

PATTERN WISE by the same author is a trim little paperback showing how to make the basic patterns of a five-piece dress, a princess-line dress, a suit, a coat, slacks and others.

150 pages; 130 line diagrams; 6s net
(M & B)

GENERAL CERTIFICATE CHEMISTRY
by C. W. Wood, M.Sc., M.Ed., Ll.B.

*'This is an orthodox, thorough, up-to-date and, in fact, scholarly 'O' level
text, complete with useful revision notes.'*—THE SCHOOL SCIENCE REVIEW

Mr Wood, late Senior Science Master at St Bees School, has related
his own subject to the universal story of man. In this way he caters most
ably for those who intend to specialise in science and also for those who
require a knowledge of chemistry only as a background to their general
education.

446 pages; illustrated with over 100 diagrams and plates; 12s 6d

ORDINARY LEVEL CHEMISTRY
by C. W. Wood, M.Sc., M.Ed., Ll.B.

A clear and concise book which will prove of the greatest assistance to the
student seeking to refresh his memory before taking 'O' level. 25 diagrams
of apparatus will enable him to do his revision without other help.
64 pages; illustrated; semi-limp 3s 9d

'O' Level Revision Notes are also available in other subjects.

ELEMENTARY SCIENCE OF FOOD
by E. M. Hildreth

This book is firmly established as a clear and comprehensive exposition
of its subject. The method of treatment makes it suitable for use in all
types of secondary school, for pupils taking the relevant G.C.E. examinations at 'O' and 'A' levels, and for students preparing for the City and
Guilds Domestic Cookery and Housecraft examinations, and for the
Housecraft Certificate of the National Council for Domestic Studies.
In addition to discussing food itself—its nature, preparation and pre-
servation—the book has a useful section on kitchen equipment in relation
to cookery and hygiene, and a short outline of the mechanism of digestion.

Fully revised and restyled edition 12s

Mills & Boon's **Science in Society** *Series*

General Editor: Dr. J. GOODIER
Head of the Science Department, Eton College

The books in this series represent an effort to bridge the notorious 'gap' between Arts and Science students, and to help science specialists understand the work of fellow-scientists in different fields. All are written by experts, and are illustrated.

Titles now available:

CHEMICALS AND PEOPLE by S. A. Gregory, B.Sc., M.I.Chem.E. 15s net (school edition 8s 6d)

A SHORT HISTORY OF MEDICINE by F. N. L. Poynter, Ph.D., F.R.S.L., F.L.A., and K. D. Keele, M.D., M.R.C.P. 17s 6d net (school edition 9s 6d)

EVOLUTION AND ITS IMPLICATIONS by Peter Kelly, B.Sc., M.A., F.Z.S. 18s 6d net (school edition 11s 6d)

ABOUT THE UNIVERSE by Ian F. Rolls, B.Sc., M.A. 20s net (school edition 14s 6d)

ATOMS AND THE CELL by P. A. Barker, M.A. 15s net (school edition 9s 6d)

BRITAIN'S ECONOMY by G. W. Smith (Assistant Editor, The Times Review of Industry). 17s 6d net (school edition 15s)

★